CHOICE AND CHANCE

CHOICE AND CHANCE

WITH ONE THOUSAND EXERCISES

BY

WILLIAM ALLEN WHITWORTH, M.A.

Prebendary of St. Paul's Cathedral
Formerly Fellow of St. John's College, Cambridge

HAFNER PUBLISHING COMPANY

New York and London

1965

Reprint of the fifth edition
much enlarged, issued in 1901

Printed and Published by
Hafner Publishing Company, Inc.
31 East 10th Street
New York, N.Y. 10003

Library of Congress Catalog Card Number: 65-23610

Printed in U.S.A. by
NOBLE OFFSET PRINTERS, INC.
NEW YORK 3, N. Y.

PREFACE TO THE FIFTH EDITION.

THIS work has been considerably enlarged since the publication of the Fourth Edition. Not only does the Volume contain some 45 pages more than its predecessor, but further space has been gained by the use of smaller type for merely illustrative matter.

The most important addition in the body of the work is the very far-reaching theorem which I have given as Prop. LVII. which enables us to write down at sight the mean value of such functions as α^3, $\alpha^3\beta^4$, $\alpha\beta\gamma$, &c., when α, β, γ, ... are the parts into which a given magnitude is divided at random. I first published this theorem in a pamphlet in the year 1898.

A new feature will be recognised in a class of problems which found scarcely any place in former editions; the class which includes investigations into the mean value of the largest part, (or the smallest, or any other in order of magnitude,) or of functions of such a part, when a magnitude is divided at random. To the same category belong questions as to the expectation of the highest (or the lowest) result obtained by some experiment or process repeated a given number of times.

The exercises at the end of the Volume are now increased in number to 1000. Solutions of 700 of these were published in 1897 in the companion volume entitled DCC EXERCISES IN CHOICE AND CHANCE. Amongst the 300 new questions now added there are some which I venture to think will be found suggestive of large fields of independent research open to the student.

W. A. WHITWORTH.

ALL SAINTS', MARGARET STREET,
LONDON.
June 13, 1901.

CONTENTS.

CHOICE.

CHAPTERS I. AND II.

CHAPTER III.

CHAPTER IV.

CHAPTER V.

CHANCE.

CHAPTERS VI. AND VII.

CHAPTER VIII.

CHAPTER IX.

CHAPTER X.

CHAPTER XI.

CHAPTER XII.

EXERCISES.

ERRATUM.

Page 217. In Prop. LXIII. *m* must not be negative.

CHOICE.

CHAPTER I.

THE THEORY OF PERMUTATIONS AND COMBINATIONS TREATED ARITHMETICALLY.

WE have continually to make our choice among different courses of action open to us, and upon the discretion with which we make it, much may depend. Of this discretion a higher philosophy must treat, and it is not to be supposed that Arithmetic has anything to do with it; but it is the province of Arithmetic, under given circumstances, to *measure* the choice which we have to exercise, or to determine precisely the number of courses open to us.

Suppose, for instance, that a member is to be returned to parliament for a certain borough, and that four candidates present themselves. Arithmetic has nothing to do with the manner in which we shall exercise our privilege as a voter, which depends on our discretion in judging the qualifications of the different candidates; but it belongs to Arithmetic, as the science of counting and calculation, to tell us that the

1

number of ways in which (if we vote at all) we can exercise
our choice, is *four*.

The operation is, indeed, in this case so simple that we
scarcely recognise its arithmetical character at all; but if we
pass on to a more complicated case, we shall observe that
some thought or calculation is required to determine the
number of courses open to us: and thought about numbers
is Arithmetic.

Suppose, then, that we are entitled to vote for *two*
members instead of one. And still suppose that we have the
same four candidates, whom we will distinguish by names,
as *A, B, C, D*. If we try to note down all the ways in which
it is possible for us to vote, we shall find them to be six in
number; thus we may vote for any of the following:—

A and *B*,	*A* and *C*,	*A* and *D*,
C and *D*,	*B* and *D*,	*B* and *C*.

But we can hardly make this experiment without perceiving
that the resulting number, *six*, must depend arithmetically
upon the number of candidates and the number of members
to be returned; or without suspecting that on some of the
principles of arithmetic we ought to be able to arrive at that
result without the labour of noting all the possible courses
open to us, and then counting them up; a labour which we
may observe would be very great if ten or twelve candidates
offered themselves, instead of four.

In the present chapter we shall establish and explain
the principles upon which such calculations are made arithmetically. It will be found that they are very simple in
nature as well as few in number. In the following chapters
we shall treat the subject somewhat more largely by algebraical methods; but the reader who is unacquainted with
algebra may pass over those chapters, and proceed with the

first chapter on Chance (Chap. VI.), in which he will find the principles of Choice applied arithmetically to the solutions of problems in Probability, a subject of great interest and some practical importance.

We found, by experiment or trial, that there were six ways of voting for two out of four candidates. So we may say that, out of any four given articles, six selections of two articles may be made. But we call special attention to the sense in which we use the words "six selections." We do not mean that a man can select two articles, and having taken them can select two more, and then two more, and so on till he has made six selections altogether; for it is obvious that the four articles would be exhausted by the second selection; but when we speak of six selections being possible, we mean that there are six different ways of making one selection, just as among four candidates there are six ways of selecting two to vote for.

This language may appear at first to be arbitrary and unnecessary, but as we proceed with the subject we shall find that it simplifies the expression of many of our results.

In making the selection of two candidates out of four, in the case just considered, it was immaterial which of the two selected ones we took first; the selection of A first, and then B, was to every intent and purpose the same thing as the selection of B first, and then A.

But if we alter the question a little, and ask in how many ways a society can select a president and vice-president out of four candidates for office, the order of selection becomes of importance. To elect A and B as president and vice-president respectively, is not the same thing as to elect B and A for those two offices respectively. Hence there are twice as many ways as before of making the election, viz.— *That is; namely*

A and *B*,	*A* and *C*,	*A* and *D*,
C and *D*,	*B* and *D*,	*B* and *C*,
B and *A*,	*C* and *A*,	*D* and *A*,
D and *C*,	*D* and *B*,	*C* and *B*.

So if four articles of any kind are given us, there will be *twelve* ways of choosing two of them in a particular order; or, as we may more briefly express it, out of four given articles, twelve arrangements of two articles can be made. But it must be observed that the same remarks apply here, which we made on the use of the phrase "six selections" on p. 3. We do not mean that twelve arrangements or six selections can be successively made; but that if one arrangement or one selection of two articles have to be made out of the four given articles, we have the choice of twelve ways of making the arrangement, and the choice of six ways of making the selection.

We may give the following formal definitions of the words *selection* and *arrangement*, in the sense in which we have used them:—

DEF. I.—A *selection* (or *combination* or *parcel*) of any number of articles, means a set of that number of articles classed together, but not regarded as having any particular order among themselves.

DEF. II.—An *arrangement* (or *permutation* or *group*) of any number of articles, means a set of that number of articles, not only classed together, but regarded as having a particular order among themselves.

Thus the six sets,

A B C,	*B C A*,	*C A B*,
A C B,	*B A C*,	*C B A*,

are all *the same* selection (or combination or parcel) of three letters, but they are all *different* arrangements (or permutations or groups) of three letters.

So, out of the four letters *A*, *B*, *C*, *D*, we can make four selections of three letters, viz.—

$$B C D,$$
$$C D A,$$
$$D A B,$$
$$A B C;$$

but out of the same four letters we can make twenty-four arrangements of three letters, viz.—

B C D,	*B D C*,	*C D B*,	*C B D*,	*D B C*,	*D C B*,
C D A,	*C A D*,	*D A C*,	*D C A*,	*A C D*,	*A D C*,
D A B,	*D B A*,	*A B D*,	*A D B*,	*B D A*,	*B A D*,
A B C,	*A C B*,	*B C A*,	*B A C*,	*C A B*,	*C B A*.

It should be noticed that the results which we have just stated are often enunciated in slightly different phraseology. There is no difference of meaning whether we say

(1) The number of selections (or combinations) of 3 things out of 4 ;

or   (2) The number of ways of selecting 3 things out of 4 ;

or   (3) The number of combinations of 4 things taken 3 at a time (or taken 3 together).

Similarly we may speak indifferently of

(1) The number of arrangements of 3 things out of 4 ;

or   (2) The number of orders of arranging 3 things out of 4 ;

or   (3) The number of permutations (or arrangements) of 4 things taken 3 at a time (or taken 3 together).

Having thus explained the language we shall have to employ, we may now proceed to establish the principles on which all calculations of choice must be founded.

The great principle upon which we shall base all our reasoning may be stated as follows:—

If one thing can be done in a given number of different ways, and then another thing in another given number of different ways, the number of different ways in which both things can be done is obtained by multiplying together the two given numbers.

We shall first illustrate this principle, and then proceed to prove it.

Suppose we have a box containing five capital letters, *A, B, C, D, E,* and three small letters, *x, y, z.*

$$
\boxed{
\begin{array}{ccccc}
A & B & C & D & E \\
x & y & z & &
\end{array}
}
$$

The number of ways in which we can select a capital letter out of the box is *five;* the number of ways in which we can select a small letter is *three;* therefore, by the principle we have just stated, the number of different ways in which we can select a capital letter and a small one is *fifteen,* which we find on trial to be correct, all the possible selections being as follows:—

Ax,	*Bx,*	*Cx,*	*Dx,*	*Ex,*
Ay,	*By,*	*Cy,*	*Dy,*	*Ey,*
Az,	*Bz,*	*Cz,*	*Dz,*	*Ez.*

Again, suppose there are four paths to the top of a mountain, the principle asserts that we have the choice of sixteen ways of ascending and descending. For there are

4 ways up,

4 ways down,

and $4 \times 4 = 16$.

We can verify this: for if P, Q, R, S be the names of the four paths, we can make our choice among the following sixteen plans, the first-mentioned path being the way up, and the second the way down:—

P and P,	P and Q,	P and R,	P and S,
Q and P,	Q and Q,	Q and R,	Q and S,
R and P,	R and Q,	R and R,	R and S,
S and P,	S and Q,	S and R,	S and S.

Or, if we had desired to ascertain what choice we had of going up and down by different paths, we might still have applied the principle, reasoning thus:

There are *four* ways of going up, and when we are at the top we have the choice of *three* ways of descending (since we are not to come down by the same path that brought us up). Hence the number of ways of ascending and descending is 4×3, or *twelve*.

These twelve ways will be obtained from the sixteen described in the former case, by omitting the four ineligible ways,

P and P, $\qquad$ Q and Q, $\qquad$ R and R, $\qquad$ S and S.

The foregoing examples will suffice to illustrate the meaning and application of our fundamental proposition. We will now give a formal proof of it. We shall henceforth refer to it as Rule I.

8 CHOICE.

RULE I.

If one thing can be done in a given number of different ways, and (when it is done in any way) another thing can be done in another given number of different ways, then the number of different ways in which the two things can be done is the product of the two given numbers.

For let *A, B, C, D, E*, &c. represent the different ways in which the first thing can be done (taking as many letters as may be necessary to represent all the different ways), and similarly let *a, b, c, d*, &c. represent the different ways of doing the second thing. Then, if we form a table as below, having the letters *A, B, C, D, E*, &c. at the head of the several columns, and the letters *a, b, c, d*, &c. at the end of the several horizontal rows, we may regard each square in the table as representing the case, in which the first thing is

		WAYS OF DOING THE FIRST THING.						
		A	*B*	*C*	*D*	*E*	*F*	*G*	*&c.*
WAYS OF DOING THE SECOND THING.	*a*								
	b			*					
	c					†			
	d								
	&c.								

done in the way marked at the head of the column in which the square is taken, and the second thing in the way marked at the end of the row.

Thus the square marked with the asterisk (*) will denote the case in which the first thing is done in the way which we called C, and the second thing in the way which we called b; and the square marked with the dagger (†) will denote the case in which the first thing is done in the way E, and the second in the way c; and so on.

Now it will be readily seen that all the squares represent different cases, and that every case is represented by some square or other. Hence the number of possible cases is the same as the number of squares. But there are as many columns as there are ways of doing the first thing, and each column contains as many squares as there are ways of doing the second thing. Therefore the number of squares is the product of the number of ways of doing the two several things, and therefore this product expresses also the whole number of possible cases, or the whole number of ways in which the two events can be done.

This proves the rule.

Question 1. A cabinet-maker has twelve patterns of chairs and five patterns of tables. In how many ways can he make a chair and a table?

Answer. The pattern for the chair can be chosen in twelve ways, and the pattern for the table in five ways : therefore both together can be chosen in 12×5 ways.

Question 2. A friend shews me five Latin books, and seven Greek books, and allows me to choose one of each. What choice have I?

Answer. $5 \times 7 = 35$.

Question 3. If a halfpenny and a penny be tossed, in how many ways can they fall?

Answer. The halfpenny can fall in two ways, and the penny in two ways, and $2 \times 2 = 4$; therefore they can fall in four ways.

The four ways, of course, are as follows :—

    (1) both heads.
    (2) both tails.
    (3) halfpenny head and penny tail.
    (4) halfpenny tail and penny head.

Question 4. If two dice be thrown together, in how many ways can they fall ?

Answer. The first can fall in six ways, and the second in six ways, and $6 \times 6 = 36$; therefore there are thirty-six ways in which the two dice can fall.

The thirty-six ways may be represented as follows :—

1 and 1,	1 and 2,	1 and 3,	1 and 4,	1 and 5,	1 and 6,
2 and 1,	2 and 2,	2 and 3,	2 and 4,	2 and 5,	2 and 6,
3 and 1,	3 and 2,	3 and 3,	3 and 4,	3 and 5,	3 and 6,
4 and 1,	4 and 2,	4 and 3,	4 and 4,	4 and 5,	4 and 6,
5 and 1,	5 and 2,	5 and 3,	5 and 4,	5 and 5,	5 and 6,
6 and 1,	6 and 2,	6 and 3,	6 and 4,	6 and 5,	6 and 6.

Question 5. In how many ways can two prizes be given to a class of ten boys, without giving both to the same boy ?

Answer. The first prize can be given in ten ways, and when it is given the second can be given in nine ways, and $10 \times 9 = 90$; therefore we have the choice of ninety ways of giving the two prizes.

Question 6. In how many ways can two prizes be given to a class of ten boys, it being permitted to give both to the same boy ?

Answer. The first prize can be given in ten ways, and when it is given the second can be given in ten ways; therefore both can be given in 10×10, or 100 ways.

Question 7. A friend shews me five Latin books, seven Greek books, and ten French books, and allows me to choose two books, on the condition that they must not be both of the same language. Of how many selections have I choice ?

Answer. I can choose a Latin and a Greek book in $5 \times 7 = 35$ ways, a Greek and a French book in $7 \times 10 = 70$ ways, a French and a Latin book in $10 \times 5 = 50$ ways. Therefore I have the choice of $35 + 70 + 50 = 155$ ways.

Question 8. Out of nine different pairs of gloves, in how many ways could I choose a right-hand glove and a left-hand glove, *which should not form a pair?*

Answer. I can choose a right-hand glove in nine ways, and a left-hand glove in nine ways, and therefore both in 81 ways, but nine of these ways would be the selection of the nine pairs; these must be rejected, and there remain 72 ways.

Or thus. I can choose a right-hand glove in nine ways, and when it is chosen there are eight left-hand gloves from which I may choose without getting a pair, therefore my choice is $9 \times 8 = 72$ ways.

Question 9. Two persons get into a railway carriage where there are six vacant seats. In how many different ways can they seat themselves?

Answer. The first person can take any of the vacant seats; therefore he can seat himself in six different ways. Then there are five seats left, and therefore the other person has the choice of five different ways of seating himself. Hence there are 6×5, or 30 different ways in which they can take their seats.

Question 10. In how many ways can we make a two-lettered word out of an alphabet of twenty-six letters, the two letters in the word being different?

Answer. We can choose our first letter in twenty-six ways, and when it is chosen we can choose the second in twenty-five ways. Therefore we have the choice of 26×25, or 650 ways.

Question 11. In how many ways can we select a consonant and a vowel out of an alphabet of twenty consonants and six vowels?

Answer. We can choose the consonant in twenty ways, the vowel in six ways, both in one hundred and twenty ways.

Question 12. In how many ways can we make a two-lettered word, consisting of one consonant and one vowel ?

Answer. By the last answer, we can choose our two letters in one hundred and twenty ways, and when we have chosen them we can arrange them in two ways. Hence we can make the word in 120×2, or 240 different ways.

Question 13. There are twelve ladies and ten gentlemen, of whom three ladies and two gentlemen are sisters and brothers, the rest being unrelated : in how many ways might a marriage be effected ?

Answer. If all were unrelated we might make the match in 12×10, or 120 ways ; but this will include the 3×2, or 6 ways in which the selected lady and gentleman are sister and brother. Therefore the number of eligible ways is $120 - 6$, or 114.

Question 14. In how many ways can the following letters be arranged in a row :

$$a, a, a, a, a, a, a, b, c\,?$$

Answer. First write down the seven letters that are alike, with space between each, thus :

$$a \quad a \quad a \quad a \quad a \quad a \quad a$$

Then there are six spaces, and we have to place b either in one of the spaces or else at one end of the row, *i.e.* we have the choice of eight ways of placing b. When b is placed, there are then eight letters in the row with seven spaces between them, and we have the choice of these seven spaces, and the two ends in placing c. Hence c can be placed in nine ways. Therefore there are 8×9 or 72 ways of placing b and c in a row with the seven a's, or of arranging the nine letters in a row.

RULE II.

If a series of things can be done successively in given numbers of ways, the number of ways in which all the things can be done is the continued product of all the given numbers.

This rule is only an extension of the former one, and scarcely needs a separate proof. Its correctness will be sufficiently evident from considering an example.

Suppose the first thing can be done in four ways, and the second in three, then the first and second together form an event or operation, which can happen (by Rule I.) in 4×3, or 12 ways. Now suppose the third thing can be done in five ways. Then, since the first and second together can happen in twelve ways, and the third in five ways, it follows from Rule I. that the first and second and the third can be done in 12×5, or 60 ways; that is, *all three* can be done in $4 \times 3 \times 5$ ways.

So if a fourth thing can be done in seven ways, then, since the first three can be done in sixty ways, and the fourth in seven ways, the first three and the fourth can be done (by Rule I.) in 60×7, or 420 ways; that is, *all four* can be done in $4 \times 3 \times 5 \times 7$ ways. And so on, however many things there may be.

Question 15. The House of Commons formerly consisted of 489 English Members, 60 Scotch, and 103 Irish. In how many ways was it possible to choose a committee of three members representing the three nationalities?

Answer. $489 \times 60 \times 103 = 3022020$.

Question 16. Twenty competitors run a race for three prizes; in how many different ways is it possible that the prizes may be given?

Answer. The first prize can be given in twenty ways; when it is given, the second may be given in nineteen; then the third can be given in eighteen ways. Hence the whole number of ways of giving the three prizes is $20 \times 19 \times 18$, or 6840.

Question 17. In how many ways can four letters be put into four envelopes, one into each?

Answer. For the first envelope we have the choice of all the letters,

or there are four ways of filling the first envelope; then there are
three letters left, and therefore three ways of filling the second envelope;
then there are two letters left, or two ways of filling the third envelope;
so there is only one way of filling the last. Hence there are

$$4 \times 3 \times 2 \times 1,$$

or 24 ways of doing the whole.

Question 18. How many different sums may be formed with a
sovereign, a half-sovereign, a crown, a half-crown, a shilling, a sixpence,
a penny, and a half-penny?

Answer. Each coin may be either taken or left, that is, it may be
disposed of in two ways, and there are eight coins. Hence (by Rule II.)
all may be disposed of in

$$2 \times 2 \times 2 \times 2 \times 2 \times 2 \times 2 \times 2, \text{ or } 256$$

ways. One of these ways would, however, consist in the rejection of *all*
the coins, which would not be a way of taking any sum. Therefore the
number of different sums that can be made is 255.

Question 19. There are twenty candidates for an office, and seven
electors. In how many ways can the votes be given?

Answer. Each man can vote in twenty ways, and there are seven
men to vote. Therefore all the votes can be given (by Rule II.) in

$$20 \times 20 \times 20 \times 20 \times 20 \times 20 \times 20, \text{ or } 1280000000$$

different ways.

Question 20. I have six letters to be delivered in different parts of
the town, and two boys offer their services to deliver them; in how
many different ways have I the choice of sending the letters?

Answer. The first letter may be sent in either of two ways; so
may the second; so may the third; and so on. Hence the whole
number of ways is, by the rule,

$$2 \times 2 \times 2 \times 2 \times 2 \times 2, \text{ or } 64.$$

Question 21. In how many ways can six different things be divided
between two boys?

Answer. This question will be seen to be almost identical with the
last. The only difference is, that among the 64 ways of sending the

notes were included the two ways in which either boy carried them all. Now six things cannot be said to be divided among two boys if they all are given to one. Hence these two ways must be rejected, and there will only be 62 ways of dividing six things between two boys.

Question 22. In how many ways can six different things be divided into two parcels?

Answer. This question seems at first to be identical with the last. But, on consideration, we observe that if *a*, *b*, *c*, *d*, *e*, *f* represent the six things, one of the ways of dividing them between the two boys would be to give

a, *b*, to the *first* boy,
c, *d*, *e*, *f*, to the *second*;

and another different way would be to give

a, *b*, to the *second* boy,
c, *d*, *e*, *f*, to the *first*;

but if the question be merely of dividing the six things into two parcels, with no distinction between them, we have now corresponding to the two ways noted for the previous question, only the one way, viz., to put

a, *b* into *one* parcel,
c, *d*, *e*, *f* into the *other*.

Thus for every two ways of dividing the things between two different boys, there is only one way of dividing them into two in-different parcels; and, therefore, we have the choice in this last case of only thirty-one ways.

The relation of the last two results may be more clearly understood by the following consideration. We have in Question 21 six articles to divide between two boys. We may resolve the operation into the two operations of (1) dividing the articles into two parcels, and (2) when these parcels are made, giving them to the two boys. Now we can form our two parcels in thirty-one ways, and when the two parcels are made, we can give them, one to each boy, in two ways; hence by Rule I. we can make the parcels and dispense them in 31 × 2 or 62 ways.

Question 23.   In how many ways can the following letters be divided between two persons :—

$$a,\ a,\ a,\ a,\ b,\ b,\ b,\ c,\ c,\ d\,?$$

Answer.   Of the *a, a, a, a,* the first person can take either *none,* or *one,* or *two,* or *three,* or *four.*   That is, the *a, a, a, a* can be divided in five different ways ; so also the *b, b, b* can be divided in four ways ; the *c, c* in three ways ; and the *d* can be disposed of in two ways.   Hence (by Rule II.) the whole division can be made in

$$5 \times 4 \times 3 \times 2, \text{ or } 120$$

different ways, including, however, the ways in which either person gets *none* and the other gets *all.*   Excluding these two ways, the number of eligible ways is 118.

Question 24.   In the ordinary system of notation, how many numbers are there which consist of five digits ?

Answer.   The first digit may be any of the ten except 0.   We have, therefore, the choice of nine ways of assigning this digit.   Each of the other four digits may be any whatever, and therefore there are ten ways of assigning each of them.   Hence, altogether (by Rule II.) the number can be formed in

$$9 \times 10 \times 10 \times 10 \times 10, \text{ or } 90000$$

different ways ; or 90000 different numbers can be thus formed.

Of course these are all the numbers from 10000 to 99999 inclusive.

Question 25.   The cylinder of a letter-lock contains four rings, each marked with twenty-six different letters ; how many different attempts to open the lock may be made by a person ignorant of the key-word ?

Answer.   The first ring can be placed in twenty-six different positions ; so may the second ; so may the third ; so may the fourth. Hence (by Rule II.) there are

$$26 \times 26 \times 26 \times 26, \text{ or } 456976$$

different positions possible, and *one* of these is the right one.   Hence it is possible to make 456975 unsuccessful trials.

RULE III.

The number of ways in which a given number of things can be arranged is the continued product of the given number, and all whole numbers less than it.

Thus, three things can be arranged in $3 \times 2 \times 1$, or 6 ways; four things in $4 \times 3 \times 2 \times 1$, or 24 ways; five things in $5 \times 4 \times 3 \times 2 \times 1$, or 120 ways.

It will be sufficient to shew the reason of this rule in a particular case. The reasoning will be of a sufficiently general character to apply to any other case.

Take for example the case of five things. We have then a choice of five ways of filling the first place in order. When that place is filled there remain four things, and therefore we have a choice of four ways of filling the second place. Then there are three things left, and we can fill the third place in three ways. So we can fill the fourth place in two ways, and the last place in only one way, since we must give to it the one thing that is now left. Hence (by Rule II.) all the places can be filled in $5 \times 4 \times 3 \times 2 \times 1$ ways, or the whole set of five things can be arranged in $5 \times 4 \times 3 \times 2 \times 1$ ways, which shews that Rule III. is true in this case.

By exactly similar reasoning, we can shew that the rule is true in any other case. Hence we may accept it universally.

NOTE. It is usual to put the mark $\lfloor$ round a number to denote the continued product of *that number and all lesser numbers*. Thus—

$\lfloor 2$ denotes 2×1, or 2;

$\lfloor 3$ denotes $3 \times 2 \times 1$, or 6;

$\lfloor 4$ denotes $4 \times 3 \times 2 \times 1$, or 24;

$\lfloor 5$ denotes $5 \times 4 \times 3 \times 2 \times 1$, or 120;

$\lfloor 6$ denotes $6 \times 5 \times 4 \times 3 \times 2 \times 1$, or 720; and so on.

Question 26.   In how many ways can we arrange six statues in six niches, one in each ?

Answer.   It might seem, at first sight, that as the statues and the niches can each of them separately be taken in any order, we should have to consider the order of both to determine what choice of arrangement we have.

But, even though we take the niches in a stated order, any possible result whatsoever may be attained by varying the order of the statues. We may, in fact, regard the niches as forming a row in fixed order, and we have only to consider in how many different orders the six statues may be taken so as to fill the six niches in order.   Consequently, the number of ways in which it is possible to arrange the six statues in the six niches is the same as the number of orders in which the six statues can themselves be taken, which by the rule is $\lfloor 6$, or 720.

This explanation will be the better understood by comparing the next two questions.

Question 27.   In how many ways can twelve ladies and twelve gentlemen form themselves into couples for a dance ?

Answer. $\lfloor 12$.   For the first gentleman can choose a partner in twelve ways ; then the second has choice of eleven ; the third has choice of ten, and so on.   Therefore they can take partners altogether in [1]

$$12.11.10.9.8.7.6.5.4.3.2.1, \text{ or } \lfloor 12$$

ways.

Question 28.   There are twelve ladies and twelve gentlemen in a ball-room ; in how many ways can they take their places for a contre-danse ?

Answer.   The couples can be formed in $\lfloor 12$ ways (last question), and when formed, the couples can be arranged in $\lfloor 12$ different orders (Rule III.).   Therefore the twelve ladies and twelve gentlemen can arrange themselves in $\lfloor 12 \times \lfloor 12$ different ways.

Or we may reason thus :

The ladies can take their places in $\lfloor 12$ different ways (by Rule III.),

[1] The full-point is used for the sign of multiplication.

and so the gentlemen can take theirs in ⌊12 different ways. Therefore (by Rule I.) the ladies and gentlemen can arrange themselves in ⌊12 × ⌊12 different ways, as before.

Question 29. In how many different orders can the letters a, b, c, d, e, f be arranged so as to begin with ab ?

Answer. 24. For our only choice lies in the arrangement of the remaining four letters, which can be put in ⌊4 or 24 different orders (by Rule III.).

Question 30. A shelf contains five volumes of Latin, six of Greek, and eight of English. In how many ways can the nineteen books be arranged, keeping all the Latin together, all the Greek together, and all the English together ?

Answer. The volumes of Latin can be arranged among themselves (by Rule III.) in ⌊5 ways, the volumes of Greek among themselves in ⌊6 ways, and the volumes of English among themselves in ⌊8 ways. Also, when each set is thus prepared, the three sets can be placed on the shelf in ⌊3 different orders. Therefore, by Rule II., the number of ways in which the whole can be done is

$$⌊5 × ⌊6 × ⌊8 × ⌊3, \text{ or } 20901888000.$$

Question 31. In how many ways could the same books be arranged indiscriminately on the shelf ?

Answer. ⌊19, or 121645100408832000 ways.

It often requires considerable thought to determine what is meant by "different ways" of forming a ring. The next three questions suggest three meanings which the words in several circumstances will bear. It will be well to consider them, and compare them carefully, that the distinctions among them may be thoroughly recognised.

Question 32. A table being laid for eight persons, in how many ways can they take their places ?

Answer. By Rule III., the number of ways is ⌊8 or 40320.

Question 33. In how many ways can eight children form themselves into a ring, to dance round a may-pole ?

Answer. In this case we have not to assign the eight children
to particular places absolutely, but only to arrange them relatively
to one another. We may, in fact, make all possible arrangements,
by placing the first child, **A**, in any fixed position, and disposing
the others, *B, C, D, E, F, G, H*, in different ways with respect to him.
Thus there is no essential difference between the first three of the
following arrangements—

```
      AB              CD              DE              AH
   H     C         B     E         C     F         B     G
   G  *  D         A  *  F         B  *  G         C  *  F
      FE              HG              AH              DE
```

but the fourth (in which the circular order is reversed) is in the
meaning of the present question an essentially different arrangement ;
and any other essentially different arrangement might be obtained
without disturbing **A**, since absolute position is not taken into account.
Now the seven children *B, C, D, E, F, G, H* can be arranged, by
Rule III., in |7 or 5040 ways. This, therefore, is the whole number
of ways in which such a ring can be formed.

Question 34. In how many ways can eight beads be strung on
an elastic band to form a bracelet ?

Answer. This question is not equivalent to the preceding one, for
if we examine the first and fourth of the arrangements, which we
marked down as examples of the different ways in which the ring
could be made, we shall observe that though they would count as
different arrangements of children round a may-pole, they would count
as the same arrangement of beads in a bracelet, presenting only
opposite views of the same bracelet ; each being, in fact, the arrangement that would be presented by turning the other completely over.
So the 5040 arrangements which we could make according to the last
question, might be disposed into 2520 pairs, each pair presenting
only opposite views of the same ring, and not representing more than
one essentially different arrangement. Hence the answer is in this
case only 2520.

NOTE. Numbers are called *successive* when they proceed in order, each one differing from the preceding one

by *unity*. The numbers are said to be *descending* when they commence with the greatest and continually decrease; they are said to be *ascending* when they commence with the least and continually increase; and such a series of numbers is said to ascend or descend (as the case may be) *from* the first number of the series.

Thus 17, 18, 19 are successive numbers ascending from 17.

So, 17, 16, 15, 14 are successive numbers descending from 17.

And ⌊5 might be described as the continued product of five successive numbers, ascending from unity (or descending from 5); ⌊7, as the continued product of seven successive numbers ascending from unity (or descending from 7), and so on.

RULE IV.

Out of a given number of things,

the number of ways in which an arrangement of two things can be made is the product of the given number and the next lesser number;

the number of ways in which an arrangement of three things can be made is the continued product of three successive numbers descending from the given number;

the number of ways in which an arrangement of four things can be made is the continued product of four successive numbers descending from the given number;

and so on.

In other words:

If an arrangement have to be made consisting of an

assigned (smaller) number of things chosen out of a given (larger) number of things, the number of ways is the continued product of the assigned smaller number of successive numbers, descending from the given larger number.

The reason of this rule will be seen at once. For suppose we have seventeen given things; then, if we wish to make an arrangement of *two* things, we have the choice of seventeen things to place first; then there are sixteen things left, out of which we have to choose one to place second, and complete our arrangement. Hence, by Rule I., the number of ways in which we can make an arrangement of two things, is 17.16.

So if we wish to make an arrangement of *three* things, we can place the first two in 17.16 ways; and we then have fifteen things left, out of which to choose one to come third, and complete our arrangement; therefore, by Rule I., the number of ways in which we can make an arrangement of three things is the product of 17.16 and 15 or 17.16.15 : and so on.

Many questions which might be considered under Rule II. may be answered directly by this rule. Thus—

Question 35. How many three-lettered words could be made out of an alphabet of twenty-six letters, not using any letter more than once ?

Answer. 26.25.24 = 15600.

Question 36. How many four-lettered words ?

Answer. 26.25.24.23 = 358800.

Question 37. How many eight-lettered words ?

Answer. 26.25.24.23.22.21.20.19 = 62990928000.

Question 38. Four flags are to be hoisted on one mast, and there are twenty different flags to choose from : what choice have we ?

Answer. By Rule IV. we have the choice of

$$20.19.18.17, \text{ or } 116280$$

different ways.

The answer would evidently be the same if the flags were to be hoisted on different masts, for so long as there are four different positions to be occupied, the operation consists in the arrangement in these positions of four out of the twenty flags.

Question 39. An eight-oared boat has to be manned out of a club consisting of fifty rowing members. In how many ways can the crew be arranged?

Answer. We have simply to arrange eight men in order out of fifty men. Therefore Rule IV. applies, and the number of ways is

$$50.49.48.47.46.45.44.43, \text{ or } 21646947168000.$$

RULE V.

The number of ways in which twenty things can be divided into two classes of twelve and eight respectively, is

$$\frac{\lfloor 20}{\lfloor 12 \cdot \lfloor 8};$$

and similarly for any other numbers.

Suppose that twenty persons have to take their places in twelve front seats and eight back seats. By Rule III., since there are 20 people and 20 seats, they can be arranged altogether in $\lfloor 20$ ways. But the operation of arranging them may be resolved into the following three operations :—

(1) The operation of dividing the twenty into two classes of twelve and eight.

(2) The operation of arranging the class of twelve in the twelve front seats.

(3) The operation of arranging the class of eight in the eight back seats.

Hence, by Rule II. $\lfloor 20$ is the product of the number of ways in which these three several operations can be performed. But by Rule III. the second can be performed in $\lfloor 12$ ways, and the third in $\lfloor 8$ ways; therefore it follows that the first can be performed in

$$\frac{\lfloor 20}{\lfloor 12 \cdot \lfloor 8}$$

ways. This, therefore, expresses the number of ways in which twenty things can be divided into two classes, of which the first shall contain twelve things, and the second shall contain eight.

And it will be observed that our reasoning throughout is perfectly general, and would equally apply if, instead of the number twenty divided into the parts twelve and eight, we had any other number divided into any two assigned parts whatever.

Hence we can write down on the same plan the number of ways in which any given number of things can be divided into two classes, with a given number in each.

Question 40. In how many ways can two men divide 30 different books between them, one to have twice as many as the other?

Answer. The 30 books have to be divided into two classes of 20 and 10. This can be done in

$$\frac{\lfloor 30}{\lfloor 20 \cdot \lfloor 10}$$

ways, or 30045015 ways.

Question 41. Eight men are to take their places in an eight-oared boat; but two of them can only row on stroke side, and one of them only on bow side; the others can row on either side. In how many ways can the men be arranged?

Answer. The operation of arranging the men may be resolved into the following three simple and successive operations, viz.,

(1) To divide the five men who can row on either side into two parties of two and three, to complete stroke side and bow side respectively.

(2) To arrange stroke side when it is thus completed ; and

(3) To arrange bow side.

The five men who can row on either side can be divided into two parties of two and three respectively, in

$$\frac{\lfloor 5}{\lfloor 3 . \lfloor 2}, \text{ or } 10$$

ways, by Rule V. And when this is done, stroke side, consisting of four men, can be arranged in $\lfloor 4$ or twenty-four different ways (Rule III.) ; and likewise bow side in twenty-four ways. Hence the whole arrangement can be made in $10 \times 24 \times 24$, or 5760 ways.

RULE VI.

The number of ways in which twenty things can be divided into three classes of five, seven, and eight, respectively, is

$$\frac{\lfloor 20}{\lfloor 5 . \lfloor 7 . \lfloor 8},$$

and similarly for any other numbers.

For, by Rule V., the twenty things can be divided into two classes of twelve and eight in

$$\frac{\lfloor 20}{\lfloor 12 . \lfloor 8}$$

different ways, and, when this is done, the class of twelve can be divided into two classes of five and seven in

$$\frac{\lfloor 12}{\lfloor 5 . \lfloor 7}$$

ways. Hence, by Rule I., both these can be done in

$$\frac{\lfloor 20}{\lfloor 12 \cdot \lfloor 8} \times \frac{\lfloor 12}{\lfloor 5 \cdot \lfloor 7}, \text{ or } \frac{\lfloor 20}{\lfloor 5 \cdot \lfloor 7 \cdot \lfloor 8}$$

different ways.

That is, twenty things can be divided into three classes of five, seven and eight severally, in

$$\frac{\lfloor 20}{\lfloor 5 \cdot \lfloor 7 \cdot \lfloor 8}$$

different ways; and since our reasoning is perfectly general, a similar result may be written down when the numbers are any other.

And it is easily seen that the reasoning may be extended, in the same manner, to the case of more than three classes.

Question 42. In how many ways can three boys divide twelve oranges, each taking four, the oranges being all of different sizes?

Answer. By Rule VI. the number of different ways in which twelve things can be divided into three classes of four each, is

$$\frac{\lfloor 12}{\lfloor 4 \cdot \lfloor 4 \cdot \lfloor 4}, \text{ or } 34650.$$

Question 43. In how many ways can they divide them, so that the eldest gets five, the next four, and the youngest three?

Answer. By Rule VI. the number of different ways is

$$\frac{\lfloor 12}{\lfloor 3 \cdot \lfloor 4 \cdot \lfloor 5}, \text{ or } 27720.$$

Question 44. If there be fifteen apples all alike, twenty pears all alike, and twenty-five oranges all alike, in how many ways can sixty boys take one each?

Answer. The boys have, in fact, to form themselves into a party of fifteen for the apples, a party of twenty for the pears, and a party of twenty-five for the oranges. They can therefore do it by Rule VI. in

$$\frac{\lfloor 60}{\lfloor 15 \cdot \lfloor 20 \cdot \lfloor 25}$$

different ways.

Question 45. In how many ways can two sixes, three fives, and an ace be thrown with six dice?

Answer. The six dice have to be divided into three sets, containing 2, 3, 1 severally, of which the first set are to be placed with *six* upwards ; the second set with *five* upwards ; and the third set with *ace* upwards. By Rule VI. it can be done in

$$\frac{\lfloor 6}{\lfloor 3 \, . \, \lfloor 2 \, . \, \lfloor 1}, \text{ or } 60$$

different ways.

Question 46. In how many ways may fifty-two cards be divided amongst four players, so that each may have thirteen?

Answer. By Rule VI.,

$$\frac{\lfloor 52}{\lfloor 13 \, . \, \lfloor 13 \, . \, \lfloor 13 \, . \, \lfloor 13}.$$

When a number of things have to be divided into *equal* sets, special care is needed to consider the circumstances of the case so as to determine whether the sets are different or indifferent, that is to say, whether a new distribution will or will not be arrived at by taking two whole sets and interchanging them. There is no difficulty when the number of things to be assigned to the different sets is unequal, as this inequality of number itself suffices to make the sets *different;* and then Rules V. and VI. are applicable without modification. But when the sets are equal, it may happen that they are indifferent, and Rules V. and VI. will not give the true result.

For example, if 22 boys have to arrange themselves into two sets of 10 and 12 respectively to play a match, the number of ways in which they can be divided is

$$\frac{\lfloor 22}{\lfloor 10 \, . \, \lfloor 12}.$$

But if they are to form two elevens, the number of ways is

$$\text{not } \frac{\lfloor 22}{\lfloor 11 \cdot \lfloor 11}, \qquad \text{but } \tfrac{1}{2} \frac{\lfloor 22}{\lfloor 11 \cdot \lfloor 11},$$

since putting a, b, c, d, e, f, g, h, j, k, l into one set, and m, n, o, p, q, r, s, t, u, v, w into the other, is the same arrangement as if these were reversed, and m, n, o, p, q, r, s, t, u, v, w put into the first set, and the rest left for the other. Consequently if we took $\dfrac{\lfloor 22}{\lfloor 11 \cdot \lfloor 11}$ as the result given by Rule V., every arrangement would be counted twice over, and the true result will therefore be obtained by dividing by **2**. If however the two sides into which the boys are to be divided are to be distinguished by two names, if one is a "First Eleven" and the other a "Second Eleven," or if one side are to wear blue uniform and the other red, if there is in fact anything to mark them as two different classes, Rule V. will apply and the result will be

$$\frac{\lfloor 22}{\lfloor 11 \cdot \lfloor 11}.$$

Whenever the sets are indifferent, Rule V. or VI. gives each arrangement repeated as many times as the sets could be permuted among themselves, *i.e.* $\lfloor 2$ times when there are 2 sets, $\lfloor 3$ times when there are 3 sets, and so on. Hence we have to divide the result of Rule VI. by $\lfloor 2$ or $\lfloor 3$ or $\lfloor 4$ or &c., according to the number of sets.

Question 47. In how many ways can 52 different cards be divided into four parcels of 13 each?

Answer. This question differs from Question 46 only by the parcels being *indifferent*. The result in that question must be divided by $\lfloor 4$ and will give

$$\frac{\lfloor 52}{\lfloor 4 \cdot \lfloor 13 \cdot \lfloor 13 \cdot \lfloor 13 \cdot \lfloor 13}.$$

Question 48.   In how many ways can 12 different books be put into three parcels, one of which is to hold 3, another 4, and the other 5 ?

Answer. $$\frac{\lfloor 12}{\lfloor 3 \,.\, \lfloor 4 \,.\, \lfloor 5} = 27720.$$

It ought to be clearly seen that in such cases as this what constitutes the parcels *different*, is that they are necessarily to have different numbers 3, 4, 5 assigned to them. In Question 22 the mere fact of our putting two things into one parcel and four into another did not constitute the parcels different, for there was nothing in the question to make one parcel always have two and another always four; *each parcel* might have any number so long as they together contained six.

It must be observed that there is some ambiguity in the manner in which the words sort and class are sometimes used, especially when we describe collections of articles as of different sorts or of the same sort, or of different classes or of the same class.

Thus, if letters have been spoken of as consonants and vowels, we may describe the alphabet as containing twenty letters of one sort, and six letters of the other sort; yet if we regard the individual character of each letter, we shall speak of a printer's fount as containing twenty-six different sorts of letters. Plainly, there are either two classes or twenty-six classes, according to the character adopted as the criterion of class.

For instance, we may describe the letters

a, a, a, x, x,

as *three of one sort and two of another sort.*   But the letters

a, e, i, x, z,

regarded as vowels and consonants, might also be described as *three of one sort and two of another sort.*

Suppose now we are asked in how many different orders we can write down five different letters, of which three are of one sort and two of another sort, the answer will depend entirely on the sense in which "sort" is understood. If we suppose the letters to be such as

$$a, a, a, x, x,$$

where those of the same sort are absolutely identical with one another, having no personal individuality (so to speak), the answer will be

$$\frac{\lfloor 5}{\lfloor 3 . \lfloor 2}$$

(by Rule V.), since our only choice lies in dividing the five places into two sets of three and two, for the $a, a, a,$ and x, x. But if the given letters be such as

$$a, e, i, x, z,$$

where the three, $a, e, i,$ are of one sort as vowels, but each has an individual character of its own, and the two, $x, z,$ are of one sort as consonants, but these also (like the vowels) distinct in their identity, then the answer becomes $\lfloor 5$, by Rule III., since the five letters are for the purposes of arrangement all different.

We shall avoid this ambiguity as much as possible, by speaking of things as of one *sort*, when there is no individual distinction amongst them, and of one *class* when they are united by a common characteristic, but capable, at the same time, of distinction one from another.

RULE VII.

The number of orders in which twenty letters can be arranged, of which four are of one sort ($a, a, a, a,$ suppose), *five of another sort (b, b, b, b, b, suppose), two of another sort (c, c, suppose), and the remaining nine all different, is*

$$\frac{\lfloor 20}{\lfloor 4 \cdot \lfloor 5 \cdot \lfloor 2} ;$$

and similarly for any other numbers.

For the operation of arranging the letters in order may be resolved into the following :—

    (1)   To divide the twenty places into four sets, of four, five, two, nine, respectively.

    (2)   To place the *a, a, a, a,* in the set of four places.

    (3)   To place the *b, b, b, b, b,* in the set of five places.

    (4)   To place the *c, c,* in the set of two places.

    (5)   To *arrange* the nine remaining letters in the set of nine places.

Now by Rule VI., the operation (1) can be done in

$$\frac{\lfloor 20}{\lfloor 4 \cdot \lfloor 5 \cdot \lfloor 2 \cdot \lfloor 9}$$

different ways.

The operation (2) can be done in only one way, since the letters are all alike.

So the operations (3) (4) can be done in only one way each.

And the operation (5) can be performed in $\lfloor 9$ ways by Rule III.

Therefore by Rule II. the whole complex operation can be performed in

$$\frac{\lfloor 20}{\lfloor 4 \cdot \lfloor 5 \cdot \lfloor 2 \cdot \lfloor 9} \times \lfloor 9, \text{ or } \frac{\lfloor 20}{\lfloor 4 \cdot \lfloor 5 \cdot \lfloor 2}$$

different ways.

And in the same way we can reason about any other case. Hence in any case, to find the number of orders in which a series of letters can be arranged which are not all alike, we have only to write down the fraction, having in the numerator the total number of the letters, and in the denominator the numbers of letters of the several sorts; each number being enclosed in the mark $\lfloor$.

Question 49. In how many orders can we arrange the letters of the word *indivisibility?*

Answer. $\dfrac{\lfloor 14}{\lfloor 6} = 14.13.12.11.10.9.8.7 = 121080960.$

Question 50. In how many orders can we arrange the letters of the word *parallelepiped?*

Answer. $\dfrac{\lfloor 14}{\lfloor 3 . \lfloor 3 . \lfloor 3 . \lfloor 2} = 201801600.$

Question 51. In how many orders can we arrange the letters of the word *llangollen?*

Answer. 75600.

RULE VIII.

Out of twenty things, a selection of twelve things can be made in the same number of ways as a selection of eight things (where $12 + 8 = 20$*); and the number of ways is*

$$\frac{\lfloor 20}{\lfloor 12 . \lfloor 8} ;$$

and similarly for other numbers of things.

For the selection of twelve (or eight) things out of twenty, consists of the operation of dividing the twenty things into two sets of twelve and eight, and rejecting one of the sets.

Therefore by Rule V., whichever set be rejected, the operation can be performed in

$$\frac{\underline{20}}{\underline{12} \cdot \underline{8}}$$

different ways.

Question 52. Out of one hundred things, in how many ways can three things be selected ?

Answer. By Rule VIII.,

$$\frac{\underline{100}}{\underline{97} \cdot \underline{3}} ;$$

or striking out from the numerator and the denominator all the successive factors from 1 to 97,

$$\frac{100 \cdot 99 \cdot 98}{\underline{3}} .$$

In the last result, we observe that the numerator 100.99.98 expresses (Rule V.) the number of ways in which an *arrangement* of three things might be made out of one hundred things.

This suggests the following rule for the number of ways of selecting any number of things out of a larger number, which will often be found more convenient than Rule VIII., although both of course lead to the same result.

RULE IX.

Out of any given number of things,
the number of selections of two things may be obtained from the number of arrangements of two things, by dividing by $\underline{2}$;

the number of selections of three things may be obtained from the number of arrangements of three things, by dividing by $\underline{3}$;

the number of selections of four things may be obtained from the number of arrangements of four things, by dividing by $\lfloor 4$;

and so on.

It will be sufficient to shew the reason of this rule in any particular case.

Suppose we have to make a selection of three things out of a given number of things; what is our choice in this case, compared with our choice in making an arrangement of three things ?

The operation of making an *arrangement* of three things may be resolved into the two operations following, viz.—

(1) To make a *selection* of three things out of the given things.

(2) To arrange in order the three selected things.

Therefore, by Rule I., the number of ways of making an *arrangement* of three things is equal to the number of ways of making a *selection* of three things, multiplied by the number of ways of arranging the three selected things.

But by Rule III., three things can be arranged in $\lfloor 3$ different ways.

Hence, the number of *arrangements* of three things, out of a greater number, is equal to the number of *selections* multiplied by $\lfloor 3$.

Or, the number of *selections* of three things is equal to the number of *arrangements* divided by $\lfloor 3$.

And the same reasoning would apply if the number of things to be selected were any other instead of 3. Therefore the rule is true always.

The student being in possession of the two rules (VIII. and IX.) for writing down the number of ways in which any number of things can be selected out of a larger number,

will, in any particular case, use the rule which may seem the
more convenient. It will be observed that Rule VIII. gives
the result in the more *concise* form when the number of
things to be selected is a high number; but the fraction
thus written down, though more concisely expressed, is not
in such low terms as˙that which would be written down by
Rule IX. Consequently, when the actual numerical value
of the result is required, Rule IX. leaves the less work to be
done, in cancelling out common factors from the numerator
and the denominator. In many cases, it is simplest to take
advantage of the principle of Rule VIII., that out of twenty
things (suppose) the number of ways in which seventeen
things can be selected is the same as the number of ways
in which 20 − 17 or three things can be selected,˙and then
to apply Rule IX. For, comparing the different forms of
the result in this case, we observe that Rule VIII. gives

$$\frac{\lfloor 20}{\lfloor 17 . \lfloor 3}$$

while Rule IX. gives

$$\frac{20.19.18.17.16.15.14.13.12.11.10.9.8.7.6.5.4}{1.2.3.4.5.6.7.8.9.10.11.12.13.14.15.16.17}$$

which might be simplified by dividing the numerator and
denominator by the factors

$$4.5.6.7.8.9.10.11.12.13.14.15.16.17.$$

But if we recognise the teaching of Rule VIII., that the
number of ways of selecting seventeen things is the same as
the number of ways of selecting three things, and then apply
Rule IX. to find the number of ways of selecting three
things, we can at once write down the result in the simple
form

$$\frac{20.19.18}{1.2.3} .$$

Question 53.   Out of a basket of twenty pears at three a penny, how many ways are there of selecting six pennyworth ?

Answer.   By Rule VIII., we can select eighteen out of twenty in as many ways as we can select two ; and, by Rule IX., this can be done in

$$\frac{20.19}{1.2}, \text{ or } 190$$

ways.

Question 54.   In how many ways can the same choice be exercised so as to include the largest pear ?

Answer.   Taking the largest pear first, our only choice now lies in selecting seventeen out of the remaining nineteen, which can be done (Rules VIII. and IX.) in

$$\frac{19.18}{1.2}, \text{ or } 171$$

ways.

Question 55.   In how many ways can the same choice be exercised without taking the smallest pear ?

Answer.   We have now to select eighteen pears out of nineteen. Therefore (Rules VIII. and IX.) our choice can be exercised in nineteen ways.

Question 56.   In how many ways can the same choice be exercised so as to include the largest, and not to include the smallest pear ?

Answer.   Taking the largest pear first, we have then to choose seventeen more out of eighteen, which can be done (Rules VIII. and IX.) in eighteen ways.

Question 57.   Out of forty-two radicals and fifty reformers, what choice is there in selecting a committee consisting of four radicals and four reformers ?

Answer.   The radical committee-men can be chosen (by Rule VIII.) in

$$\frac{42.41.40.39}{1.2.3.4}, \text{ or } 111930$$

different ways, and the reformers in

$$\frac{50.49.48.47}{1.2.3.4}, \text{ or } 230300$$

different ways.   Hence (by Rule I.) the whole choice can be exercised in

$$111930 \times 230300, \text{ or } 25777479000$$

different ways.

Question 58.   A company of volunteers consists of a captain, a lieutenant, an ensign, and eighty rank and file.   In how many ways can ten men be selected so as to include the captain?

Answer.   Since the captain is to be one of the ten, the only choice lies in the selection of nine men out of the remaining eighty-two, which can be done (Rule VIII. or IX.) in

$$\frac{\lfloor 82}{\lfloor 9 . \lfloor 73}, \text{ or } \frac{82.81.80.79.78.77.76.75.74}{\lfloor 9}$$

different ways.

Question 59.   In how many ways can ten men be selected so as to include *at least one* officer?

Answer.   By Rule VIII., ten men can be selected out of the whole company in

$$\frac{\lfloor 83}{\lfloor 10 . \lfloor 73}$$

ways altogether.   But the number of different ways that will include *no officer* will be the number of ways in which ten can be selected out of the eighty rank and file, that is (by Rule VIII.),

$$\frac{\lfloor 80}{\lfloor 10 . \lfloor 70}.$$

These must be subtracted from the whole number of ways in which ten men might be selected, and the remainder

$$\frac{\lfloor 83}{\lfloor 10 . \lfloor 73} - \frac{\lfloor 80}{\lfloor 10 . \lfloor 70}$$

will be the number of ways in which they may be selected so as to include at least one officer.

Question 60. In how many ways can ten men be selected so as to include *exactly one* officer ?

Answer. The nine rank and file can be selected in

$$\frac{\lfloor 80}{\lfloor 9 \cdot \lfloor 71}$$

ways, and the one officer in three ways. Therefore the ten can be selected in

$$\frac{3 \times \lfloor 80}{\lfloor 9 \cdot \lfloor 71}$$

different ways.

Question 61. There are fifteen candidates for admission into a society which has two vacancies. There are seven electors, and each can either vote for two candidates, or plump for one. In how many ways can the votes be given ?

Answer. Each voter can plump in fifteen ways, and can vote for two candidates in

$$\frac{15 \cdot 14}{1 \cdot 2}, \text{ or } 105$$

ways (Rule IX.). Therefore each elector can vote altogether in 120 ways. And there are seven electors; therefore all the votes can be given (by Rule II.) in

$$120 \times 120 \times 120 \times 120 \times 120 \times 120 \times 120,$$

or 358318080000000 different ways.

It will be well to notice particularly the points which distinguish the next three examples.

In all of them we suppose twenty things of one class and six things of another class set before us, the individuals of each class being distinct; and in all of them a selection has to be made of three things out of each class. But while the first is a case of simple selection, in the second each set of three things has separately to be arranged in order, and in the third the whole six selected things have to be together arranged in order.

Question 62.   Out of twenty men and six women, what choice have we in selecting three men and three women ?

Answer.   The men can be selected in

$$\frac{20 \cdot 19 \cdot 18}{1 \cdot 2 \cdot 3}, \text{ or } 1140$$

different ways (Rule IX.), and the women in

$$\frac{6 \cdot 5 \cdot 4}{1 \cdot 2 \cdot 3}, \text{ or } 20$$

different ways.   Therefore, we have the choice of

$$1140 \times 20, \text{ or } 22800$$

different ways of making our selection.

Question 63.   Out of twenty men and six women, what choice have we in filling up six different offices, three of which must be filled by men, and the other three by women ?

Answer.   We can allot the first three offices to three men in 20 . 19 . 18 or 6840 different ways (Rule IV.); and we can allot the other three offices to three women in 6 . 5 . 4 or 120 different ways. Therefore, we have the choice of

$$6840 \times 120, \text{ or } 820800$$

different ways of making our arrangement.

Question 64.   Out of twenty consonants and six vowels, in how many ways can we make a word, consisting of three different consonants, and three different vowels ?

Answer.   We can select three consonants in

$$\frac{20 \cdot 19 \cdot 18}{1 \cdot 2 \cdot 3}, \text{ or } 1140$$

different ways, and three vowels in

$$\frac{6 \cdot 5 \cdot 4}{1 \cdot 2 \cdot 3}, \text{ or } 20$$

different ways.   Therefore (by Rule I.), the six letters can be selected in

$$1140 \times 20, \text{ or } 22800$$

different ways; and when they are so selected, they can be arranged (by Rule III.), in $\lfloor 6$ or 720 different orders. Hence (by Rule I.), there are 22800×720, or 16416000 different ways of making the word.

Question 65. Out of the twenty-six letters of the alphabet, in how many ways can we make a word consisting of four different letters, one of which must be always a?

Answer. Since we are always to use a, we must choose three letters out of the remaining twenty-five. This can be done in

$$\frac{25 \cdot 24 \cdot 23}{1 \cdot 2 \cdot 3}, \text{ or } 2300$$

ways. Then the whole set of four letters can be arranged in $\lfloor 4$ or 24 different orders. Hence we have the choice of

$$2300 \times 24, \text{ or } 55200$$

different ways of making the word.

The last answer might have been arrived at in another way, as follows:—

Without the limitation, we could make a word of four different letters in $26.25.24.23$, or 358800 different ways. The question is how many of these will contain a. Now if all the 358800 words were written down on paper, since each is made of four letters, our paper would contain 358800×4, or 1435200 letters. And since no letter of the alphabet has been used with more favour than any other, it follows that each would occur $1435200 \div 26$, or 55200 times. Therefore a must occur 55200 times; and since no word contains a more than once, 55200 words must contain a. That is, the number of words formed of four different letters of which a is one is 55200, as before.

Question 66. Out of the twenty-six letters of the alphabet, in how many ways can we make a word consisting of four different letters, two of which must be a and b?

Answer. We can choose the other two letters out of the remaining twenty-four in

$$\frac{24 \cdot 23}{1 \cdot 2}, \text{ or } 276$$

ways, and then we can arrange the whole set of four letters in $\lfloor 4$ or 24 different orders. Hence we have the choice of

$$276 \times 24, \text{ or } 6624$$

different ways of making the word.

Question 67. Out of twenty consonants and six vowels, in how many ways can we make a word consisting of three different vowels and two different consonants, one of the vowels being always *a*?

Answer. We can choose the other two vowels in

$$\frac{5 \cdot 4}{1 \cdot 2}, \text{ or } 10$$

ways, and the two consonants in

$$\frac{20 \cdot 19}{1 \cdot 2}, \text{ or } 190$$

ways; hence our letters can be selected in 1900 ways, and when they are selected the set of five can be arranged in $\lfloor 5$ or 120 ways. Hence the whole number of ways of making the word is

$$1900 \times 120, \text{ or } 228000.$$

Question 68. There are ten different situations vacant, of which four must be held by men, and three by women; the remaining three may be held by either men or women. If twenty male and six female candidates present themselves, in how many ways can we fill up the situations?

Answer. The men's situations can be filled up in $20 \cdot 19 \cdot 18 \cdot 17$ or 116280 different ways, and the women's in $6 \cdot 5 \cdot 4$ or 120 different ways. When this is done, there are nineteen persons left, all of whom are eligible for the other three situations. Hence these three can be filled up in $19 \cdot 18 \cdot 17$ or 5814 different ways. Therefore, the whole election can be made in

$$116280 \times 120 \times 5814, \text{ or } 81126230400$$

different ways.

RULE X.

Out of any number of things, the number of ways of selecting 5 *things when repetitions are allowed is the same as if there were* 5 − 1, *or* 4 *more things to be selected from, without repetitions; and so for any other number.*

A selection of 5 letters out of the alphabet when repetitions are allowed will include such selections as *aaaaa, aabcc, abbbc,* as well as those like *abcde, afghk,* which are alone valid when repetitions are not allowed.

The rule states that, repetitions being allowed, the number of selections of 5 letters out of (say) the 26 letters of the alphabet, is the same as the number of selections of 5 things out of 30 without repetitions, that is,

$$\frac{26 \cdot 27 \cdot 28 \cdot 29 \cdot 30}{1 \cdot 2 \cdot 3 \cdot 4 \cdot 5}.$$

Suppose the selections were all written down, add to each of them the whole alphabet.

Then each selection becomes a selection of 31 letters, in which each letter of the alphabet occurs at least once; and we have thus all possible selections of 31 letters, subject to the condition that each appears at least once.

By trying to construct these selections of 31 letters by another process, we shall find how many of them there must be.

To construct such a selection, since the order of the letters is immaterial, we are introducing no new limit if we determine to arrange the letters of each selection in any order; say, in alphabetical order.

Let us mark 31 places for the 31 letters in the selection, thus :

- -

We have to fill one or more of these places with a's, then one or more with b's, and so on. Now there are 30 spaces between the 31 places, and (when the 26 sorts of letter are put in) there will be 25 spaces between a's and b's, between b's and c's, and so on, and the remaining 5 spaces will be between repeated letters. All our choice resolves itself therefore into the number of ways in which we can choose 5 spaces out of 30 to come between the repeated letters.

Therefore the choice of selecting 5 out of 26 with repetitions is the same as the choice of selecting 5 out of 30 without repetitions. And the same argument would hold for any numbers, therefore the rule is true.

Question 69. Out of a large number of pennies, half-pennies, and farthings, in how many ways can one select four coins ?

Answer. The choice of selecting four coins out of the three with repetitions is the same as the choice of selecting four out of $3+4-1$, or 6, without repetitions : it is therefore

$$\frac{6.5.4.3}{1.2.3.4}, \text{ or } 15.$$

The fifteen selections are as follows :

$pppp,$	$pphh,$	$phhh,$	$pfff,$	$hhff,$
$ppph,$	$pphf,$	$phhf,$	$hhhh,$	$hfff,$
$pppf,$	$ppff,$	$phff,$	$hhhf,$	$ffff.$

Question 70. In how many ways can three glasses be filled without mixing, if we have five sorts of wine ?

Answer. To select three out of five, repetitions being permitted, is the same as to select three out of $5+3-1=7$ without repetitions. The number of ways is therefore

$$\frac{7.6.5}{1.2.3}, \text{ or } 35.$$

If a, e, i, o, u represent the five sorts of wine, the 35 ways are as follows :

$a\,a\,a$,	$a\,e\,e$,	$a\,i\,o$,	$e\,e\,e$,	$e\,i\,o$,	$i\,i\,i$,	$i\,u\,u$,
$a\,a\,e$,	$a\,e\,i$,	$a\,i\,u$,	$e\,e\,i$,	$e\,i\,u$,	$i\,i\,o$,	$o\,o\,o$,
$a\,a\,i$,	$a\,e\,o$,	$a\,o\,o$,	$e\,e\,o$,	$e\,o\,o$,	$i\,i\,u$,	$o\,o\,u$,
$a\,a\,o$,	$a\,e\,u$,	$a\,o\,u$,	$e\,e\,u$,	$e\,o\,u$,	$i\,o\,o$,	$o\,u\,u$,
$a\,a\,u$,	$a\,i\,i$,	$a\,u\,u$,	$e\,i\,i$,	$e\,u\,u$,	$i\,o\,u$,	$u\,u\,u$.

It is understood that the glasses are all alike, so that the arrangement $a\,e\,i$ is the same as $e\,a\,i$ or $e\,i\,a$. If the glasses be different then each can be filled in 5 ways, and all three in 125 ways.

Question 71. In how many ways can a dozen marbles be selected at a shop where they sell 5 kinds of marbles ?

Answer. The choice will be the same as in selecting 12 out of $12 + 5 - 1 = 16$, without repetitions ;

$$\frac{16 \cdot 15 \cdot 14 \cdot 13}{1 \cdot 2 \cdot 3 \cdot 4} = 1820.$$

Question 72. How many dominoes are there in a set numbered from double blank to double nine ?

Answer. Each domino is made by a selection of two numbers out of the ten 0, 1, 2, 3, 4, 5, 6, 7, 8, 9 ; and repetitions are allowed (*i.e.* the two numbers on a domino may be alike). Therefore the number is the same as the number of selections of two out of $10 + 2 - 1 = 11$, without repetitions, that is

$$\frac{11 \cdot 10}{1 \cdot 2} = 55.$$

ARRANGEMENTS OUT OF A NUMBER OF THINGS NOT ALL DIFFERENT.

We considered under Rule VII. the modifications of the case of Rule III., when the things out of which the arrangement is to be made are not all different. The corresponding modifications of Rule IV. are too intricate to be brought under general rules by arithmetical methods; but each case, as it arises, may be resolved into cases to which the preceding rules will apply. The manner of proceeding will be sufficiently illustrated by the following questions.

When however the number of things of each sort is not less than the whole number of things to be chosen, the problem resolves itself into the case of arrangements when repetitions are allowed, and comes under a very simple rule, to be presently given (Rule XI.).

Question 73. In how many ways can an arrangement of four letters be made out of the letters of the words *choice and chance?*

Answer. There are fifteen letters altogether, of eight different sorts, viz. *c, c, c, c ; h, h ; a, a ; n, n ; e, e ; o ; i ; d.* The different ways of selecting the four letters may, therefore, be classified as follows :

(1) all four alike,

(2) three alike and one different,

(3) two alike and two others alike,

(4) two alike and the other two different,

(5) all four different.

Now, the selection (1) can be made in only one way (viz. by selecting *c, c, c, c*), and when this selection of letters is made they can be arranged in only one order ;

therefore (1) gives rise to only one arrangement.

The selection (2) can be made in seven ways, for three letters alike can be selected in only one way (viz. *c, c, c*), and one different one in seven ways (*a, e, i, o, h, n, d*). And when this selection of letters is made, they can be arranged in four ways (Rule VII.) ;

therefore (2) gives rise to 7×4, or 28 arrangements.

The selection (3) can be made in $\dfrac{5 \cdot 4}{1 \cdot 2}$, or 10 ways (Rule IX.), since we have to select two out of the five pairs, *cc, hh, aa, nn, ee*. And when this selection of letters is made, they can be arranged in $\dfrac{\lfloor 4}{\lfloor 2 \cdot \lfloor 2}$, or 6 ways (Rule VII.) ;

therefore (3) gives rise to 10×6, or 60 arrangements.

The selection (4) can be made in 5×21, or 105 ways, for we can select one of the five pairs, *cc, hh, aa, nn, ee* in five ways, and two out of the seven different sorts of letters that will then be left, in $\dfrac{7 \cdot 6}{1 \cdot 2}$, or 21 ways (Rule IX.); and when this selection of letters is made, they can be arranged in $\dfrac{\lfloor 4}{\lfloor 2}$, or 12 ways (Rule VII.);

therefore (4) gives rise to 105×12, or 1260 arrangements.

The selection (5) of four different letters must be made out of the eight, *c, h, a, n, e, o, i, d*; therefore the number of arrangements which will come from such a selection must be $8 \cdot 7 \cdot 6 \cdot 5$ or 1680.

Hence, the whole number of arrangements of four letters out of the fifteen given letters is

$$1 + 28 + 60 + 1260 + 1680, \text{ or } 3029.$$

Question 74. In how many ways can an arrangement of three things be made out of fifteen things, of which five are of one sort, four of another sort, three of another sort, and the remaining three of another sort?

Answer. The three selected things may be either—

(1) all three alike,

or (2) two alike and one different,

or (3) all different.

Now, the selection of all three alike can be made in 4 ways, since we can take one of the four different sorts. And when this selection is made, the selected things can be arranged in only one order;

therefore (1) gives rise to only four arrangements.

The selection of two alike and one different can be made in 4×3, or 12 ways (Rule I.); for the two alike can be of any of the four sorts, and the one different of any one of the remaining three sorts. And when this selection is made, the things selected can be arranged in $\dfrac{\lfloor 3}{\lfloor 2}$, or three ways (Rule VII.);

therefore (2) gives rise to 12×3, or 36 arrangements.

And if all three selected things are to be different we shall have $4 \cdot 3 \cdot 2$, or 24 arrangements (Rule IV.).

Hence, the whole number of arrangements of three things out of the fifteen given things is

$$4+36+24, \text{ or } 64.$$

Question 75. In how many ways can an arrangement of five things be made out of the fifteen things given in the last question?

Answer. The different ways of selecting five things may be classified as follows :—

    (1) all five alike,

    (2) four alike and one different,

    (3) three alike and two others alike,

    (4) three alike and two different,

    (5) two alike, two others alike, and one different,

    (6) two alike and three different.

Now by the application of Rules II., VII., IX., as in the preceding questions, it will be easily seen that

the selection (1) can be made in one way, and leads to one arrangement :

the selection (2) can be made in six ways, and leads to 6×5 or 30 arrangements :

the selection (3) can be made in twelve ways, and leads to 12×10 or 120 arrangements :

the selection (4) can be made in twelve ways, and leads to 12×20 or 240 arrangements :

the selection (5) can be made in twelve ways, and leads to 12×30 or 360 arrangements :

the selection (6) can be made in four ways, and leads to 4×60 or 240 arrangements.

Hence the whole number of different arrangements is

$$1+30+120+240+360+240, \text{ or } 991.$$

RULE XI.

Out of 12 *things, the number of arrangements of* 5 *things when repetitions are allowed, is the continued product of* 12 *written down* 5 *times* $= 12 \times 12 \times 12 \times 12 \times 12$, *and so for any other numbers.*

For in making an arrangement of 5 things, we have the choice of 12 things to occupy the first place : and when the first place is filled we have still the choice of 12 things for the second place (since we are at liberty to repeat in the second place the same thing which we assigned to the first place). And when these two places are filled we have still the choice of 12 things for the third place, and so on. Therefore by Rule II. our whole choice is $12 \times 12 \times 12 \times 12 \times 12$. Q. E. D.

Question 76. In how many ways could a four-lettered word be made of an alphabet of 20 letters, repetitions being allowed ?

Answer. $20 \times 20 \times 20 \times 20 = 160000$.

Question 77. How many five-lettered words could be made of the five vowels, repetitions allowed ?

Answer. $5 \times 5 \times 5 \times 5 \times 5 = 3125$.

Question 78. With 10 figures, how many numbers can be made consisting of not more than 6 figures ?

Answer. We may suppose all the required numbers to be written with six figures, because if we have less than six we may insert cyphers at the beginning. Thus 473 may be written 000473. Hence every possible arrangement of 6 figures out of the ten will give the required set of numbers, except 000000, which must be struck out. The number of numbers is therefore

$$10 \times 10 \times 10 \times 10 \times 10 \times 10 - 1 = 999999.$$

RULE XII.

The whole number of ways in which a person can select some or all (as many as he pleases) of a given number of things, is one less than the continued product of 2 repeated the given number of times.

For since he is at liberty to take none or all or as

many as he pleases of the different things, he can dispose of each thing in two ways, for he can either take it or leave it. Now suppose there are five things, then he can act altogether in

$$2 \times 2 \times 2 \times 2 \times 2$$

different ways. But if he is not to reject *all* the things, the number of courses open to him will be one less than this, or

$$2 \times 2 \times 2 \times 2 \times 2 - 1.$$

And the same reasoning would apply if the number of things were any other number instead of five. Hence, the rule will be true always.

Question 79. One of the stalls in a bazaar contains twenty-seven articles exposed for sale. What choice has a purchaser?

Answer. He may buy either one thing or more, and there are twenty-seven things: therefore (by Rule X.), the number of courses open to him is one less than the continued product of twenty-seven *twos*, or 134217727.

Question 80. What is the greatest number of different amounts that can be made up by selection from five given weights?

Answer. By Rule XII., $2 \times 2 \times 2 \times 2 \times 2 - 1$ or 31.

In the case of the last question, the different selections will not always produce different sums. Hence, we cannot always make thirty-one different sums. But under favourable circumstances, as, for instance, when the weights are 1 lb., 2 lbs., 4 lbs., 8 lbs., 16 lbs., all the different selections will produce different sums, and then the number of different sums is thirty-one. Hence, thirty-one is the *greatest* number of different weights that can be made by a selection from five given weights.

In the case of the five weights, 1 lb., 2 lbs., 4 lbs., 8 lbs., 16 lbs., the thirty-one different amounts that can be weighed consist of every integral number of pounds from one to thirty-one.

Thus, with single weights, we can weigh the following numbers of pounds, viz., 1, 2, 4, 8, 16; and then we have

$3 = 1 + 2,$	$7 = 1 + 2 + 4,$	$15 = 1 + 2 + 4 + 8,$
$5 = 1 + 4,$	$11 = 1 + 2 + 8,$	$23 = 1 + 2 + 4 + 16,$
$6 = 2 + 4,$	$13 = 1 + 4 + 8,$	$27 = 1 + 2 + 8 + 16,$
$9 = 1 + 8,$	$14 = 2 + 4 + 8,$	$29 = 1 + 4 + 8 + 16,$
$10 = 2 + 8,$	$19 = 1 + 2 + 16,$	$30 = 2 + 4 + 8 + 16,$
$12 = 4 + 8,$	$21 = 1 + 4 + 16,$	
$17 = 1 + 16,$	$22 = 2 + 4 + 16,$	$31 = 1 + 2 + 4 + 8 + 16.$
$18 = 2 + 16,$	$25 = 1 + 8 + 16,$	
$20 = 4 + 16,$	$26 = 2 + 8 + 16,$	
$24 = 8 + 16,$	$28 = 4 + 8 + 16,$	

It may be observed that, if we had a 32 lbs. weight, by adding it to each of the sets already obtained, we should get all the numbers from 33 to 63 inclusive; hence all the weights

1 lb.   2 lbs.   4 lbs.   8 lbs.   16 lbs.   32 lbs.

would enable us to weigh any number of pounds from 1 to 63.

Then the addition of a 64 lbs. weight would enable us to weigh any number up to 127, and so on.

Question 81. What is the greatest number of different amounts that can be weighed with five weights, when each weight may be put into either scale?

Answer. This is not a direct example of our rule, but it may be solved on a like principle to that by which the rule itself was established.

Each weight can be disposed of in three ways, that is, it can be placed either in the weight-pan, or in the pan with the substance to be weighed, or it can be left out altogether. Hence, all the weights can be disposed in $3 \times 3 \times 3 \times 3 \times 3$, or 243 ways (Rule II.). But one of these ways would consist in rejecting *all* the weights; this must be cast out, and then there remain 242 ways. But in the most favourable case, half of these ways would consist in placing a less weight in the weight-pan than in the other, and these must be cast out. Hence there remain 121 different amounts that can be weighed under the most favourable circumstances with five weights, when it is permitted to place weights in the pan with the substance to be weighed.

The weights 1 lb., 3 lbs., 9 lbs., 27 lbs., 81 lbs., will afford an instance of the most favourable case. In this instance, the 121 amounts that can be weighed consist of every integral number of pounds from 1 to 121. Thus—

$2 = 3 - 1,$	$15 = 27 - 9 - 3,$
$4 = 3 + 1,$	$16 = 27 - 9 - 3 + 1,$
$5 = 9 - 3 - 1,$	$17 = 27 - 9 - 1,$
$6 = 9 - 3,$	$18 = 27 - 9,$
$7 = 9 - 3 + 1,$	$19 = 27 - 9 + 1,$
$8 = 9 - 1,$	$20 = 27 - 9 + 3 - 1,$
$10 = 9 + 1,$	$21 = 27 - 9 + 3,$
$11 = 9 + 3 - 1,$	$22 = 27 - 9 + 3 + 1,$
$12 = 9 + 3,$	$23 = 27 - 3 - 1,$
$13 = 9 + 3 + 1,$	$24 = 27 - 3,$
$14 = 27 - 9 - 3 - 1,$	&c.

RULE XIII.

The whole number of ways in which a person can select some or all (as many as he pleases) out of a number of things which are not all different, is one less than the continued product of the series of numbers formed by increasing by unity the several numbers of things of the several sorts.

Thus, suppose we have the letters—

$$a, a, a, a, a,$$
$$b, b, b,$$
$$c, c, c, c,$$
$$d,$$
$$e,$$

viz., five of one sort, three of another, four of a third sort, one of a fourth sort, and one of a fifth.

The numbers of letters in the several classes are 5, 3, 4, 1, 1, and these, severally increased by unity, give the new series of numbers 6, 4, 5, 2, 2. The rule states that the whole number of ways in which a person may take some or all (as many as he pleases) of the given letters, is

$$6 \times 4 \times 5 \times 2 \times 2 - 1, \text{ or } 479.$$

The reason of the rule will be seen from the following considerations. Suppose the person were at liberty to take *none*, or all, or as many as he pleased of the letters. He could then dispose of the five a, a, a, a, a in *six* different ways, for he might take 5 or 4 or 3 or 2 or 1 or *none* of them. So he could dispose of the three, b, b, b in *four* ways, for he might take 3 or 2 or 1 or *none* of them. Similarly he could dispose of the c, c, c, c in *five* ways, and of the d in *two* ways, and of the e in *two* ways. Hence he might act altogether, in

$$6 \times 4 \times 5 \times 2 \times 2$$

different ways (Rule II.). But if he is not to reject *all* the things, the number of courses open to him will be one less than this, or

$$6 \times 4 \times 5 \times 2 \times 2 - 1.$$

And the same reasoning would apply to any other **case.** Hence we may accept the rule as true always.

Question 82.   In how many ways can two booksellers divide between them 200 copies of one book, 250 of another, 150 of a third, and
100 of a fourth ?

Answer.   Either man can take any number of books, but not either
none or *all.*   Therefore, the number of ways is one less than that
given by the rule : *i.e.*, the division can be made in

$$201 \times 251 \times 151 \times 101 - 2$$

different ways ; or in

$$769428201 - 2, \text{ or } 769428199$$

different ways.

The student who is unfamiliar with algebraical processes
may omit the next four chapters.   If he has thoroughly
mastered the present chapter, he will have no difficulty
in proceeding at once with the theory of Chance which is
treated arithmetically in Chapter VI.

CHAPTER II.

We shall now exhibit with the advantage of algebraical notation the principles which we established by purely arithmetical methods in the previous chapter. The "Propositions" of Chapter II. correspond seriatim to the "Rules" of Chapter I.

PROPOSITION I.

If one operation can be performed in m ways, and (when it has been performed in any way) a second operation can then be performed in n ways, there will be mn ways of performing the two operations.

For if we confine our attention to the case in which the former operation is performed in its *first* way, we can associate with this way any of the *n* ways of performing the latter operation: and thus we shall have *n* ways of performing the two operations, without recognising more than the *first* way of performing the former one.

Then, if we consider the *second* way of performing the former operation, we can associate with this way any of the *n* ways of performing the latter operation: and thus we shall have *n* ways of performing the two operations, using only the *second* way of performing the former one.

And so, corresponding to *each* of the m ways of performing the former operation, we shall have n ways of performing the two operations.

Hence, altogether we shall have m times n, or mn ways of performing the two operations.   Q. E. D.

PROPOSITION II.

If one operation can be performed in m ways, and then a second can be performed in n ways, and then a third in r ways, and then a fourth in s ways (and so on), the number of ways of performing all the operations will be $m \times n \times r \times s \times$ &c.

For by Prop. I., the first and second can be performed in mn ways.

Then if we treat these two as forming one complete operation, and associate with it the third operation (which can be performed in r ways), it follows again from Prop. I., that both these can be performed in $mn \times r$ different ways. That is, the first, second, and third of the original operations can be performed in mnr ways.

Again, if we treat these three as forming one complete operation, and associate with it the fourth operation (which can be performed in s ways), it follows again from Prop. I. that both these can be performed in $mnr \times s$ different ways. That is, the first, second, third, and fourth operations can be performed in $mnrs$ ways; and so on.   Q. E. D.

COROLLARY. *If there be x operations which can be performed successively in m ways each, then all can be performed in m^x ways.*

This follows from the proposition, by considering the particular case in which m, n, r, s, &c. are all equal.

EXAMPLES. If there are p candidates for the office of president, s candidates for that of secretary, and t candidates for that of treasurer, the election of the three officers can be made in pst different ways.

If a telegraph has m arms, and each arm is capable of n different positions, including the position of rest, the number of signals that can be made is $n^m - 1$.

If there be x things to be given to n persons, n^x will represent the whole number of different ways in which they may be given.

PROPOSITION III.

The number of different orders in which n different things can be arranged is

$$n(n-1)(n-2) \ldots \ldots 3.2.1.$$

For, having to arrange the n things, we may arrive at any possible arrangement, by taking them one by one, and placing them in the n places in order.

The first place may be filled up by any of the n things : that is, it may be filled up in n different ways.

Then the second place may be filled up by any of the $n - 1$ things that are left : that is, it may be filled up in $n - 1$ different ways.

Then the third place may be filled up by any of the $n - 2$ things that are now left : that is, it may be filled up in $n - 2$ different ways.

Similarly the fourth place may be filled up in $n - 3$ ways, the fifth in $n - 4$ ways, and so on ; and ultimately the last place may be filled up in only one way.

Hence (Prop. II.) the whole number of ways of filling up all the places, or making the whole arrangement, is the continued product of all these numbers, or

$$n(n-1)(n-2) \ldots \ldots 3.2.1.$$

COROLLARY. *If n given things have to be devoted to n given objects, one to each, the distribution can be made in* $\lfloor n$ *ways.*

EXAMPLES. The number of ways in which n persons can stand in a row is $\lfloor n$. The number of ways in which they can form a ring is $\lfloor n-1$. (See page 19.)

The number of ways in which m ladies and m gentlemen can form a ring, no two ladies being together, is $\lfloor m \cdot \lfloor m-1$, or $\{\lfloor m \}^2 \div m$.

PROPOSITION IV.

Out of n different things, the number of ways in which an arrangement of r things can be made is

$$n (n - 1) (n - 2)\ldots\ldots to\ r\ factors,$$
or $\quad\quad n (n - 1) (n - 2)\ldots\ldots(n - r + 1).$

For we have to fill up r different places in order with some of the n given things. As in the last proposition, the first place can be filled up in n ways, the second in $n - 1$ ways, the third in $n - 2$ ways; and so on for all the r places.

Hence the whole number of ways of filling up all the r places, or making the required arrangement, is

$$n (n - 1) (n - 2)\ldots\ldots to\ r\ factors.$$

Or, observing that the

1st factor is	n,	
2nd	„	$n - 1$,
3rd	„	$n - 2$,
&c.		&c.
rth	„	$n - (r - 1)$ or $n - r + 1$,

we may write the result,—

$$n (n - 1)(n - 2)\ldots\ldots(n - r + 1).$$

EXAMPLE. The number of times a company of mn men can form a rectangular column, having m men in front, so as to present a different front each time, is

$$mn\,(mn-1)\,(mn-2)\,\ldots\ldots\,(mn-m+1).$$

PROPOSITION V.

The number of ways in which $x + y$ things can be divided into two classes, so that one may contain x and the other y things, is

$$\frac{\lfloor x + y}{\lfloor x \rfloor \lfloor y}.$$

For suppose N represents the number of ways in which the division could be made; then the things in the first class can be arranged in $\lfloor x$ different orders (Prop. III.), and the things in the second class in $\lfloor y$ different orders, and therefore the whole set of $x + y$ things can be arranged in x places of one class, and y places of another class, in $N\,.\,\lfloor x\,.\,\lfloor y$ different ways (Prop. II.). But this must be the same as the number of ways in which the whole set of $x + y$ things can be arranged into any $x + y$ different places, which, by Prop. III., is $\lfloor x + y$. Hence we have the equation

$$N\,.\,\lfloor x\,.\,\lfloor y = \lfloor x + y,$$

or

$$N = \frac{\lfloor x + y}{\lfloor x \rfloor \lfloor y}.$$

That is, the number of ways in which the required division can be made is

$$\frac{\lfloor x + y}{\lfloor x \rfloor \lfloor y},$$

which was to be proved.

DIVISION INTO CLASSES. 59

PROPOSITION VI.

The number of ways in which $x+y+z$ things can be divided into three classes, so that they may contain x, y, and z things severally, is

$$\frac{\lfloor x+y+z}{\lfloor x\,\lfloor y\,\lfloor z}.$$

For, by Prop. V., the $x+y+z$ things can be divided into two classes, containing x and $y+z$ things in

$$\frac{\lfloor x+y+z}{\lfloor x\,\lfloor y+z}$$

ways ; and then the class of $y+z$ things can be subdivided into two classes, containing y and z things in

$$\frac{\lfloor y+z}{\lfloor y\,\lfloor z}.$$

Therefore the three classes of x, y, z things can be made in

$$\frac{\lfloor x+y+z}{\lfloor x\,\lfloor y+z}\times\frac{\lfloor y+z}{\lfloor y\,\lfloor z},\text{ or }\frac{\lfloor x+y+z}{\lfloor x\,\lfloor y\,\lfloor z}$$

ways (Prop. I.), which was to be proved.

COROLLARY. We might similarly extend the reasoning if there were any more classes. Thus, *the number of ways in which $v+w+x+y+z$ things can be divided into five classes, containing respectively v, w, x, y, z things, is*

$$\frac{\lfloor v+w+x+y+z}{\lfloor v\,\lfloor w\,\lfloor x\,\lfloor y\,\lfloor z}.$$

EXAMPLE. The number of ways in which mn things can be equally divided among n persons, is

$$\lfloor mn\div(\lfloor m)^{n}.$$

PROPOSITION VII.

The number of different orders in which n things can be arranged, whereof p are all alike (of one sort), q all alike (of another sort), r all alike (of another sort); and the rest all different, is

$$\frac{\lfloor n}{\lfloor p \lfloor q \lfloor r}.$$

For the operation of making this arrangement may be resolved into the several operations following:—

(1) to divide the n places which have to be filled up into sets of p places, q places, r places, and $n-p-q-r$ places respectively:

(2) to place the p things all alike in the set of p places, the q things all alike in the set of q places, the r things all alike in the set of r places:

(3) to arrange the remaining $n-p-q-r$ things which are all different in the remaining set of $n-p-q-r$ places.

Now the operation (1) can be performed, by Prop. VI., in

$$\frac{\lfloor n}{\lfloor p \lfloor q \lfloor r \lfloor n-p-q-r}$$

different ways: the operation (2) can be performed in only one way: the operation (3), by Prop. III., in $\lfloor n-p-q-r$ ways.

Hence (Prop. II.) the whole operation can be performed in

$$\frac{\lfloor n}{\lfloor p \lfloor q \lfloor r \lfloor n-p-q-r} \times \lfloor n-p-q-r, \text{ or } \frac{\lfloor n}{\lfloor p \lfloor q \lfloor r}$$

different ways. Q. E. D.

COROLLARY. The same argument would apply if the number of sets of things alike were any other than three. Thus, for instance, *the number of orders in which n things can be arranged, whereof p are alike, q others alike, r others alike, s others alike, and t others alike, is*

$$\frac{\lfloor n}{\lfloor p \lfloor q \lfloor r \lfloor s \lfloor t}.$$

EXAMPLE. If there be m copies of each of n different volumes, the number of different orders in which they can be arranged on one shelf is $\lfloor mn \div (\lfloor m)^n$.

PROPOSITION VIII.

Out of n different things, the number of different ways in which a selection of r things can be made, is the same as the number of different ways in which a selection of $n - r$ things can be made, and is

$$\frac{\lfloor n}{\lfloor r \lfloor n - r}.$$

For either operation simply requires the n things to be divided into two sets of r and $n - r$ things respectively, whereof one set is to be taken and the other left.

Therefore (by the last proposition) whichever set be rejected, the operation can be performed in

$$\frac{\lfloor n}{\lfloor r \lfloor n - r}$$

different ways.

The expression $\dfrac{\lfloor n}{\lfloor r \lfloor n - r}$ may be written

$$\frac{n(n-1)(n-2)\ldots\ldots\ldots 3.2.1}{\lfloor r .(n-r)(n-r-1)\ldots 3.2.1}$$

or, dividing the numerator and denominator of the fraction by all the successive integers from 1 to $n-r$,

$$\frac{n(n-1)(n-2)\ldots(n-r+1)}{\lfloor r}.$$

This result might have been obtained quite independently, as follows :

PROPOSITION VIII. (bis).

To shew that the number of ways of selecting r things out of n is

$$\frac{n(n-1)(n-2)\ldots(n-r+1)}{\lfloor r}.$$

Let x represent the number of ways of making a selection of r things out of n things. The r things thus selected might be arranged (Prop. III.) in $\lfloor r$ different orders. Therefore (Prop. I.) $x \times \lfloor r$ is the number of ways in which r things can be selected out of n things, and arranged in order. But by Prop. IV. this can be done in $n(n-1)(n-2)\ldots(n-r+1)$ different ways. Therefore we have the equation

$$x \times \lfloor r = n(n-1)(n-2)\ldots(n-r+1),$$

which gives us

$$x = \frac{n(n-1)(n-2)\ldots(n-r+1)}{\lfloor r},$$

the required expression.

EXAMPLES. The number of ways in which a committee of p reformers and q radicals can be selected out of $m+p$ reformers and $n+q$ radicals, is

$$\frac{\lfloor m+p \lfloor n+q}{\lfloor m \lfloor p \lfloor n \lfloor q}.$$

If there be $n-1$ sets containing $2m$, $3m$, $4m$, ... nm things respectively, the number of ways in which a selection can be made, consisting of m things out of each set, is

$$\frac{\lfloor 2m}{\lfloor m \lfloor m} \times \frac{\lfloor 3m}{\lfloor 2m \lfloor m} \times \frac{\lfloor 4m}{\lfloor 3m \lfloor m} \times \dots \times \frac{\lfloor mn}{\lfloor (n-1)\, m \lfloor m} = \frac{\lfloor mn}{(\lfloor m)^n}.$$

PROPOSITION IX.

The number of ways of selecting r things out of n when repetitions are allowed is the same as the number of ways of selecting r things out of $n + r - 1$ without repetitions.

By adding all the n things to each selection of r out of n, we shall get a selection of $r + n$ things subject to the condition that each thing appears at least once in every selection.

Hence the number of ways required is the same as the number of ways of selecting $n + r$ things subject to this condition.

To make a selection of $n + r$ things subject to this condition we may take $n + r$ blank places. Put the things into any defined order, and fill up one or more of the first places with the first thing; then one or more of the next places with the next thing, and so on. In passing from one place to the next we shall always either *repeat* the thing we last assigned or *change* to the next. Altogether in going from one end of the row to the other we make $n + r - 1$ steps, of which $n - 1$ must be *changes,* and r must be *repetitions.* Our only choice is to select r out of the $n + r - 1$ steps for our r repetitions. Therefore the choice required is the choice of r things out of $n + r - 1$. Q. E. D.

NOTE. The number of ways may be written thus:

$$\frac{\lfloor n + r - 1}{\lfloor n - 1 \lfloor r} = \frac{n\,(n+1)\,(n+2)\dots(n+r-1)}{1 \cdot 2 \cdot 3 \dots r}.$$

EXAMPLES. The number of dominoes in a set which goes from double blank to double n will be

$$\tfrac{1}{2}(n+1)(n+2).$$

A wood is full of primroses, violets, anemones and bluebells : in how many ways can we compose a nosegay of n flowers?

Answer. $\qquad \tfrac{1}{6}(n+1)(n+2)(n+3).$

The number of homogeneous products of r dimensions that can be made out of n letters is

$$n(n+1)(n+2)\dots(n+r-1)\div\lfloor \underline{r}.$$

COROLLARY. When repetitions are permitted the number of combinations of r things out of $n+1$ is the same as the number of combinations of n things out of $r+1$.

NOTATION.

We shall use the symbol P_r^n to denote the number of *permutations* of n things taken r at a time, *i.e.*, the number of ways in which an arrangement of r things can be made out of n things, as in Prop. IV.

We shall use the symbol C_r^n to denote the number of *combinations* of n things taken r at a time, *i.e.*, the number of ways of selecting r things out of n things, as in Prop. VIII.

And we shall use the symbol R_r^n to denote the number of ways of selecting r things out of n when repetitions are allowed as in Prop. IX.

It is convenient to consider that the full symbol for the number of combinations of $x+y$ things taken x together or y together, or for the number of ways of dividing $x+y$ things into a set of x and a set of y things is $C_{x,y}^{x+y}$. But as the affix in this symbol is always the sum of the two suffixes, it is only necessary to write two of the three. Thus we may write indifferently

$$C_x^{x+y}, \quad C_y^{x+y}, \quad \text{or} \quad C_{x,y},$$

and again

$$C_r^n, \quad C_{n-r}^n \text{ or } C_{r,\,n-r}.$$

Remember that

$$P_r^n = n\,(n-1)\,(n-2)\,\dots\,(n-r+1),$$

$$C_r^n = \frac{n\,(n-1)\,(n-2)\,\dots\,(n-r+1)}{1\,.\,2\,.\,3\,\dots\,r} = \frac{\lfloor n}{\lfloor r\,\lfloor n-r},$$

$$R_r^n = \frac{n\,(n+1)\,(n+2)\,\dots\,(n+r-1)}{1\,.\,2\,.\,3\,\dots\,r} = \frac{\lfloor n+r-1}{\lfloor r\,\lfloor n-1}.$$

And
$$R_n^{m+1} = C_{m,\,n} = R_m^{n+1}.$$

It is convenient to notice that

$$C_{m+1,\,n-1} = \frac{n}{m+1}\,C_{m,\,n};$$

and, therefore,

$$C_{m,\,n} - C_{m+1,\,n-1} = \frac{m-n+1}{m+1}\,C_{m,\,n} = \frac{m-n+1}{m+n+1}\,C_{m+1,\,n},$$

and, as a particular case,

$$C_{n,\,n} - C_{n+1,\,n-1} = \frac{1}{n+1}\,C_{n,\,n} = 2C_{n,\,n} - \tfrac{1}{2}C_{n+1,\,n+1}.$$

Also that
$$C_{n,\,n-1} = \tfrac{1}{2}C_{n,\,n}.$$

PROPOSITION X.

Out of n different things, when each may be repeated as often as we please, the number of ways in which an arrangement of r things can be made is n^r.

For the first place can be filled up in n ways, and when it is filled up the second place can also be filled up in n ways (since we are not now precluded from repeating the selection already made); and so the third can be filled up in n ways, and so on, for all the r places.

Hence (Prop. II., Cor.) all the r places can be filled up, or the whole arrangement can be made, in n^r different ways. Q. E. D.

PROPOSITION XI.

The whole number of ways in which a selection can be made out of n different things is $2^n - 1$.

For each thing can be either taken or left; that is, it can be disposed of in two ways. Therefore (Prop. II., Cor.) all the things can be disposed of in 2^n ways. This, however, includes the case in which *all* the things are rejected, which is inadmissible; therefore the whole number of admissible ways is $2^n - 1$. Q. E. D.

COROLLARY. Since the total number of selections must be made up of the combinations taken one at a time, two together, three together, &c. and n together, we must have

$$C_1^n + C_2^n + C_3^n + \dots + C_n^n = 2^n - 1,$$

or

$$1 + \frac{n}{1} + \frac{n(n-1)}{1 \cdot 2} + \frac{n(n-1)(n-2)}{1 \cdot 2 \cdot 3} + \&c. \text{ to } (n+1) \text{ terms} = 2^n.$$

PROPOSITION XII.

The whole number of ways in which a selection can be made out of $p + q + r + \&c.$, things, whereof p are all alike (of one sort), q all alike (of another sort), r all alike (of another sort), &c., is

$$(p+1)(q+1)(r+1) \dots \&c. - 1.$$

For, of the set of p things all alike, we may take either 0 or 1 or 2 or 3 or &c. or p, and reject all the rest; that is, the p things can be disposed of in $p + 1$ ways. Similarly, the q things can be disposed of in $q + 1$ ways, the r things in $r + 1$ ways, and so on. Hence (Prop. II.) all the things can be disposed of in $(p + 1)(q + 1)(r + 1)\ldots$ ways. This, however, includes the case in which *all* the things are rejected, which is inadmissible; therefore the whole number of admissible ways is

$$(p + 1)(q + 1)(r + 1)\ldots \&c. - 1. \qquad \text{Q. E. D.}$$

EXAMPLES. If there be m sorts of things and n things of each sort, the number of ways in which a selection can be made from them is $(n + 1)^m - 1$.

If there be m sorts of things, and one thing of the first sort, two of the second, three of the third, and so on, the number of ways in which a selection can be made from them is $\lfloor m + 1 - 1$.

PROPOSITION XIII.

To prove that if x and y be positive integers

$$x^n + C_1^n x^{n-1} y + C_2^n x^{n-2} y^2 + \ldots + C_r^n x^{n-r} y^r + \ldots + y^n = (x + y)^n.$$

Suppose we have n things to give to x men and y women without any restriction as to the number given to each.

Since there are $x + y$ persons, we may give the things in $(x + y)^n$ ways.

But we may classify these ways according to the number of things given to men and women respectively. If we give $n - r$ things to men and r things to women, we may select the r things for the women in C_r^n ways, and then assign the remaining $n - r$ things to the men, and the selected r to the women, in $x^{n-r} y^r$ ways. Thus we get $C_r^n x^{n-r} y^r$ different dispositions of the things. And r may have all values from 0 to n.

Giving r all these values in succession we get $n + 1$ sets of ways of disposing of the things, which together must be the total number of ways $(x + y)^n$ which we obtained at first. Thus we have

$$x^n + C_1^n x^{n-1} y + C_2^n x^{n-2} y^2 + \ldots + C_r^n x^{n-r} y^r + \ldots + y^n = (x + y)^n.$$

COROLLARY. The proposition must also be true when x and y are not positive integers. For the result of the continued multiplication of $x + y$ by itself must be the same in form whatever x and y may represent. Therefore always, if n be a positive integer,

$$(x + y)^n = x^n + \frac{n}{1} x^{n-1}y + \frac{n(n-1)}{1 \cdot 2} x^{n-2}y^2 + \dots$$
$$+ C_r^n \, x^{n-r}y^r + \dots + y^n.$$

This formula for the expansion of $(x + y)^n$ is called the Binomial Theorem.

PROPOSITION XIV.

If there be N sets of letters[1], and if out of r assigned letters $\alpha, \beta, \gamma \dots$ each letter such as α occur in N_1 sets; each combination of two letters (such as α, β) in N_2 sets; each combination of three letters (such as α, β, γ) occur in N_3 sets; and so on; and finally all the r letters occur in N_r sets, then the number of sets free from all the letters will be

$$N - \frac{r}{1} N_1 + \frac{r(r-1)}{1 \cdot 2} N_2 - \frac{r(r-1)(r-2)}{1 \cdot 2 \cdot 3} N_3 + \&c. \dots \pm N_r,$$

the coefficients following the law of the Binomial Theorem.

The number of sets free from α is ....$N - N_1$

Among these, β is found in ....$N_1 - N_2$

$\therefore$ (by Subtraction) the number of sets free from α or β is....................$N - 2N_1 + N_2$

---

[1] It should be observed that the sets may be parcels or groups, selections or arrangements, with or without repetitions, and they will not necessarily all contain the same number of letters.

Among these, γ is found in ....$N_1 - 2N_2 + N_3$
(for, if we had introduced from the beginning the condition that γ be present we should have had throughout N_1, N_2, N_3 for N, N_1, N_2, respectively.)
$\therefore$ (by Subtraction) the number of sets free from α, β, or γ is.......................$N - 3N_1 + 3N_2 - N_3$

Among these δ is found in ....$N_1 - 3N_2 + 3N_3 - N_4$
(for, if we had introduced from the beginning the condition that δ be always present we should have had N_1, N_2, N_3 ... for N, N_1, N_2 ... respectively.)
$\therefore$ (by Subtraction) the number of sets free from α, β, γ or δ, is ....$N - 4N_1 + 6N_2 - 4N_3 + N_4$.
And so on.

Now we may observe that the successive operations performed at the right-hand side of the page are identical with the operation of constantly multiplying by $1 - N$ except that we have N, N_1, N_2, N_3... in place of 1, N, N^2, N^3... respectively. Therefore the coefficients must be the same as in the involution of $1 - N$, $i.e.$ they must follow the law of the Binomial Theorem.

Therefore we have (after r operations), the number of sets free from any of the r letters, viz.:

$$N - \frac{r}{1} N_1 + \frac{r(r-1)}{1 \cdot 2} N_2 - \frac{r(r-1)(r-2)}{1 \cdot 2 \cdot 3} N_3 + \&\text{c.} \dots \pm N_r.$$

Q. E. D.

COROLLARY I. If all the sets must contain some of the letters the expression just found must be zero, and therefore we find N in terms of N_1, N_2, N_3, &c.; thus

$$N = \frac{r}{1} N_1 - \frac{r(r-1)}{1 \cdot 2} N_2 + \frac{r(r-1)(r-2)}{1 \cdot 2 \cdot 3} N_3 - \&\text{c.} \dots \mp N_r.$$

COROLLARY II. Suppose the N sets of letters are the combinations of m letters taken n at a time. The number free from any of r assigned letters will be C_n^{m-r}. And we have

$$N = C_n^m, \qquad N_1 = C_{n-1}^{m-1}, \qquad N_2 = C_{n-2}^{m-2}, \qquad \text{and so on.}$$

Therefore

$$C_n^{m-r} = C_n^m - C_1^r C_{n-1}^{m-1} + C_2^r C_{n-2}^{m-2} - \&\text{c.} \pm C_{n-r}^{m-r}.$$

In the particular case when $n = m - r$ we get

$$1 = C_r^m - C_r^{m-1} C_1^r + C_r^{m-2} C_2^r - \&\text{c. to } (r+1) \text{ terms.}$$

COROLLARY III. Our reasoning being perfectly general we may enunciate the proposition in general terms, as follows.

If there be N events or operations and if (out of r possible conditions α, β, γ, ...) every one condition (such as α) be fulfilled in N_1 of the events; and every combination of two simultaneous conditions (such as α, β) be fulfilled in N_2 of the events; and every combination of three simultaneous conditions (such as α, β, γ) be fulfilled in N_3 of the events; and so on; and finally all the r conditions be simultaneously fulfilled in N_r of the events; then the number of events free from all these conditions is

$$N - \frac{r}{1} N_1 + \frac{r(r-1)}{1.2} N_2 - \frac{r(r-1)(r-2)}{1.2.3} N_3 + \&\text{c.} \dots \pm N_r.$$

EXAMPLE. A symmetrical function of a, b, c, d has one term without any of these letters; a is found in 9 terms, ab in 5 terms, abc in 3 terms, and $abcd$ in 2 terms. How many terms are there altogether?

Here we have $N_1 = 9$, $N_2 = 5$, $N_3 = 3$, $N_4 = 2$, and

$$1 = N - 4N_1 + 6N_2 - 4N_3 + N_4,$$

or

$$1 = N - 36 + 30 - 12 + 2;$$

$$\therefore \quad N = 17.$$

N.B. The seventeen terms may be such as

$$1 + a^2 + b^2 + c^2 + d^2 + bcd + acd + abd + abc + abcd + a^3b^3$$
$$+ c^3d^3 + a^3c^3 + b^3d^3 + a^3d^3 + b^3c^3 + a^2b^2c^2d^2.$$

Again to determine the number of orders in which four men and their wives can enter a room without any man coming next to his own wife, we have $N = \lfloor 8$, $N_1 = 2 \lfloor 7$, $N_2 = 2^2 \lfloor 6$, &c. Therefore the required number is

$$\lfloor 8 - 4 . 2 \lfloor 7 + 6 . 2^2 \lfloor 6 - 4 . 2^3 \lfloor 5 + 2^4 \lfloor 4 = 13824.$$

EXCURSUS.

ON THE SUMMATION OF CERTAIN SERIES.

THE theory of Choice may often be applied to obtain the sum of algebraical series. Examples of such summation have already occurred (Prop. XI. Cor., Prop. XIII. Cor., Prop. XIV. Cor. 2). In the present Excursus we exhibit a fuller application of the method.

1. All the combinations of n things 0, 1, 2, 3 ... or n together are formed by dealing with each of the n things in either of two ways (*i.e.* each must either be selected or rejected). Hence we write down

$$1 + C_1^n + C_2^n + C_3^n + ... + C_n^n = 2^n.$$

2. But if one of the things (say α) is always to be used there will be only 2^{n-1} combinations. Hence we have (multiplying throughout by n)

$$C_1^n + 2C_2^n + 3C_3^n + ... + nC_n^n = n2^{n-1}.$$

Similarly if we introduced the condition that two of the things (say α, β) are always to be used we should get

$$1 . 2C_2^n + 2 . 3C_3^n + 3 . 4C_4^n + ... + n(n-1)C_n^n = n(n-1)2^{n-2}.$$

3. Again, let us have $m + 1$ letters of which one is α. The number of combinations n-together when repetitions are allowed is R_n^{m+1}. Analyse these according as α occurs $n, n - 1, n - 2, \ldots$ or 1 or 0 times, and we write

$$1 + R_1^m + R_2^m + R_3^m + \ldots + R_n^m = R_n^{m+1},$$

or $\qquad 1 + C_1^m + C_2^{m+1} + C_3^{m+2} + \ldots + C_n^{m+n-1} = C_n^{m+n}.$

4. Writing $m + 1$ for m, and $n - 1$ for n, we get

$$1 + C_m^{m+1} + C_m^{m+2} + C_m^{m+3} + \ldots \text{ to } n \text{ terms} = C_{m+1}^{m+n}$$

or, multiplying throughout by $\lfloor m$,

$$P_m^m + P_m^{m+1} + P_m^{m+2} + \ldots \text{ to } n \text{ terms} = P_{m+1}^{m+n}/(m + 1).$$

Giving m the values $1, 2, 3 \ldots$ in succession, we get the following series each summed to n terms,

$$1 + 2 + 3 + \ldots \qquad\qquad = \tfrac{1}{2} n (n + 1),$$
$$1 . 2 + 2 . 3 + 3 . 4 + \ldots \qquad = \tfrac{1}{3} n (n + 1) (n + 2),$$
$$1 . 2 . 3 + 2 . 3 . 4 + 3 . 4 . 5 + \ldots = \tfrac{1}{4} n (n + 1) (n + 2) (n + 3),$$

and so on.

5. Out of the $n + 2$ numbers $1, 2, 3 \ldots (n + 2)$ a selection of three numbers can be made in C_3^{n+2} ways. The lowest number chosen may be $n, n - 1, n - 2 \ldots 3, 2, 1$. Counting these separately we get

$$C_2^2 + C_2^3 + C_2^4 + \ldots + C_2^{n+1} = C_3^{n+2},$$

or $\qquad 1 . 2 + 2 . 3 + 3 . 4 + \ldots + n (n + 1) = \tfrac{1}{3} n (n + 1) (n + 2),$

as in the last article. Or we may count the ways separately according as the middle number is $2, 3, 4 \ldots$ or $(n + 1)$. Then we obtain the very useful summation,

$$1 . n + 2 (n - 1) + 3 (n - 2) + \ldots + n . 1 = \tfrac{1}{6} n (n + 1) (n + 2).$$

6. Another series

$$1 + C_1^m C_1^n + C_2^m C_2^n + \ldots + C_n^m C_n^n = C_n^{m+n}$$

(m not being less than n) simply expresses the fact that if an equal number of men and women are to be selected out of m men and n women, all possible results can be effected by selecting n persons out of the whole number and combining the selected men with the non-selected women.

This series is of frequent occurrence in the particular case when $m = n$,

$$1 + (C_1^n)^2 + (C_2^n)^2 + \ldots + (C_n^n)^2 = Y_n,$$

where Y_n denotes[1] the number of combinations of $2n$ things n-together, or the number of ways of dividing $2n$ things into two equal parcels; that is

$$Y_n = C_n^{2n} = C_{n,\,n} = R_n^{n+1} = 2R_n^n.$$

7. Out of an alphabet of p consonants and q vowels a selection of n letters without repetitions can be made in C_n^{p+q} ways. Considering the selections when $0, 1, 2, 3 \ldots$ or n vowels are used we find

$$C_n^p + C_{n-1}^p C_1^q + C_{n-2}^p C_2^q + C_{n-3}^p C_3^q + \ldots + C_n^q = C_n^{p+q}.$$

So if repetitions be allowed

$$R_n^p + R_{n-1}^p R_1^q + R_{n-2}^p R_2^q + R_{n-3}^p R_3^q + \ldots + R_n^q = R_n^{p+q}.$$

8. If we write $p + 1$ and $q + 1$ for p and q respectively, the last identity becomes

$$C_{p,\,n} + C_{p,\,n-1} C_{q,\,1} + C_{p,\,n-2} C_{q,\,2} + \ldots + C_{q,\,n} = C_{p+q+1,\,n},$$

a very useful summation.

[1] The student who has read the Integral Calculus will note that in virtue of Wallis' formula $4^n / Y_n$ lies between $\sqrt{\pi n}$ and $\sqrt{\pi (n+\frac{1}{2})}$. This sometimes helps us to approximate to the numerical value of factorials of a high order.

9. We may classify the selections of n things out of m when repetitions are allowed according as 1, 2, 3... or n of the m things are used ; (noting that the number of selections of n things out of x when repetitions are allowed and all the x things must be used is $R_{n-x}^{x} = C_{x-1}^{n-1}$). Thus we get

$$C_1^m + C_2^m C_1^{n-1} + C_3^m C_2^{n-1} + \dots \text{ to } n \text{ terms} = R_n^m,$$

or multiplying throughout by n,

$$C_1^m C_1^n + 2C_2^m C_2^n + 3C_3^m C_3^n + \dots + nC_n^m C_n^n = \frac{\lfloor m+n-1}{\lfloor m-1 \lfloor n-1}.$$

10. In the series of Art. 8 the general term is $C_{p,\,n-x} . C_{q,\,x}$. If we write m for $p + q + n$ this becomes

$$C_x^n . C_{q+n}^m . C_n^{q+n} \div C_{q+x}^m,$$

and the sum of the series becomes C_n^{m+1}. Hence dividing throughout by $C_{q+n}^m C_n^{q+n}$, we have

$$\frac{1}{C_q^m} + \frac{C_1^m}{C_{q+1}^m} + \frac{C_2^n}{C_{q+2}^m} + \dots + \frac{1}{C_{q+n}^m} = \frac{m+1}{q+1} \div C_{q+1}^{m-n+1}.$$

11. The results of the last ten articles may be tabulated as follows : the summation being in all cases from $x = 0$ to $x = n$, or, where $x = 0$ is inadmissible, from $x = 1$ to $x = n$.

$$\Sigma \{C_x^n\} = 2^n \qquad\qquad\qquad \text{Art. 1}$$

$$\Sigma \{xC_x^n\} = n2^{n-1} \qquad\qquad\quad \text{Art. 2}$$

$$\Sigma \{x(x-1)\,C_x^n\} = n(n-1)\,2^{n-2} \qquad \text{Art. 2}$$

$$\Sigma \{R_x^m\} = R_n^{m+1} \qquad\qquad\quad \text{Art. 3}$$

$$\Sigma \{C_{m,\,x}\} = C_{m+1,\,n} \qquad\qquad \text{Art. 4}$$

$$\Sigma \{P_m^{m+x}\} = P_{m+1}^{m+1+n} \div (m+1) \qquad \text{Art. 4}$$

$$\Sigma \{x(n-x)\} = \tfrac{1}{6}n(n+1)(n+2) \qquad \text{Art. 5}$$

$$\Sigma \{C_x^m . C_x^n\} = C_{m,\,n} \qquad\qquad \text{Art. 6}$$

$$\Sigma \{C_{n-x}^p C_x^q\} = C_n^{p+q} \qquad\qquad \text{Art. 7}$$

$$\Sigma \left\{ R^p_{n-x} R^q_x \right\} = R^{p+q}_n \qquad \text{Art. 7}$$

$$\Sigma \left\{ C_{p,\, n-x} C_{q,\, x} \right\} = C_{p+q+1,\, n} \qquad \text{Art. 8}$$

$$\Sigma \left\{ x C^m_x C^n_x \right\} = n C_{m-1,\, n} \qquad \text{Art. 9}$$

$$\Sigma \left\{ C^n_x \div C^m_{q+x} \right\} = \frac{m+1}{q+1} \div C^{m-n+1}_{q+1} \qquad \text{Art. 10.}$$

12. In Prop. XIII. Cor. we proved the Binomial Theorem for a positive integral exponent. We must refer to treatises on algebra for the proof that it is true whatever the exponent be ; so that always

$$(1+x)^n = 1 + \frac{n}{1}x + \frac{n(n-1)}{1.2}x^2 + \frac{n(n-1)(n-2)}{1.2.3}x^3 + \&c.$$

the series stopping at the $(n+1)$th term when n is a positive integer but going on *ad infinitum* when n is fractional or negative.

As $C^n_1, C^n_2, C^n_3 \ldots$ are the coefficients in the expansion of $(1+x)^n$, n being a positive integer, so $R^n_1, R^n_2, R^n_3 \ldots$ are the coefficients in the expansion of $(1-x)^{-n}$, and $Y_1, Y_2, Y_3 \ldots$ the coefficients in the expansion of $1 \div \sqrt{1-4x}$. Thus

$$(1+x)^n = 1 + C^n_1 x + C^n_2 x^2 + C^n_3 x^3 + \ldots$$
$$(1-x)^{-n} = 1 + R^n_1 x + R^n_2 x^2 + R^n_3 x^3 + \ldots$$
$$(1-4x)^{-\frac{1}{2}} = 1 + Y_1 x + Y_2 x^2 + Y_3 x^3 + \ldots.$$

The student may also verify the following results :

$$Y_n (1-4x)^{-n-\frac{1}{2}} = Y_n + Y_{n+1} C_{n,1} x + Y_{n+2} C_{n,2} x^2 + \ldots$$

$$\frac{(1-4x)^{n-\frac{1}{2}}}{Y_n} = \frac{1}{Y_n} - \frac{C^n_1 x}{Y_{n-1}} + \frac{C^n_2 x^2}{Y_{n-2}} - \frac{C^n_3 x^3}{Y_{n-3}} + \ldots$$

$$\pm x^n \left\{ 1 + \frac{Y_1 x}{C_{n,1}} + \frac{Y_2 x^2}{C_{n,2}} + \ldots \right\},$$

$$\frac{1 - \sqrt{1-4x}}{2x} = 1 + \frac{Y_1 x}{2} + \frac{Y_2 x}{3} + \frac{Y_3 x}{4} + \ldots.$$

This last is a particular case of the more general theorem:

$$\frac{1}{p}\left(\frac{1-\sqrt{1-4x}}{2x}\right)^p = \frac{1}{p} + \frac{R_1^{p+1}x}{p+1} + \frac{R_2^{p+2}x^2}{p+2} + \frac{R_3^{p+3}x^3}{p+3} + \ldots.$$

13. Since the product of $(1-4x)^{\frac{1}{2}}$ and $(1-4x)^{-\frac{1}{2}}$ is unity, the coefficient of x^{n+1} in the product of their expansions must be zero. Therefore

$$Y_{n+1} - 2\left\{Y_n + \tfrac{1}{2}Y_{n-1}Y_1 + \tfrac{1}{3}Y_{n-2}Y_2 + \ldots + \frac{1.}{n+1}Y_n\right\} = 0,$$

or

$$Y_n + \tfrac{1}{2}Y_1Y_{n-1} + \tfrac{1}{3}Y_2Y_{n-2} + \tfrac{1}{4}Y_3Y_{n-3} + \ldots + \frac{1}{n+1}Y_n$$
$$= \tfrac{1}{2}Y_{n+1} = C_n^{2n+1}.$$

14. From the expansion of $(1-4x)^{-\frac{1}{2}}$, squaring, we obtain

$$(1-4x)^{-1} = \{1 + Y_1x + Y_2x^2 + Y_3x^3 + \ldots\}^2.$$

But by the Binomial Theorem

$$(1-4x)^{-1} = 1 + 4x + (4x)^2 + (4x)^3 + \ldots$$

Equating the coefficients of x^n in these two expansions we get

$$Y_n + Y_1Y_{n-1} + Y_2Y_{n-2} + Y_3Y_{n-3} + \ldots + Y_n = 4^n = 2^{2n},$$

a result which we shall quote in Chapter V.

15. If we write $y - y^2$ for x in the expansion of $(1-4x)^{-\frac{1}{2}}$ we obtain

$$(1-2y)^{-1} = 1 + Y_1y(1-y) + Y_2y^2(1-y)^2 + \&c.$$

But by the Binomial Theorem

$$(1-2y)^{-1} = 1 + (2y) + (2y)^2 + (2y)^3 + \ldots\ldots$$

Equating the coefficients of y^n we obtain

$$Y_n - C_1^{n-1}Y_{n-1} + C_2^{m-2}Y_{2n-2} - \&c. \pm C_k^{n-k}Y_{n-k} = 2^n,$$

the number of terms in the series being $\frac{1}{2}(n+1)$ when n is odd and $\frac{1}{2}n+1$ when n is even.

16. Another series which we shall make use of in subsequent chapters is the expansion of e^x where e denotes the limiting value to which $\left(1+\dfrac{1}{x}\right)^x$ tends when x is indefinitely increased. We must again refer to Treatises on Algebra for proofs that

$$e^x = 1 + x + \frac{x^2}{\lfloor 2} + \frac{x^3}{\lfloor 3} + \frac{x^4}{\lfloor 4} + \&c.$$

and therefore (putting $x=1$)

$$e = 1 + 1 + \frac{1}{\lfloor 2} + \frac{1}{\lfloor 3} + \frac{1}{\lfloor 4} + \&c.$$

The numerical value of e calculated from this last series is $2.718281828\ldots$ or approximately $617 \div 227$.

Putting $x=-1$, we obtain

$$\frac{1}{e} = \frac{1}{\lfloor 2} - \frac{1}{\lfloor 3} + \frac{1}{\lfloor 4} - \frac{1}{\lfloor 5} + \&c.$$

17. If we expand $(e^x-1)^n$ by the Binomial Theorem we obtain
$$(e^x-1)^n = e^{nx} - C_1^n e^{(n-1)x} + C_2^n e^{(n-2)x} - \&c.$$

If we expand each of the powers of e in the right-hand member and write down the coefficient of x^r in each expansion we find that the coefficient of x^r in $(e^x-1)^n$ is

$$\frac{1}{\lfloor r} \left\{ n^r - C_1^n (n-1)^r + C_2^n (n-2)^r - C_3^n (n-3)^r + \&c. \right\},$$

an expression which we shall meet with in Chapter III.

18. The following table of expansions will facilitate the working of some of the exercises.

$$e^x - 1 \ = x \ + \frac{1}{2} x^2 + \frac{1}{6} \ x^3 + \frac{1}{24} \ x^4 + \frac{1}{120} \ x^5 + \frac{1}{720} \ x^6 + \ldots$$

$$(e^x - 1)^2 = x^2 + \ x^3 + \frac{7}{12} \ x^4 + \frac{1}{4} \ x^5 + \frac{31}{360} \ x^6 + \frac{1}{40} \ x^7 + \ldots$$

$$(e^x - 1)^3 = x^3. + \frac{3}{2} x^4 + \frac{5}{4} \ x^5 + \frac{3}{4} \ x^6 + \frac{43}{120} \ x^7 + \frac{23}{160} \ x^8 + \ldots$$

$$(e^x - 1)^4 = x^4 + 2x^5 + \frac{13}{6} \ x^6 + \frac{5}{3} \ x^7 + \frac{81}{80} \ x^8 + \frac{37}{72} \ x^9 + \ldots$$

$$(e^x - 1)^5 = x^5 + \frac{5}{2} x^6 + \frac{10}{3} \ x^7 + \frac{25}{8} \ x^8 + \frac{331}{144} \ x^9 + \frac{45}{32} \ x^{10} + \ldots$$

$$(e^x - 1)^6 = x^6 + 3x^7 + \frac{19}{4} \ x^8 + \frac{21}{4} \ x^9 + \frac{1087}{240} \ x^{10} + \frac{259}{80} \ x^{11} + \ldots$$

$$(e^x - 1)^7 = x^7 + \frac{7}{2} x^8 + \frac{77}{12} \ x^9 + \frac{49}{6} \ x^{10} + \frac{1939}{240} \ x^{11} + \frac{4753}{720} \ x^{12} + \ldots$$

$$(e^x - 1)^8 = x^8 + 4x^9 + \frac{25}{3} \ x^{10} + 12 \ x^{11} + \frac{4819}{360} \ x^{12} + \frac{123}{10} \ x^{13} + \ldots$$

$$(e^x - 1)^9 = x^9 + \frac{9}{2} x^{10} + \frac{21}{2} \ x^{11} + \frac{135}{8} \ x^{12} + \frac{419}{20} \ x^{13} + \frac{171}{8} \ x^{14} + \ldots$$

$$(e^x - 1)^{10} = x^{10} + 5x^{11} + \frac{155}{12} \ x^{12} + \frac{275}{12} \ x^{13} + \frac{94}{3} \ x^{14} + \frac{1265}{36} \ x^{15} + \ldots$$

$$e^{e^x} \div e \ \ = 1 + \ x + \ x^2 + \frac{5}{6} \ x^3 + \frac{5}{8} \ x^4 + \frac{13}{30} x^5 + \frac{203}{720} x^6 + \ldots$$

$$e^x/(1 - x) = 1 + 2x + \frac{5}{2} x^2 + \frac{8}{3} \ x^3 + \frac{65}{24} \ x^4 + \frac{163}{60} \ x^5 + \ldots$$

$$e^x/(1 - x)^2 = 1 + 3x + \frac{11}{2} x^2 + \frac{49}{6} \cdot x^3 + \frac{87}{8} \ x^4 + \frac{1631}{120} \ x^5 + \ldots$$

$$e^x/(1 - x)^3 = 1 + 4x + \frac{19}{2} x^2 + \frac{53}{3} \ x^3 + \frac{685}{24} \ x^4 + \frac{632}{15} \ x^5 + \ldots$$

$$e^x/(1 - x)^4 = 1 + 5x + \frac{29}{2} x^2 + \frac{193}{6} \ x^3 + \frac{1457}{24} \ x^4 + \frac{12341}{120} \ x^5 + \ldots$$

$$e^x/(1 - x)^5 = 1 + 6x + \frac{41}{2} x^2 + \frac{158}{3} \ x^3 + \frac{907}{8} \ x^4 + \frac{12973}{60} \ x^5 + \ldots$$

$$e^x/(1 - x)^6 = 1 + 7x + \frac{55}{2} x^2 + \frac{481}{6} \ x^3 + \frac{4645}{24} \ x^4 + \frac{49171}{120} \ x^5 + \ldots$$

The table for the expansion of $e^x/(1-x)^r$ is easily extended, each coefficient being obtained by the addition of the coefficient above it and the coefficient to the left of it.

CHAPTER III.

DISTRIBUTIONS.

MOST of the questions of Permutations and Combinations which we have considered have involved the division of a given series of things into two parts, one part to be chosen, and the other rejected. The theorem expressed arithmetically in Rule VI. (page 25), and algebraically in Proposition VI. (page 59), is the only one in which we have contemplated distribution into more than two classes. But as the number of things to be given to each class was in the terms of that theorem assigned, the problem was reduced to a case of successive selection, and was therefore classed with other questions of combinations. But when the number of elements to be distributed to each several class is unassigned, and left to the exercise of a further choice, the character of the problem is very much altered, and the problem ranks among a large variety which we class together as problems of *Distribution*.

Distribution is the separation of a series of elements into a series of classes. The great variety that exists among problems of distribution may be mostly traced to five principal elements of distinction, which it will be well to consider in detail before enunciating the propositions on which the solution of the problems will depend.

I. *The things to be distributed may be different or indifferent.* The number of ways of distributing five gifts among
three recipients, will depend upon whether the gifts are
all alike or various.   If they are all alike (or, though unlike,
yet indifferent as far as the purposes of the problem are
concerned), the only questions will be (i) whether we shall
divide them into sets of 2, 2, 1 or 3, 1, 1, and (ii) how we
shall assign the three sets to the three individuals.   If on
the contrary the five gifts are essentially different, as *a, b,
c, d, e,* then they may be divided into sets of 2, 2, 1 in 15
ways, and into sets of 3, 1, 1 in 10 ways, and then we shall
have to assign the three sets which are in this case all essentially different (because their component elements are so), to
the three individuals.   In the first case, the sets could be
formed in 2 ways, and when formed in either way they could
be assigned in 3 ways, thus giving a complete choice of 6
distributions.   In the second case, the sets could be formed
in 25 ways, and when formed in any way they could be
assigned in 6 ways, thus giving a complete choice of 150
distributions.

II. *The classes into which the things are to be distributed
may be themselves different or indifferent.* We here use
the adjectives *different* or *indifferent* to qualify the abstract
classes regarded as ends or objects to which the articles are
to be devoted, without any reference to à *posteriori* differences existing merely in differences of distribution into the
classes.

Where five gifts were to be distributed to three recipients, the distinct personality of the three recipients made
the classes characteristically different, quite apart from the
consideration of the differences of the elements which composed them.   But if we had only to wrap up five books in

three different parcels, and no difference of destination were assigned to the parcels, we should speak of the parcels as *indifferent*. The problem would be simply to divide the five things into three sets, without assigning to the sets any particular order. The distribution could be made in 2 ways if the things themselves were indifferent, and in 25 ways if they were different.

III. *The order of the things in the classes may be different or indifferent*, that is, the classes may contain permutations or combinations. Of course this distinction can only arise when the things themselves are different, for we cannot recognise any order among indifferent elements. We shall avoid confusion by distinguishing arranged and unarranged classes respectively as *groups* and *parcels*. If three men are to divide a set of books amongst them, it is a case of division into *parcels*, for it does not matter in what order or arrangement any particular man gets his books. But if a series of flags are to be exhibited as a signal on three masts, it is a case of division into *groups*, for every different arrangement of the same flags on any particular mast would constitute a different signal.

IV. *It may or may not be permissible to leave some of the possible classes empty.* It will entirely depend upon the circumstances out of which the problem arises, whether it shall be necessary to place at least one element in every class, or whether some of them may be left vacant; in fact, whether the number of classes named in the problem is named as a limit not to be transgressed, or as a condition to be exactly fulfilled. If we are to distribute five gifts to three recipients, it will probably be expected, and unless otherwise expressly stated it will be implied, that no one goes away empty. But if it be asked how many signals can be displayed by the aid of five flags on a three-masted ship, it will be necessary to include the signals which could be given by placing all the flags on one mast, or on two masts.

V. *It may or may not be permissible to leave some of the distributable things undistributed.* This will be illustrated by a comparison of the Propositions XV. and XVIII. below.

The following table in which the cases considered in the present chapter are classified, will be useful as an index to the propositions.

Nature of the distribution.		Whether blank lots are allowed.	Whether all the things must be distributed.	PROP.
Distribution of different things into	different groups	Yes	Yes	XV.
	different ,,	No	Yes	XVI.
	indifferent ,,	No	Yes	XVII.
	different ,,	Yes	No	XVIII.
	different ,,	No	No	XIX.
	indifferent ,,	No	No	XX.
Distribution of different things into different parcels		Yes	Yes	XXI.
		No	Yes	XXII.
Distribution of different things into indifferent parcels		No	Yes	XXIII.
		Yes	Yes	XXIV.
Distribution of indifferent things into different parcels		No	Yes	XXV.
		Yes	Yes	XXVI.
		{ the lots }	Yes	XXVII.
		{ limited }	Yes	XXVIII.
Distribution of indifferent things into indifferent parcels		No	Yes	{ XXIX. XXX. }

PROPOSITION XV.

The number of ways in which n different things can be arranged in r different groups (blank groups being admissible) is

$$r(r+1)(r+2)\ldots(r+n-1).$$

For we shall obtain the arrangements by taking the n different things and putting with them $r-1$ indifferent points of partition, and arranging these $n+r-1$ things in all possible orders. Since $r-1$ of them are alike the number of arrangements is by Prop. VII.

$$\lfloor n+r-1 \div \lfloor r-1,$$

or $\qquad r(r+1)(r+2)\ldots(r+n-1).$ Q. E. D.

EXAMPLE. The number of ways of arranging n flags on r masts when all the flags must be displayed, but all the masts need not be used, is

$$r(r+1)(r+2)\ldots(r+n-1).$$

PROPOSITION XVI.

The number of ways in which n different things can be arranged in r different groups (none being blank) is

$$\lfloor n \; C_{r-1}^{n-1} \;\text{ or }\; \frac{\lfloor n \lfloor n-1}{\lfloor n-r \lfloor r-1}.$$

For we shall obtain the arrangements by (1) arranging the n things in all possible orders, and (2) inserting $r-1$ points of partition in a selection of $r-1$ out of the $n-1$ intervals between them.

The arrangement (1) can be made in $\lfloor n$ ways, and the selection (2) in C_{r-1}^{n-1} ways. Therefore our distribution can be made in

$$\lfloor n \; C_{r-1}^{n-1} \quad \text{or} \quad \lfloor n \lfloor n-1 \div \lfloor n-r \lfloor r-1$$

different ways. Q. E. D.

EXAMPLE. The number of ways in which n flags can be arranged on r masts so that every mast has at least one flag is

$$\lfloor n \lfloor n-1 \div \lfloor n-r \lfloor r-1.$$

PROPOSITION XVII.

The number of ways in which n different things can be arranged in r indifferent groups (none being blank) is

$$\frac{\lfloor n}{\lfloor r} C_{r-1}^{n-1} \quad \text{or} \quad \frac{\lfloor n \lfloor n-1}{\lfloor n-r \lfloor r \lfloor r-1}.$$

For it is plain that for any one distribution in this case we must have $\lfloor r$ arrangements when the groups are not indifferent. Hence we have only to divide the result of the last proposition by $\lfloor r$; which gives the required expression.

PROPOSITION XVIII.

Out of n different things the total number of ways in which r different groups can be made (blank groups being admissible) is $\lfloor n$ times the coefficient of x^n in the expansion of $e^x/(1-x)^r$.

For if we use x things we may select them in C_x^n ways, and then distribute them (by Prop. XV.) in

$$r(r+1)(r+2) \ldots (r+x-1) \text{ ways.}$$

Thus we get

$$C_x^n \cdot r(r+1)(r+2) \ldots (r+x-1)$$

distributions. And (including the case when all the groups are blank) x may have every value from 0 to n. Therefore the total number of distributions is

$$\lfloor n \left\{ \frac{1}{\lfloor n} + \frac{r}{\lfloor 1 \rfloor \lfloor n-1} + \frac{r(r+1)}{\lfloor 2 \rfloor \lfloor n-2} + \frac{r(r+1)(r+2)}{\lfloor 3 \rfloor \lfloor n-3} + \&c. \right\},$$

to $n+1$ terms. But the series within the bracket is the coefficient of x^n in the product of the two series

$$1 + \frac{x}{\lfloor 1} + \frac{x^2}{\lfloor 2} + \frac{x^3}{\lfloor 3} + \&c.,$$

and $\quad 1 + \frac{r}{\lfloor 1} x + \frac{r(r+1)}{\lfloor 2} x^2 + \frac{r(r+1)(r+2)}{\lfloor 3} x^3 + \&c.,$

and these are respectively the expansions of e^x and $(1-x)^{-r}$. Hence the total number of distributions is $\lfloor n$ times the coefficient of x^n in the expansion of $e^x/(1-x)^r$.

EXAMPLES. This proposition will give the total number of signals which can be made by displaying arrangements out of n flags upon r masts, when one is not required to use either all the masts or all the flags. Writing $n=12$ and $r=8$, we should have the number of ways in which a lady with 12 rings could wear some or all of them on her 8 fingers.

PROPOSITION XIX.

Out of n different things the total number of ways in which r different groups can be made (without blanks) is $\lfloor n$ times the coefficient of x^{n-r} in the expansion of $e^x/(1-x)^r$.

For if we use x things, we may select them in $\lfloor n \div \lfloor n-x \lfloor x$ ways, and then distribute them (by Prop. XVI.) in

$$\lfloor x \lfloor x-1 \div \lfloor x-r \lfloor r-1 \text{ ways.}$$

Thus we get $\qquad \lfloor n \lfloor x-1 \div \lfloor n-x \lfloor x-r \lfloor r-1$

distributions. And x may have every value from r to n inclusive. Therefore the total number of distributions is $\lfloor n$ times

$$\frac{1}{\lfloor n-r} + \frac{r}{\lfloor 1 \lfloor n-r-1} + \frac{r(r+1)}{\lfloor 2 \lfloor n-r-2} + \frac{r(r+1)(r+2)}{\lfloor 3 \lfloor n-r-3} + \&c.,$$

which (as in the last proposition) is $\lfloor n$ times the coefficient of x^{n-r} in the expansion of $e^x/(1-x)^r$.   Q. E. D.

PROPOSITION XX.

Out of n different things the total number of ways in which r indifferent groups can be made (without blanks) is $\lfloor n / \lfloor r$ times the coefficient of x^{n-r} in the expansion of $e^x/(1-x^r)$.

This follows from Prop. XIX., as Prop. XVII. from Prop. XVI.

EXAMPLE. This proposition will give the number of ways of forming r trains at a railway station at which there are n carriages.

The foregoing propositions have related to distribution into *groups*, the remainder of this chapter will be devoted to distribution into *parcels*.

PROPOSITION XXI.

The number of ways in which n different things can be distributed into r different parcels is r^n, when blank lots are admissible.

For each of the n different things can be assigned to any one of the r parcels without thought of how the others are disposed of. Hence the n things can be successively disposed of in r ways each, and therefore (Prop. II.) all can be disposed of in r^n different ways. Q. E. D.

PROPOSITION XXII.

The number of ways in which n different things can be distributed into r different parcels (without blank lots) is $\lfloor n$ times the coefficient of x^n in the expansion of $(e^x - 1)^r$.

For by the last proposition, the number of distributions when blanks are allowed is r^n. And the number of distributions subject to the condition that an assigned parcel is blank is $(r-1)^n$. And the number of distributions subject to the condition that two assigned parcels are blank is $(r-2)^n$ and so on. Hence, by Prop. XIV. Cor. 3, the number of distributions in which none of the r parcels are blank is

$$r^n - \frac{r}{1}(r-1)^n + \frac{r(r-1)}{1 \cdot 2}(r-2)^n - \frac{r(r-1)(r-2)}{1 \cdot 2 \cdot 3}(r-3)^n$$

$$+ \&c. \dots \pm \frac{r}{1} \cdot 2^n \mp 1,$$

that is (Excursus, Art. 17), $\lfloor n$ times the coefficient of x^n in the expansion of $(e^x - 1)^r$. Q. E. D.

EXAMPLES. The number of ways in which five different commissions can be executed by three messengers is 3^5 or 243. But if no one of the messengers is to be unemployed, the number of ways will be $\lfloor 5$ times the coefficient of x^5 in the expansion of $(e^x - 1)^3$; that is (Excursus, Art. 18),

$$\lfloor 5 \times 5/4, \text{ or } 150.$$

There are 8^{11} or 8589934592 ways of giving 11 different gifts to 8 boys. But if no boy is to be without a gift the number of ways is $\lfloor 11$ times the coefficient of x^{11} in the expansion of $(e^x - 1)^8$; that is, $12 \times \lfloor 11$, or 479001600.

PROPOSITION XXIII.

The number of r-partitions of n different things, i.e. the number of ways in which n different things can be distributed into r indifferent parcels, with no blank lots, is $\lfloor n / \lfloor r$ times the coefficient of x^n in the expansion of $(e^x - 1)^r$.

This follows from Prop. XXII., as Prop. XVII. from Prop. XVI., or Prop. XX. from Prop. XIX.

EXAMPLE. To divide the letters a, b, c, d, e into three parcels. The number of ways will be $\lfloor 5 / \lfloor 3$ times the coefficient of x^5 in the expansion of $(e^x - 1)^3$; that is (Excursus, Art. 18), $5 . 4 \times 5/4 = 25$.

The twenty-five partitions are easily seen to be ten such as abc, d, e, and fifteen such as ab, cd, e.

PROPOSITION XXIV.

The total number of ways in which n different things can be distributed into 1, 2, 3... or n indifferent parcels is $\lfloor n$ times the coefficient of x^n in the expansion of e^{e^x}/e.

Let N_r denote the number of r-partitions of n different things; then

$$N_1 = \lfloor n \text{ times the coefficient of } x^n \text{ in } \frac{e^x - 1}{\lfloor 1},$$

$$N_2 = \dotfill \frac{(e^x - 1)^2}{\lfloor 2},$$

$$N_3 = \dotfill \frac{(e^x - 1)^3}{\lfloor 3},$$

and so on.

Therefore by addition

$$N_1 + N_2 + N_3 + \ldots + N_n$$

is equal to $\lfloor n$ times the coefficient of x^n in the expansion of

$$\frac{e^x - 1}{\lfloor 1} + \frac{(e^x - 1)^2}{\lfloor 2} + \frac{(e^x - 1)^3}{\lfloor 3} + \&c.,$$

this last series being carried to infinity if we please, since the terms beyond the nth do not involve x^n, and therefore the inclusion of them will not affect the coefficient of x^n.

But this series is the expansion of $e^{e^x - 1} - 1$, and the coefficient of x^n therein is the same as in the expansion of $e^{e^x - 1}$ or $e^{e^x} \div e$. Hence

$$N_1 + N_2 + N_3 + \ldots + N_n$$

is equal to $\lfloor n$ times the coefficient of x^n in the expansion of e^{e^x}/e. Q. E. D.

PROPOSITION XXV.

The number of ways in which n indifferent things can be distributed into r different parcels (blank lots being inadmissible) is the number of combinations of n − 1 things taken r − 1 at a time.

For we may perform the operation by placing the n things in a row, then placing $r - 1$ points of partition amongst them, and assigning the r parts thus created, in order, to the r parcels in order.

Hence the number of ways is the number of ways of placing $r - 1$ points of partition in a selection out of $n - 1$ intervals. Therefore it is the same as the number of combinations of $n - 1$ things taken $r - 1$ at a time. Q. E. D.

PROPOSITION XXVI.

The number of ways in which n indifferent things can be distributed into r different parcels (blank lots being admissible) is the number of combinations of $n + r - 1$ things taken $r - 1$ at a time.

For the distribution of n things, when blank lots are admissible, is the same as the distribution of $n + r$ things when they are not admissible, since in the latter case we have to place one thing in each of the r parcels, and then to distribute the remainder as if blank lots were admissible. Hence, writing $n + r$ for n in the result of Proposition XXV., we obtain the number required.

EXAMPLES. Twenty shots are to be fired ; the work can be distributed among four guns in C_3^{19} or 969 ways, without leaving any gun unemployed. Or, neglecting this restriction, the work can be done in C_3^{23} or 1771 ways.

Again, five partners in a game require to score 36 to win. The number of ways in which they may share this score (not all necessarily contributing) is C_4^{40} or 91390 different ways.

Again, in how many ways can five oranges be distributed amongst seven boys ? Evidently two or more of them will get none. The answer is C_6^{11} or 462.

PROPOSITION XXVII.

The number of ways in which n indifferent things can be distributed into r different parcels, no parcel to contain less than q things, is the number of combinations of $n - 1 - r(q - 1)$ things taken $r - 1$ at a time.

For if we first place q things in each of the r parcels we shall have $n - qr$ things left, and it will only remain to dis tribute them among the same r parcels according to Proposition XXVI., which shews that the number of ways of making the distribution is the number of combinations of $n - qr + r - 1$ things taken $r - 1$ at a time.   Q. E. D.

PROPOSITION XXVIII.

The number of ways in which n indifferent things can be distributed into r different parcels, no parcel to contain less than q things, nor more than $q + z - 1$ things, is the coefficient of x^{n-qr} in the expansion of

$$\left(\frac{1 - x^z}{1 - x}\right)^r.$$

For if we multiply together r factors, each represented by

$$x^q + x^{q+1} + \ldots\ldots + x^{q+z-1},$$

we shall have in our result a term x^n for every way in which we can make up n by the addition of one index q or $q + 1$ or $q + 2$ or &c., or $q + z - 1$ from each of the r factors.   Hence we shall have x^n as many times as there are ways of distributing n into r different parts, no part less than q nor greater than $q + z - 1$.   Therefore the number of ways of so distributing n is the coefficient of x^n in the expansion of

$$(x^q + x^{q+1} + \ldots + x^{q+z-1})^r,$$

or of $$x^{qr}(1 + x + x^2 + \ldots + x^{z-1})^r,$$

which is the coefficient of x^{n-qr} in the expansion of

$$(1 + x + x^2 + \ldots + x^{z-1})^r,$$

or of $$\left(\frac{1 - x^z}{1 - x}\right)^r.$$ Q. E. D.

EXAMPLE. The number of ways in which four persons, each throwing a single die once, can score 17 amongst them will be obtained by putting $q=1$, $z=6$, $x=17$, $r=4$. Thus it is the coefficient of x^{17-4} in the expansion of

$$\left(\frac{1-x^6}{1-x}\right)^4.$$

Now

$$(1-x^6)^4 = 1 - 4x^6 + 6x^{12} - \&c.$$

$$(1-x)^{-4} = \frac{1}{6}\left\{1.2.3 + 2.3.4x + 3.4.5x^2 + ...\right\}.$$

And the coefficient of x^{13} in the product

$$= \frac{1}{6}\left\{14.15.16 - 4.8.9.10 + 6.2.3.4\right\}$$

$$= 104.$$

The following notation will be sometimes convenient.

Let n be a number not divisible by r. Then $\dfrac{n}{r}$ is not an integer, it therefore lies between two consecutive integers. *Let* $\dfrac{n-}{r}$ *denote the lesser of these and let* $\dfrac{n+}{r}$ *denote the greater.* Then we shall have

$$\frac{n+}{r} - \frac{n-}{r} = 1.$$

Also let $\dfrac{n\pm}{r}$ *denote the integer nearest to* $\dfrac{n}{r}$, so that

$$\frac{n\pm}{r} = \frac{n+}{r} \text{ or } \frac{n-}{r},$$

according as the division of n by r leaves a remainder greater or less than $\dfrac{r}{2}$.

It must only be noted that if the remainder is equal to $\dfrac{r}{2}$ the expression $\dfrac{n\pm}{r}$ would be ambiguous, and we must use either $\dfrac{n+}{r}$ or $\dfrac{n-}{r}$ as the case requires.

Further, let it be understood that if n happen to be divisible by r, each of the expressions $\dfrac{n+}{r}$, $\dfrac{n-}{r}$, $\dfrac{n\pm}{r}$ must be interpreted to mean $\dfrac{n}{r}$.

Then, generally,

$\dfrac{n-}{r}$ *is the greatest integer in* $\dfrac{n}{r}$,

$\dfrac{n\pm}{r}$ *is the nearest integer to* $\dfrac{n}{r}$,

$\dfrac{n+}{r}$ *is the least integer not less than* $\dfrac{n}{r}$.

PROPOSITION XXIX.

To find the number of ways in which n indifferent things can be distributed into r indifferent parcels (no blank lots).

OR

To find the number of different r-partitions of n.

Let Π_r^n denote the number of r-partitions of n, or the number of ways of distributing n indifferent elements into r indifferent parcels.

Suppose that in any distribution, $x+1$ is the smallest number found in any parcel. Then setting aside a parcel which contains $x+1$ all the other parcels contain not less than $x+1$, and therefore more than x. If we place x in each of these $r-1$ parcels, the distribution can then be completed by distributing the remaining $n-1-rx$ things among the same $r-1$ parcels, and this can be done in Π_{r-1}^{n-1-rx} ways. In this way we shall obtain all the distributions, by giving x successively all its possible values. But since $x + 1$ is the smallest number found in any parcel, $x + 1$ cannot be greater than the greatest integer in $\dfrac{n}{r}$, or $\dfrac{n-}{r}$.

Then x must have all values from 0 to $\dfrac{n-}{r} - 1$, and therefore

$$\Pi_r^n = \Pi_{r-1}^{n-1} + \Pi_{r-1}^{n-1-r} + \Pi_{r-1}^{n-1-2r} + \ldots \text{ to } \frac{n-}{r} \text{ terms.}$$

Now it is plain that $\Pi_1^n = 1$ for all values of n.

Hence $\Pi_2^n = \Pi_1^{n-1} + \Pi_1^{n-3} + \Pi_1^{n-5} + \ldots \text{ to } \dfrac{n-}{2} \text{ terms} = \dfrac{n-}{2}$.

Again $\Pi_3^n = \Pi_2^{n-1} + \Pi_2^{n-4} + \Pi_2^{n-7} + \ldots \text{ to } \dfrac{n-}{3} \text{ terms}$

$$= \frac{n-1-}{2} + \frac{n-4-}{2} + \frac{n-7-}{2} + \ldots \text{ to } \frac{n-}{3} \text{ terms.}$$

The summation will depend upon the form of n; thus,

$$\text{If } n = 6q \quad \text{then } \Pi_3^n = \frac{n^2}{12}$$

$$n = 6q \pm 1 \quad \Pi_3^n = \frac{n^2 - 1}{12}$$

$$n = 6q \pm 2 \quad \Pi_3^n = \frac{n^2 - 4}{12}$$

$$n = 6q + 3 \quad \Pi_3^n = \frac{n^2 + 3}{12}.$$

Therefore Π_3^n is always *the integer nearest to* $\dfrac{n^2}{12}$, or

$$\Pi_3^n = \frac{n^2 \pm}{12}.$$

Again, $\Pi_4^n = \Pi_3^{n-1} + \Pi_3^{n-5} + \Pi_3^{n-9} + \ldots$ to $\dfrac{n-}{4}$ terms

$$= \frac{(n-1)^2 \pm}{12} + \frac{(n-5)^2 \pm}{12} + \frac{(n-9)^2 \pm}{12} + \ldots \text{ to } \frac{n-}{4} \text{ terms.}$$

The summation will depend upon the form of n; thus,

If $n = 12q$ then $\Pi_4^n = \dfrac{n^3 + 3n^2}{144}$

$n = 12q + 1$ $\Pi_4^n = \dfrac{n^3 + 3n^2 - 9n + 5}{144}$

$n = 12q + 2$ $\Pi_4^n = \dfrac{n^3 + 3n^2 - 20}{144}$

$n = 12q + 3$ $\Pi_4^n = \dfrac{n^3 + 3n^2 - 9n - 27}{144}$

$n = 12q + 4$ $\Pi_4^n = \dfrac{n^3 + 3n^2 + 32}{144}$

$n = 12q + 5$ $\Pi_4^n = \dfrac{n^3 + 3n^2 - 9n - 11}{144}$

$n = 12q + 6$ $\Pi_4^n = \dfrac{n^3 + 3n^2 - 36}{144}$

$n = 12q - 5$ $\Pi_4^n = \dfrac{n^3 + 3n^2 - 9n + 5}{144}$

$n = 12q - 4$ $\Pi_4^n = \dfrac{n^3 + 3n^2 + 16}{144}$

$n = 12q - 3$ $\Pi_4^n = \dfrac{n^3 + 3n^2 - 9n - 27}{144}$

$n = 12q - 2$ $\Pi_4^n = \dfrac{n^3 + 3n^2 - 4}{144}$

$n = 12q - 1$ $\Pi_4^n = \dfrac{n^3 + 3n^2 - 9n - 11}{144}$.

Therefore,
$$\begin{cases} \Pi_4^n = \dfrac{n^3 + 3n^2 \pm}{144} \text{ when } n \text{ is even:} \\[3mm] \Pi_4^n = \dfrac{n^3 + 3n^2 - 9n \pm}{144} \text{ when } n \text{ is odd.} \end{cases}$$

By a like process we may deduce successively Π_5^n, Π_6^n, &c., and thus we may find Π_r^n for any values of n and r, although we cannot write down a general expression for Π_r^n in any simple terms.

EXAMPLES.   There are twelve 3-partitions of 12, viz.

1, 1, 10	1, 3, 8	1, 5, 6	2, 3, 7	2, 5, 5	3, 4, 5
1, 2, 9	1, 4, 7	2, 2, 8	2, 4, 6	3, 3, 6	4, 4, 4

There are fifteen 4-partitions of 12, viz.

1, 1, 1, 9	1, 1, 4, 6	1, 2, 3, 6	1, 3, 4, 4	2, 2, 4, 4
1, 1, 2, 8	1, 1, 5, 5	1, 2, 4, 5	2, 2, 2, 6	2, 3, 3, 4
1, 1, 3, 7	1, 2, 2, 7	1, 3, 3, 5	2, 2, 3, 5	3, 3, 3, 3

The number of 4-partitions of 13 is the integer nearest to $(n^3 + 3n^2 - 9n) \div 144$ when $n = 13$. Therefore there are 18 partitions, viz.

1, 1, 1, 10	1, 1, 5, 6	1, 2, 5, 5	2, 2, 2, 7	2, 3, 4, 4
1, 1, 2, 9	1, 2, 2, 8	1, 3, 3, 6	2, 2, 3, 6	3, 3, 3, 4
1, 1, 3, 8	1, 2, 3, 7	1, 3, 4, 5	2, 2, 4, 5	
1, 1, 4, 7	1, 2, 4, 6	1, 4, 4, 4	2, 3, 3, 5	

It appears from what precedes that the number of r-partitions of any number is easily calculated if we have a register of the $(r-1)$-partitions of lower numbers. There is no difficulty therefore in constructing a table of the number of r-partitions of n for a series of consecutive values of r and n, commencing with unity. Such a table is given on page 99. It is however most readily constructed by the aid of the following theorem.

PROPOSITION XXX.

To prove that the number of r-partitions of n exceeds the number of (r − 1)-partitions of n − 1, by the number of r-partitions of n − r.

To make every *r*-partition of *n*, we must first take *r* of the elements and place one of them in each of the proposed parcels. We have then to distribute the remaining *n − r* elements into 1, 2, 3 … or more of the parcels. Hence

$$\Pi_r^n = \Pi_1^{n-r} + \Pi_2^{n-r} + \Pi_3^{n-r} + \dots + \Pi_{r-1}^{n-r} + \Pi_r^{n-r}.$$

Now write *n* − 1 for *n*, and *r* − 1 for *r*, then

$$\Pi_{r-1}^{n-1} = \Pi_1^{n-r} + \Pi_2^{n-r} + \Pi_3^{n-r} + \dots + \Pi_{r-1}^{n-r},$$

therefore by subtraction

$$\Pi_r^n - \Pi_{r-1}^{n-1} = \Pi_r^{n-r}.$$

COROLLARY. If $n - r < r$, that is if $r > \dfrac{n}{2}$,

$$\Pi_r^n = \Pi_{r-1}^{n-1}.$$

We proceed to shew how the table of partitions given on page 99 is most readily constructed, or how it can be most readily extended at will.

We commence by observing that for all values of *n*

$$\Pi_1^n = 1, \quad \Pi_n^n = 1, \quad \Pi_{n-1}^n = 1;$$

therefore we may fill the highest row and the two lowest diagonal rows with unity.

Also, since if $x > n$, $\Pi_x^n = 0$, we may regard all the blank spaces below the lowest diagonal as filled with zero.

This makes a sufficient commencement of the table, though it may be most convenient to insert at once the row of 2-partitions, which we know to be 1, 1, 2, 2, 3, 3, &c. since

$$\Pi_2^n = \frac{n-}{2} .$$

We have now to see how the table when once commenced and carried to any extent may be further extended.

Take any vertical column, as for instance, the column under the head 7. It reads thus

$$1, \ 3, \ 4, \ 3, \ 2, \ 1, \ 1, \ 0, \ 0, \ 0, \ \&c.$$

Add up the sum of this series first to one term, then add another term, and another, and so on; we get

$$1, \ 4, \ 8, \ 11, \ 13, \ 14, \ 15, \ 15, \ 15, \ 15, \ \&c.$$

But by the proposition these sums must be respectively Π_1^8, Π_2^9, Π_3^{10}, and so on, ad infinitum. That is, they constitute a *diagonal* of our table commencing under the head 8, and extending indefinitely downwards to the right.

In this way it is quite easy to write out the table to any extent, proceeding by successive diagonals, each entry in the table being found by the simple addition of two numbers.

TABLE OF THE NUMBER OF r-PARTITIONS OF n.

r\\n	1	2	3	4	5	6	7	8	9	10	11	12	13	14	15	16	17	18	19	20	21	22	23	24	25	26	27
1	1	1	1	1	1	1	1	1	1	1	1	1	1	1	1	1	1	1	1	1	1	1	1	1	1	1	1
2		1	1	2	2	3	3	4	4	5	5	6	6	7	7	8	8	9	9	10	10	11	11	12	12	13	13
3			1	1	2	3	4	5	7	8	10	12	14	16	19	21	24	27	30	33	37	40	44	48	52	56	61
4				1	1	2	3	5	6	9	11	15	18	23	27	34	39	47	54	64	72	84	94	108	120	136	150
5					1	1	2	3	5	7	10	13	18	23	30	37	47	57	70	84	101	119	141	164	192	221	255
6						1	1	2	3	5	7	11	14	20	26	35	44	58	71	90	110	136	163	199	235	282	331
7							1	1	2	3	5	7	11	15	21	28	38	49	65	82	105	131	164	201	248	300	364
8								1	1	2	3	5	7	11	15	22	29	40	52	70	89	116	146	186	230	288	352
9									1	1	2	3	5	7	11	15	22	30	41	54	73	94	123	157	201	252	318
10										1	1	2	3	5	7	11	15	22	30	42	55	75	97	128	164	212	267
11											1	1	2	3	5	7	11	15	22	30	42	56	76	99	131	169	219
12												1	1	2	3	5	7	11	15	22	30	42	56	77	100	133	172
13													1	1	2	3	5	7	11	15	22	30	42	56	77	101	134
14														1	1	2	3	5	7	11	15	22	30	42	56	77	101
15															1	1	2	3	5	7	11	15	22	30	42	56	77
16																1	1	2	3	5	7	11	15	22	30	42	56
17																	1	1	2	3	5	7	11	15	22	30	42
18																		1	1	2	3	5	7	11	15	22	30
19																			1	1	2	3	5	7	11	15	22
20																				1	1	2	3	5	7	11	15

Note that the successive values of n are given at the head of the columns, and the successive values of r in the column to the left of the table.

CHAPTER IV.

DERANGEMENTS.

WHEN we place a series of elements in a particular order we are said to *arrange* them. But if they have been already arranged, or if they have a proper order of their own, and we place them in other order, we are said to *derange* them. Thus derangement implies a previous arrangement in which each element had its own proper place, either naturally belonging to it or arbitrarily assigned to it.

If we begin with unity and multiply successively by 1, 2, 3 … as if we were going to form $\lfloor n$, but let every even product be increased by unity and every odd product be diminished by unity, we shall obtain a series of numbers which we shall denote by the symbols $\Vert 1$, $\Vert 2$, $\Vert 3$, &c.

Thus multiply by 1 *and subtract* 1 : we get $\Vert 1 = 0$,

then multiply by 2 *and add* 1 : we get $\Vert 2 = 1$,

then multiply by 3 *and subtract* 1 : we get $\Vert 3 = 2$,

then multiply by 4 *and add* 1 : we get $\Vert 4 = 9$,

and so on.

Or, more fully,

$$\Vert 1 = \lfloor 1 - 1,$$

$$\Vert 2 = 2 \cdot 1 - 2 + 1,$$

$$\Vert 3 = 3 \cdot 2 \cdot 1 - 3 \cdot 2 + 3 - 1,$$

$$\Vert 4 = 4 \cdot 3 \cdot 2 \cdot 1 - 4 \cdot 3 \cdot 2 + 4 \cdot 3 - 4 + 1,$$

and finally

$$\|n = \lfloor n \left\{ 1 - \frac{1}{\lfloor 1} + \frac{1}{\lfloor 2} - \frac{1}{\lfloor 3} + \cdots \pm \frac{1}{\lfloor n} \right\}.$$

As $\lfloor n$ is called *factorial-n* it is convenient to read $\|n$ as *sub-factorial-n*. The values of the first twelve factorials and sub-factorials, and their ratios, are given on page 107.

Since by definition

$$\|n+1 = (n+1)\,\|n \pm 1,$$

and

$$\|n = n\,\|n-1 \mp 1,$$

we have by addition

$$\|n+1 + \|n = (n+1)\,\|n + n\,\|n-1,$$

or

$$\|n+1 = n\,(\|n + \|n-1).$$

This equation expresses the law connecting each sub-factorial with the two preceding ones; and it is curious to note that *the same law* holds good for factorials and for sub-factorials, since

$$\lfloor n+1 = n\,(\lfloor n + \lfloor n-1).$$

Comparing the series for $\|n$ with the expansion of e^{-1} (page 77) we deduce

$$\|n = \frac{\lfloor n}{e} \pm H, \qquad \begin{array}{l}\text{upper sign when } n \text{ is even,}\\ \text{lower sign when } n \text{ is odd,}\end{array}$$

where H is a small fraction lying between $\frac{1}{n+1}$ and $\frac{1}{n+2}$.

In other words, $\|n$ *is the integer nearest to* $\lfloor n \div e$.

PROPOSITION XXXI.

The number of ways in which a row of n elements may be so deranged that no element shall be in its proper place is $\lfloor\!\lfloor n$, or the integer nearest to $\lfloor n \div e$.

For the total number of arrangements is $\lfloor n$. The number fulfilling the condition that any assigned one (at least) is *in situ* is $\lfloor n-1$. The number fulfilling the condition that two assigned elements are *in situ* is $\lfloor n-2$, and so on. Hence by Prop. XIV. Cor. 3, the number of arrangements in which none of the n elements are *in situ* is

$$\lfloor n - \frac{n}{1}\lfloor n-1 + \frac{n(n-1)}{1.2}\lfloor n-2 - \frac{n(n-1)(n-2)}{1.2.3}\lfloor n-3 + \&c.$$

to $n+1$ terms

$$= \lfloor n \left\{ 1 - \frac{1}{\lfloor 1} + \frac{1}{\lfloor 2} - \frac{1}{\lfloor 3} + \dots \pm \frac{1}{\lfloor n} \right\} = \lfloor\!\lfloor n. \quad \text{Q. E. D.}$$

COROLLARY. *The number of ways in which n elements can be deranged so that not any one of r assigned elements may be in its proper place (the rest being unrestricted) is*

$$\lfloor n - \frac{r}{1}\lfloor n-1 + \frac{r(r-1)}{1.2}\lfloor n-2 - \dots \pm \lfloor n-r.$$

EXAMPLE. Suppose we have the four elements a, b, c, d; the number of derangements, so that all may be displaced, is (by the proposition) $\lfloor\!\lfloor 4$ or 9.

These nine derangements are as follows:

$$
\begin{array}{ccc}
b\,d\,a\,c & c\,a\,d\,b & d\,c\,a\,b \\
b\,a\,d\,c & c\,d\,b\,a & d\,c\,b\,a \\
b\,c\,d\,a & c\,d\,a\,b & d\,a\,b\,c \\
\end{array}
$$

If it be required to derange the same terms so that two may remain *in situ* and two be displaced, the number of derangements is, by the Corollary,

$$12\left(1-1+\frac{1}{2}\right)=6.$$

These six derangements are as follows :

$$\begin{array}{ccc} a\,b\,d\,c & a\,d\,c\,b & a\,c\,b\,d \\ b\,a\,c\,d & c\,b\,a\,d & d\,b\,c\,a \end{array}$$

PROPOSITION XXXII.

The number of ways of deranging a series of n terms so that no term may be followed by the term which originally followed it, is $\lfloor n + \lfloor n - 1$, or the integer nearest to $\lfloor n + 1 \div ne$.

Let α, β, γ, $\ldots \kappa$ represent the n terms. Then amongst the $\lfloor n$ arrangements of which the terms are capable there will be $\lfloor n - 1$ in which any assigned sequence $\alpha\beta$ occurs : (for these arrangements will be obtained by regarding $\alpha\beta$ as one term and then arranging it with the remaining $n - 2$ terms). Similarly any two sequences which can consistently occur (as $\alpha\beta$, $\beta\gamma$, or $\alpha\beta$, $\gamma\delta$*) will be found in $\lfloor n - 2$ different arrangements. Any three consistent sequences will be found in $\lfloor n - 3$ different arrangements : and so on.

Therefore the number of arrangements free from any of the $n - 1$ sequences is, by Prop. XIV. Cor. 3,

$$\lfloor n - (n-1)\lfloor n-1 + \frac{(n-1)(n-2)}{1.2}\lfloor n-2$$

$$-\frac{(n-1)(n-2)(n-3)}{1.2.3}\lfloor n-3 + \&c. \text{ to } n \text{ terms}$$

$$=\lfloor n-1\left\{n-\frac{n-1}{\lfloor 1}+\frac{n-2}{\lfloor 2}-\frac{n-3}{\lfloor 3}+\frac{n-4}{\lfloor 4}-\&c. \pm\frac{1}{\lfloor n}\right\},$$

* Of course such sequences as $\alpha\beta$ $\alpha\gamma$ could not consistently occur, as α could not at the same time be followed by β and γ.

which is easily seen to be equivalent to $\|n + \|n-1$, or $\|n+1 \div n$ (page 101), which is the integer nearest to $\lfloor n+1 \div ne$.   Q. E. D.

COROLLARY.   *The number of derangements of a series of n terms, free from any of r assigned sequences (capable of occurring simultaneously in one arrangement), is*

$$\lfloor n - \frac{r}{1}\lfloor n-1 + \frac{r(r-1)}{1.2}\lfloor n-2 - \ldots \pm \lfloor n-r.$$

EXAMPLE.   Let us derange the series of four elements *abcd* so as to exclude the sequences *ab bc cd*.

By the proposition the number of derangements is

$$\|4 + \|3 = 9 + 2 = 11.$$

And they are found on trial to be

a c b d	b d c a	c a d b	d b a c
a d c b	b a d c	c b a d	d c b a
	b d a c	c b d a	d a c b

PROPOSITION XXXIII.

The number of ways of deranging the series of n terms α, β, γ, ... ι, κ, *so that none of the n sequences* αβ, βγ, ... ικ, κα *may occur, is* $n\|n-1$, *or n times the integer nearest to* $\lfloor n-1 \div e.$*

For, as before, there are $\lfloor n$ arrangements of the *n* terms, and any assigned sequence will be found in $\lfloor n-1$ of them; any two assigned sequences in $\lfloor n-2$, any three assigned

* Or 1 more (*n* odd) or 1 less (*n* even) than the integer nearest to $\lfloor n \div e.$

sequences in $\underline{|n-3}$ of them, and so on for $n-1$ sequences; but as all the n sequences cannot occur at once, the number of arrangements with n sequences is not 1 but 0.

Therefore (by Prop. XIV. Cor. 3) the whole number of admissible arrangements is

$$\underline{|n} - n\underline{|n-1} + \frac{n(n-1)}{1 \cdot 2}\underline{|n-2} - \&c.$$

to n terms [not $n+1$ terms], which may be written $\underline{\|n \pm 1}$, or $n\underline{\|n-1}$; that is, n times the greatest integer in $\underline{|n-1 \div e}$. Q. E. D.

EXAMPLE. Let us derange the series of four elements *abcd* so as to exclude the sequences *ab bc cd da*.

By the proposition the number of derangements is $4\ \underline{\|3}$ or $4 \times 2 = 8$; and the eight derangements are found to be

$$a\ c\ b\ d \qquad b\ d\ c\ a \qquad c\ a\ d\ b \qquad d\ b\ a\ c$$
$$a\ d\ c\ b \qquad b\ a\ d\ c \qquad c\ b\ a\ d \qquad d\ c\ b\ a$$

PROPOSITION XXXIV.

If n terms be arranged in circular procession the number of ways in which they can be deranged so that no term may be followed by the term which originally followed it, is

$$\underline{\|n-1} - \underline{\|n-2} + \underline{\|n-3} - \underline{\|n-4} + \dots.$$

For the whole number of arrangements of n things in circular procession is $\underline{|n-1}$; and any assigned sequence is found in $\underline{|n-2}$ of them; any two assigned consistent sequences in $\underline{|n-3}$, and so on, till we come to the case of n consistent sequences, which can evidently be found in 1 arrangement. Hence provided we replace the final $\lfloor-1$ by unity we may write down, (by Prop. XIV. Cor. 3), the number of arrangements free from any of the n sequences as follows;

$$\lfloor n-1 - n\lfloor n-2 + \frac{n(n-1)}{1 \cdot 2}\lfloor n-3 - \&\text{c. to } (n+1) \text{ terms.}$$

If we call this $f(n)$ we see that $f(n) + f(n-1) = \lVert n-1$; whence

$$f(n) = \lVert n-1 - \lVert n-2 + \lVert n-3 - \lVert n-4 + \ldots \quad \text{Q. E. D.}$$

EXAMPLES :

If $n=3$, the number of derangements may be written

$$2-1=1,$$

or the only availab'.. derangement is one, viz. the one in which the order of the terms is reversed.

If $n=5$, we have

$$9-2+1=8.$$

If *abcde* represent the original order, the eight derangements may be exhibited as follows :

$$a\,c\,b\,e\,d \qquad a\,e\,b\,d\,c \qquad a\,c\,e\,d\,b \qquad a\,e\,c\,b\,d \qquad a\,d\,c\,e\,b$$
$$a\,d\,b\,e\,c \qquad a\,c\,e\,b\,d \qquad a\,e\,d\,c\,b$$

In the foregoing propositions we have investigated the number of ways of deranging groups of elements subject to various laws. But as there can scarcely be a limit to the variety of laws which might be proposed to regulate the distribution in different cases, it would be an endless task to undertake a strictly complete discussion of the subject, or to make our treatise exhaustive. The cases which we have considered are those which most obviously arise, and the methods which we have applied to them will be easily adapted to a variety of other cases, or will suggest other methods of still wider applicability.

To save trouble in working out numerical examples we append a table of the values of the first 12 factorials and sub-factorials, and of their ratios. It will be seen that the ratio of $\lfloor n : \lVert n$ converges with great rapidity towards its ultimate value e, the successive values of the ratio being alternately greater and less than e.

$n.$	$\lfloor n$	$\lVert n$	$\lfloor n \div \lVert n$	$\lVert n \div \lfloor n$
1	1	0	∞	0·000000
2	2	1	2·000000	0·500000
3	6	2	3·000000	0·333333
4	24	9	2·666666	0·375000
5	120	44	2·727272	0·366666
6	720	265	2·716981	0·368055
7	5040	1854	2·718446	0·367857
8	40320	14833	2·718262	0·367881
9	362880	133496	2·718283	0·367879
10	3628800	1334961	2·718281	0·367879
11	39916800	14684570	2·718281	0·367879
12	479001600	176214841	2·718281	0·367879

CHAPTER V.

SOME QUESTIONS OF PRIORITY.

WE shall consider in the present chapter some questions of order amongst things of two or more classes, when limits are placed upon the excess at any point of things of one class above things of the other.

If a man possessed of only £5 makes 24 successive bets of £1, winning 12 times and losing 12 times, the number of orders in which his successes and failures can occur will naturally be limited by the fact that the losses must never exceed the gains by more than £5.

A variety of questions may be proposed in which similar conditions are assigned.

For example, if an urn contain black balls and white balls which are to be drawn out in succession, the order in which they are drawn out may be limited by the condition that the number of white balls drawn must never exceed the number of black balls; or, again, by the condition that the excess of black balls over white must never be more than a given number.

Or there may be a question of taking m paces horizontally and n paces vertically without ever crossing that oblique line which is reached when the number of paces in each direction is the same.

This last case suggests a graphic representation which will equally apply to the other cases, and will help to fix our ideas. The horizontal paces may be taken to represent successes and the vertical paces failures; or the one may represent the drawing of black balls and the other of white balls. In stating our propositions we shall speak for shortness of gains and losses, but it will be observed that the reasoning is quite general.

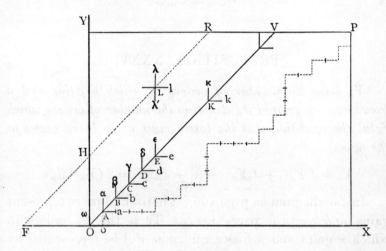

From any origin O draw OX horizontally and OY vertically, and let P be the point which would be reached by starting from O and taking m paces horizontally in the direction OX and n paces vertically parallel to OY.

Let A be the point reached by taking one pace horizontally and one pace vertically, B the point reached by taking two paces in each direction, C by taking three paces in each direction, and so on; so that $ABC...$ lie in the straight line bisecting the right angle XOY.

Let $o, a, b, c ...$ be the points reached by taking one horizontal pace from each of the points $O, A, B, C ...$ and $\omega, \alpha, \beta, \gamma ...$ the points reached by taking one pace vertically from $O, A, B, C ...$ respectively.

In considering the number of routes from one point to another we shall proceed on the understanding that each route is to be traversed by paces taken only horizontally and vertically, and without retrogression.

It is plain that the whole number of routes from O to P is $$C_m^{m+n} \text{ or } C_{m,\,n}.*$$

PROPOSITION XXXV.

Y_n being the number of orders in which n gains and n losses can occur, and J_n denoting the number of orders which fulfil the condition that the losses must never be in excess of the gains,

$$Y_n + J_1 Y_{n-1} + J_2 Y_{n-2} + \ldots + J_{n-1} Y_1 = 2\,(Y_n - J_n).$$

In the diagram on page 109, let horizontal paces represent gains and vertical paces losses. Then the Y_n orders in which n gains and n losses can come will be represented by all possible routes from O to V, and the J_n orders which fulfil the stated condition will be represented by all routes from O to V which do not pass to the left of the diagonal OV. The remaining routes ($Y_n - J_n$ in number) may be classified according to the point at which they *first* pass to the left of the diagonal whether they recross more than once or not, that is according as they first traverse the pace $O\omega$ or $A\alpha$ or $B\beta$ or &c.

Consider the routes which cross the diagonal at K, after making (say) r horizontal and r vertical paces, without

---

* Throughout this chapter we shall use $C_{r,\,n-r}$ in preference to C_r^n, and $C_{x,\,y}$ in preference to C_x^{x+y} or C_y^{x+y} to denote $\dfrac{\lfloor n}{\lfloor r\,\lfloor n-r}$ and $\dfrac{\lfloor x+y}{\lfloor x\,\lfloor y}$ respectively.

having crossed before, but independently of any consideration of the number of times they may cross afterwards.

Any such route $OK\kappa P$ may be divided into three portions OK, $K\kappa$, κP, of which OK can be made in J_r ways, $K\kappa$ in one way and κP in $C_{n-r,n-r-1} = \frac{1}{2} Y_{n-r}$ ways. Therefore the whole number of ways in which the route $OK\kappa P$ can be made is $\frac{1}{2} J_r Y_{n-r}$.

Giving r all values from 0 to $n-1$ we get all routes comprehended in the number $Y_n - J_n$. Therefore

$$\Sigma_{r=0}^{r=n-1} \left\{ \tfrac{1}{2} J_r Y_{n-r} \right\} = Y_n - J_n,$$

or, $Y_n + J_1 Y_{n-1} + J_2 Y_{n-2} + \ldots + J_{n-1} Y_1 = 2 (Y_n - J_n)$. Q.E.D.

PROPOSITION XXXVI.

Of the orders in which n gains and n losses can occur, one $(n+1)$th of the whole number fulfil the condition that the losses must never exceed the gains.

The number of orders in which n gains and n losses can occur is Y_n.

With the notation already adopted we have to prove that

$$J_n = \frac{Y_n}{n+1}.$$

We know that

$$Y_0 = 1, \quad Y_1 = 2, \quad Y_2 = 6, \quad Y_3 = 20, \quad Y_4 = 70;$$

and actually counting the orders included in J_n when $n = 1, 2, 3$, or 4, we find that

$$J_0 = 1, \quad J_1 = 1, \quad J_2 = 2, \quad J_3 = 5, \quad J_4 = 14.$$

Hence the proposition is true as long as n does not exceed 4.

To prove it generally, we shall shew that if it be true when $n = 0, 1, 2, \ldots$ or $x - 1$ it will also be true when $n = x$.

By the last proposition we have

$$J_0 Y_x + J_1 Y_{x-1} + J_2 Y_{x-2} + \ldots + J_{n-1} Y_1 = 2Y_n - 2J_n.$$

But since our present proposition is by hypothesis true when $n = 0, 1, 2 \ldots$ or $x - 1$, we have

$$J_0 = Y_0,$$
$$J_1 = \tfrac{1}{2} Y_1,$$
$$J_2 = \tfrac{1}{3} Y_2,$$
$$\&c. = \&c.$$
$$J_{x-1} = \frac{1}{x} Y_{x-1}.$$

Substituting these values we get

$$Y_0 Y_x + \tfrac{1}{2} Y_1 Y_{x-1} + \tfrac{1}{3} Y_2 Y_{x-2} + \ldots + \frac{1}{x} Y_{x-1} Y_1 = 2Y_x - 2J_x,$$

or (Excursus, Art. 13, page 76)

$$\tfrac{1}{2} Y_{x+1} - \frac{1}{x+1} Y_x = 2Y_x - 2J_x,$$

whence $J_x = Y_x \div (x + 1);$

that is, if the proposition is true for the first $x - 1$ values of n, it is true for the next value. But we have found that it was true for initial values; therefore universally

$$J_n = Y_n \div (n + 1).$$

Q. E. D.

COR. The number of orders in which the condition is not fulfilled may be written

$$C_{n+1,\, n-1}.$$

LEMMA.

To sum the series

$$Y_0 C_{m,n} + \tfrac{1}{2} Y_1 C_{m-1, n-1} + \tfrac{1}{3} Y_2 C_{m-2, n-2} + \ldots + \frac{1}{n+1} Y_n C_{m-n, 0}.$$

In the diagram already constructed, since all the routes from O to P commence at the point O on the diagonal and terminate at the point P to the right of the diagonal, they may be classified according to the points at which they *first* pass to the right of the diagonal: *i.e.* according as they first pass along Oo, or Aa or Bb, &c. Consider those which pass along Kk. Any such route consists of three portions OK, Kk, kP, of which OK lies altogether to the left of the diagonal, and can therefore be described in $Y_r/(r+1)$ ways (Prop. XXXVI.); Kk can be described in one way, and kP can be described in $C_{m-r-1, n-r}$ ways. Hence there are $Y_r C_{m-r-1, n-r}/(r+1)$ such routes; and giving r all values from 0 to n inclusive we must obtain all the $C_{m, n}$ routes from O to P. Therefore we must have identically

$$Y_0 C_{m-1, n} + \tfrac{1}{2} Y_1 C_{m-2, n-1} + \tfrac{1}{3} Y_2 C_{m-3, n-2} + \ldots$$
$$\ldots + \frac{1}{n+1} Y_n C_{m-n-1, 0} = C_{m, n}.$$

This is true for all values of m and n; therefore, writing $m+1$ for m we obtain

$$Y_0 C_{m, n} + \tfrac{1}{2} Y_1 C_{m-1, n-1} + \tfrac{1}{3} Y_2 C_{m-2, n-2} + \ldots$$
$$\ldots + \frac{1}{n+1} Y_n C_{m-n, 0} = C_{m+1, n}.$$

NOTE. If we make $m = n$, we obtain a series already summed (Excursus, Art. 13, page 76).

PROPOSITION XXXVII.

$C_{m,\,n}$ *being the number of orders in which* m *gains and* n *losses can occur, and* $J_{m,\,n}$ *denoting the number of orders which fulfil the condition that the losses must never be in excess of the gains,*

$$C_{m,\,n-1} + J_1 C_{m-1,\,n-2} + J_2 C_{m-2,\,n-3} + \ldots$$
$$\ldots + J_{n-1} C_{m-n+1,\,0} = C_{m,\,n} - J_{m,\,n}.$$

[Observe that for brevity, when the two suffixes are alike, we write J_n instead of $J_{n,\,n}$.]

Proceeding step by step as in Prop. XXXV., but considering the routes from O to P instead of O to V, we find that each route $OK\kappa P$ may be made in $J_r C_{m-r,\,n-r-1}$ ways.

Hence
$$\Sigma_{r=0}^{r=n-1} \{J_r C_{m-r,\,n-r-1}\} = C_{m,\,n} - J_{m,\,n},$$
or
$$C_{m,\,n-1} + J_1 C_{m-1,\,n-2} + J_2 C_{m-2,\,n-3} + \ldots$$
$$\ldots + J_{n-1} C_{m-n+1,\,0} = C_{m,\,n} - J_{m,\,n}.$$

Q. E. D.

PROPOSITION XXXVIII.

Of the orders in which m *gains and* n *losses can occur* $\dfrac{n}{m+1}$ *ths of the whole number will fail to fulfil the condition that the losses must never exceed the gains.*

We found in Prop. XXXVI. the values of J_0, J_1, J_2, &c. in the form $J_n = Y_n/(n+1)$.

Substitute these values in the result of Prop. XXXVII. and we obtain

$$C_{m,\,n-1} + \tfrac{1}{2} Y_1 C_{m-1,\,n-2} + \tfrac{1}{3} Y_2 C_{m-2,\,n-3} + \cdots$$

$$\cdots + \frac{1}{n} Y_{n-1} C_{m-n+1,\,0} = C_{m,\,n} - J_{m,\,n}.$$

But by the Lemma (page 113) writing $n-1$ for n in its result, the first member of this equation is equal to $C_{m+1,\,n-1}$.

Therefore

$$C_{m,\,n} - J_{m,\,n} = C_{m+1,\,n-1}$$

$$= \frac{n}{m+1} C_{m,\,n}.$$

Q. E. D.

COROLLARY. $J_{m,\,n} = \dfrac{m-n+1}{m+1} C_{m,\,n}.$

EXTENSION OF THE LEMMA.

If in the proof of the Lemma (page 113) the routes instead of starting from O had started from the point F situated h paces horizontally to the left of O, the whole number of routes would have been $C_{m+h,\,n}$. And classifying them as before, any route passing along Kk would have consisted of three parts, FK, Kk, kP, of which FK could be described in $\dfrac{h+1}{r+h+1} C_{r+h,\,r}$ ways (Prop. XXXVIII.), Kk in one way, kP in $C_{m-r-1,\,n-r}$ ways.

Hence there are $\dfrac{h+1}{r+h+1} C_{m-r-1,\,n-r} C_{r+h,\,r}$ such routes. And giving r all values from 0 to n we obtain the identity

$$C_{h,\,0}, C_{m-1,\,n} + \frac{h+1}{h+2} C_{h+1,\,1}, C_{m-2,\,n-1} + \frac{h+1}{h+3} C_{h+2,\,2}, C_{m-3,\,n-2} + \cdots$$

$$\cdots + \frac{h+1}{h+n+1} C_{h+n,\,h}, C_{m-n-1,\,0} = C_{m+h,\,n},$$

or

$$\frac{C_{h,\,0}C_{m-1,\,n}}{h+1} + \frac{C_{h+1,\,1}C_{m-2,\,n-1}}{h+2} + \frac{C_{h+2,\,2}C_{m-3,\,n-2}}{h+3} + \cdots$$

$$\cdots + \frac{C_{h+n,\,n}C_{m-n-1,\,0}}{h+n+1} = \frac{C_{m+h,\,n}}{h+1}.$$

Write h for $h+1$ and m for $m-1$, and we have

$$\frac{C_{m+h,\,n}}{h} = \frac{C_{h-1,\,0}C_{m,\,n}}{h} + \frac{C_{h,\,1}C_{m-1,\,n-1}}{h+1} + \cdots + \frac{C_{h+n-1,\,n}C_{m-n,\,0}}{h+n}.$$

Now write $n-h$ for n, and we have

$$\frac{C_{m+h,\,n-h}}{h} = \frac{C_{h-1,\,0}C_{m,\,n-h}}{h} + \frac{C_{h,\,1}C_{m-1,\,n-h-1}}{h+1} + \cdots$$

$$\cdots + \frac{C_{n-1,\,n-h}C_{m-n+h,\,0}}{n}.$$

PROPOSITION XXXIX.

Among the $C_{m,\,n}$ orders in which m gains and n losses can occur, there will be $C_{m+h,\,n-h}$ orders in which the losses will at some time be at least h in excess of the gains.

With the same diagram as before, the orders will be represented by routes from O to P which touch or cross a line HR parallel to the diagonal OK, at a vertical distance of h paces above it.

The routes may be classified according to the points at which they first touch the line HR.

Let $O\lambda'LP$ be any route which first reaches this line at a point L, distant r horizontal paces and $r+h$ vertical paces from O, and let $\lambda'L$ be the pace by which the point L is approached.

The route may be divided into three parts $O\lambda'$, $\lambda'L$, and LP; of which

$O\lambda'$ can be made in $\dfrac{h}{r+h}\,C_{r+h-1,\,r}$ ways (Prop. XXXVIII.),

$\lambda'L$ in one way,

LP in $C_{m-r,\,n-r-h}$ ways;

therefore the number of routes first touching at L is

$$\frac{h}{r+h}\,C_{r+h-1,\,r}\,C_{m-r,\,n-r-h},$$

and the whole number of routes will be got by giving r all values from 0 to $n-h$ inclusive, and adding.

The summation is that of the final series of the extension of the Lemma (page 116).

Hence, the whole number of routes is $C_{m+h,\,n-h}$, which therefore represents the number of orders required.

Q. E. D.

COROLLARY. It follows that *the number of orders in which m gains and n losses can occur so that there shall never be an excess of h losses, is* $C_{m,\,n}-C_{m+h,\,n-h}$.

Similarly, *the number of orders so that there shall never be an excess of k gains, is* $C_{m,\,n}-C_{m-k,\,n+k}$.

If $h=1$ this reduces to the case of Prop. XXXVIII.

CHANCE.

CHAPTER VI.

THE THEORY OF PROBABILITY TREATED ARITHMETICALLY.

"THERE is very little chance of fine weather."
"Is there much chance of his recovery?"
"There is no chance of finding it."
"There is a great probability of war."
"This is a more probable result than the other."
"That is more likely to be mine than yours."
"There is less chance of her coming than of his."

These are expressions in common use amongst us; the very commonness of their use shews that people in general have some idea of chance, and some conception of different degrees of probability in the occurrence of doubtful events. All understand what is meant by much chance and little chance; they distinguish events as very probable, probable, improbable, or very improbable; but no attempt is made in common conversation to measure with any accuracy the amount of probability attaching to any given event. If a Doctor is asked what chance there is of a patient's recovery, he may answer that there is much chance or little chance, but he cannot express with any precision the exact magnitude of his hope or of his fear. Yet his expectation of the event has a certain magnitude. He has a greater expectation of this patient's recovery than he has of the recovery of another, whose symptoms are more aggravated, and less expectation than in another case where the constitution is stronger. His expectation has a definite value, and if he were a gambler, he would be prepared to offer or take certain definite odds on the event. But in common language, this definite amount of expectation or probability cannot be precisely expressed, because we have no recognised standard with which to compare it, no recognised amount of expectation or probability by which to measure it.

In fact, in describing the magnitude of any expectation which we entertain, we are in the same position as if we had to describe the length of a room. or the height of a tower, to a man who was not acquainted with a foot or a yard, or any of our standards of length. We could speak of the room as very long or very short, we could speak of the tower as very high or very low, but without some standard length recognised alike by ourselves and those whom we addressed, we could not give an accurate answer to either of the questions, How long is the room? or How high is the tower?

So when we are asked what chance we think there is of a fine afternoon, we may say that there is much chance or little chance, or we may even go further, and establish in our own minds a scale of expressions, distinguishing the different degrees of probability in some such way as follows:

It is certain not to rain.
It is very unlikely to rain.
It is unlikely to rain.
It is as likely to rain as not.
It is likely to rain.
It is very likely to rain.
It is certain to rain.

But these expressions, except the first, fourth, and last, are vague and indefinite, nor can we ever be sure that those with whom we are conversing attach exactly the same idea to each expression that we do.

This vagueness is of little consequence in common life, because in most cases it is impossible to make an accurate estimate of a chance, and the expressions are, perhaps, as accurate as the estimates themselves which we wish to express. But there are other classes of events concerning which it is possible to form accurate estimates of their degree of probability or likelihood of happening, and in these cases it is well to have some more precise method of expressing different degrees of probability, than is afforded by the common expressions which we have quoted.

We must observe at the outset, that we use the words *chance* and *probability* as strictly synonymous. In common language, it is usual to prefer the former word when the expectation is small, and the latter when it is large. Thus we generally hear of "little chance," or of "great probability," but not so often of "great chance," or "little probability." This distinction, however, is not universal, and we shall entirely disregard it, using the two words chance and probability in the same sense.

It will be seen that probability always implies some ignorance on the part of the person entertaining the expectation, and the amount of probability attaching to any event will depend upon the degree of this ignorance. With omniscience, degrees of probability are incompatible; for omniscience implies certainty, and certainty precludes doubt, and degrees of probability are the measures of doubt.

Hence, there is no such thing as the *absolute* probability of an event, all probability being conditional on our ignorance, and varying when that condition varies. Thus the same event will be unequally probable to different persons, whose knowledge of the circumstances relating to the event is different. And to the same person, the expectation of any event will be effected by any accession of knowledge concerning the event.

For instance, suppose we see a friend set out with five other passengers in a ship whose crew number thirty men: and suppose we presently hear that a man fell overboard on the passage and was lost. So long as our knowledge is confined to the fact that one individual only has been lost out of the thirty-six on board, the probability that it is our friend is very small. The odds against it would be said to be thirty-five to one. But suppose our knowledge is augmented by the news that the man who has been lost is a passenger; though we still feel that it is equally likely to be any of the other five passengers, yet our apprehension that it is our friend becomes much greater than it was before. The odds against it are now described as five to one. Thus the probability that our friend is lost is seen to be entirely conditional on the respective degrees of our knowledge and ignorance; and so soon as our ignorance vanishes—so soon as we know all about the event, and become *as far as that event is concerned* omniscient,—then there no longer remains a question of probability; the probability is replaced by certainty.

This example will also illustrate the meaning of the ratio of probabilities. Since each of the passengers was equally likely to have been lost, it was evidently always six times as likely that the man lost was *some passenger*, as that it was our friend. So it was five times as likely that it was *a passenger, but not our friend*, as that it was our friend. Therefore, also, the probability that it was *a passenger, but not our friend*, was to the probability that it was a passenger in the *ratio* of 5 to 6.

Let us suppose another case. A number of articles are placed in a bag, and amongst them are three balls, alike in all respects, except that two of them are coloured white and the third black: all the other articles we will suppose to be coins, or anything distinguishable without difficulty from balls.

We present this bag to a stranger, and we give him leave to put in his hand in the dark, and to take out any one article he likes. But before he does this, we may consider what chance there is of his taking out a ball, or what chance there is of his taking out the black ball. Obviously we cannot form any accurate estimate of this chance, because it must depend upon the wants or the taste of the stranger influencing his will, whether he will prefer to take a ball or a coin, and being ignorant of his will in the matter, we cannot say whether it is likely or unlikely that he will select a ball.

But it is axiomatic, that if he draws a ball at all, it is twice as likely to be a white ball as to be a black one, or the respective chances of his drawing white or black are in the ratio of 2 to 1, and these chances are respectively two-thirds and one-third of the chance that he draws a ball at all.

We now proceed to shew how the magnitude of a chance may be definitely expressed. We have already pointed out that the expressions used in common language are wanting in definiteness and precision, and we compared the expedients by which degrees of probability are usually indicated to the attempts which we should make to give an idea of the length of a room to a person unacquainted with the measures of a foot and a yard.

Now we observe, that the difficulty in this latter case ceases, so soon as the person with whom we are speaking

agrees with us in his conception of any definite length whatever.   If he can once recognise what we mean by the length
of a hand, for instance, we can express to him with perfect
accuracy the length of the room as so many hands; or, if he
have an idea of what a mile is, we can precisely express the
length of the room as some certain fraction of a mile.   So,
also, as soon as we have fixed upon any standard amount of
probability that can be recognised and appreciated by all
with whom we have to do, we shall be able to express any
other amount of probability numerically by reference to that
standard.   The numbers 2, 3 would express probabilities
twice or three times as great as the standard probability;
and the fractions $\frac{1}{2}$, $\frac{1}{3}$, $\frac{2}{3}$ would express probabilities half,
one-third, or two-thirds of the standard.

Now, it matters not how great or how small the standard
be, provided it be a probability which all can recognise, and
which all will alike appreciate.   This is, indeed, the one
essential which it has to fulfil; it must be such that all
persons will make the same estimate of it.   And that which
best satisfies this condition, and, therefore, the most convenient standard with which to compare other probabilities,
is that supreme amount of probability which attaches to an
event which we know to be *certain* to happen.   All understand what *certainty* is: it is a standard which all estimate
alike.   *Certainty*, therefore, shall be our unit of probability;
and other degrees of probability shall be expressed as fractions of certainty.

But it may be asked, Is certainty a degree of probability
at all, or can smaller degrees of probability be said to have
any ratio to certainty ?   Yes.   For if we refer to the instance
already cited of the six passengers in the ship, we observe
that the chance of the lost man being a passenger is six
times as great as the chance of its being our friend.   This

is the case however great our ignorance of the circumstances of the event; and it will evidently remain true until we attain to some knowledge which affects our friend differently from his fellow-passengers. But the news that the lost man was a passenger does not affect one passenger more than another. Therefore, after receiving this news, it will still hold good that the chance of the lost man being a passenger is six times as great as the chance of its being our friend. But it is now certain that the lost man was a passenger; therefore the probability that it was our friend is one-sixth of certainty. Again, in the instance of the balls and coins in the bag, we have already noticed that the chances of drawing white or black are respectively two-thirds and one-third of the chance of drawing a ball at all. And this is the case whatever this last chance may be. But suppose the man tells us that he is drawing a ball, not a coin, then this last chance becomes certainty; and therefore the chances of drawing white or black, become respectively two-thirds and one-third of certainty. Thus it is seen that certainty, while it is the supreme degree, is some degree of probability, or is such that another degree of probability can be compared to it and expressed as a fraction of it.

Of course, when we use unity to express certainty, the probability of the lost passenger being our friend will be expressed by the fraction $\frac{1}{6}$, and the chances of the ball drawn being white or black, will be expressed by the fractions $\frac{2}{3}$ and $\frac{1}{3}$.

After the explanations which we have already given, the reader will have no difficulty in accepting the following axiom.

AXIOM.

If an event can happen in a number of different ways (of which only one can occur), the probability of its happening at all is the sum of the several probabilities of its happening in the several ways.

For instance, let the event be the falling of a coin. It can fall either *head* or *tail*, and only one of these ways can occur. The probability that it falls at all must be made up by addition of the probability that it falls *head* and the probability that it falls *tail*.

Again, let the event be that either A, B, or C should win a race in which there are any number of competitors. The event can happen in three ways, viz., by A winning, by B winning, or by C winning; and only one of these ways can occur. The probability that one of the three should win is equal to the sum of the probabilities that A should win, that B should win, and that C should win.

This is only saying that if a man would give £2 for A's chance of the prize, £3 for B's chance, and £4 for C's chance, he would give £2 + £3 + £4, or £9 for the promise that he should have the prize if any one of the three should win.

Again, if $\frac{1}{10}$ be the chance of a shot aimed at a target hitting the bull's eye, $\frac{1}{6}$ the chance of its hitting the first ring, and $\frac{1}{4}$ the chance of its hitting the outer ring, the chance that it hits one of these, *i.e.*, the chance of its hitting the target at all, is $\frac{1}{10} + \frac{1}{6} + \frac{1}{4}$, or $\frac{31}{60}$.

RULE I.

The probability of an event not happening is obtained by subtracting from unity the probability that it will happen.

For it is certain that it will either happen or not happen,
or the probability that it will either happen or not happen
is unity; and only one of these two (the happening and the
not happening) can occur. Therefore, by the axiom, unity
is the sum of the probabilities of the event happening and
not happening; or the probability of its not happening is
obtained by subtracting from unity the probability of its
happening.

Question 83.   If the chance of an event happening is $\frac{2}{5}$, what is the
chance of its not happening ?

Answer. $1 - \frac{2}{5}$, or $\frac{3}{5}$.

Question 84.   If the chance of an experiment succeeding is $\frac{7}{10}$,
what is the chance of its failing ?

Answer. $\frac{3}{10}$.

Question 85.   If the chance of a shot hitting a target be $\frac{31}{60}$, what
is the chance of its missing ?

Answer. $\frac{29}{60}$.

Question 86.   If the chance of A winning a certain race be $\frac{1}{6}$, and
the chance of B winning it $\frac{1}{8}$, what is the chance that neither should
win ?

Answer. $\frac{17}{24}$.   For, by the axiom, the chance that one of them
should win is $\frac{1}{8} + \frac{1}{6}$, or $\frac{7}{24}$; and therefore, by Rule I., the chance that
this should not happen is $1 - \frac{7}{24}$, or $\frac{17}{24}$.

DEFINITION I.   Two probabilities which together make
up unity, are called *complementary* probabilities.

DEFINITION II. When it is said that the odds are three to two against an event, it is meant that the chance of the event failing is to the chance of its happening as three to two; and when it is said that the odds are three to two in favour of an event, it is meant that the chance of its happening is to the chance of its failing as three to two; and so for any other numbers.

RULE II.

If the odds be three to two against an event, the chance of the event not happening is

$$\frac{3}{3+2},$$

and the chance of its happening is

$$\frac{2}{3+2};$$

and so for any other numbers; the numerators of the two fractions being the two given numbers, and their common denominator the sum of the numbers.

For the two fractions satisfy the condition required by Rule I., viz., that their sum should be unity, and that required by the definition, viz., that their ratio should be the same as the ratio expressing the given odds. Similarly,

If the odds be three to two in favour of an event, the chance of the event happening is

$$\frac{3}{3+2},$$

and the chance of its not happening is

$$\frac{2}{3+2};$$

and so for any other numbers; the numerators of the two fractions being the two given numbers, and their common denominator the sum of the numbers.

Question 87. If the odds be ten to one against an event, what is the probability of its happening?

Answer. $\dfrac{1}{11}$.

Question 88. If the odds be five to two in favour of the success of an experiment, what are the respective chances of success and failure?

Answer. The chance of success is $\dfrac{5}{7}$ and the chance of failure $\dfrac{2}{7}$.

RULE III.

If an event can happen in five ways, and fail in seven ways, and if these twelve ways are all equally probable, and only one of them can occur, the odds against the event are seven to five, and the chances of its happening and failing are respectively

$$\frac{5}{12} \ \ and \ \ \frac{7}{12};$$

and similarly for any other numbers.

For since the event must either happen or fail, one of the twelve ways must occur; therefore the sum of their several probabilities is unity. But all the twelve ways are equally probable. Therefore the chance of the occurrence of any particular one is $\dfrac{1}{12}$, and the chance of the occurrence of some one of the five which cause the event to happen is five times this, or $\dfrac{5}{12}$. So the chance of the occurrence of some one of the seven which cause the event to fail is $\dfrac{7}{12}$.

Suppose, for example, that a die has twelve faces, of which five are coloured white and seven black. A person throws the die, and is to receive a prize if it fall white.

The odds are seven to five against his winning the prize. The chance that he wins is $\frac{5}{12}$, and the chance that he loses is $\frac{7}{12}$.

For all the twelve faces are equally likely to turn up, and one must turn up. Therefore the chance of any particular face turning up is $\frac{1}{12}$, and the chance of a white face turning up is five times this, or $\frac{5}{12}$.

Or we might put it thus: Since there are five white and seven black faces, it is axiomatic that the chance of a white face is to the chance of a black face as five to seven. Now as soon as it is certain that the die is to be thrown, it is certain that either a white or a black face must turn up. The two chances must therefore now make up unity. But they still retain the ratio of five to seven, therefore they become respectively

$$\frac{5}{5+7} \text{ and } \frac{7}{5+7}.$$

And in the same way we might reason if the numbers were any other.

Question 89. A party of twenty-three persons take their seats at a round table; shew that the odds are ten to one against two specified persons sitting together.

Answer. Call the two specified persons A and B. Then besides A's place (wherever it may be) there are twenty-two places, of which two are adjacent to A's place and the other twenty not adjacent. And B is equally likely to be in any of these twenty-two places. Therefore

(Rule III.) the odds are twenty to two, or ten to one, against his taking a place next to A.

The last rule may be expressed in a somewhat different form as follows :

RULE IV.

If there be a number of events of which one must happen and all are equally likely, and if any one of a (smaller) number of these events will produce a certain result which cannot otherwise happen, the probability of this result is expressed by the ratio of this smaller number to the whole number of events.

For instance; if a man has purchased five tickets in a lottery, in which there are twelve tickets altogether and only one prize, his chance of the prize would be expressed by the ratio 5 : 12, or by the fraction $\frac{5}{12}$.

For convenience of reference we have given distinct numbers to the two Rules III. and IV., although they are only different statements of one and the same principle. This will be immediately seen, by considering the case of the lottery just instanced. We might at once have said that there were twelve ways of drawing a ticket, and five of these would cause the man to win, while the other seven would cause him to lose. Rule III. is therefore immediately applicable.

Question 90. If from a set of dominoes numbered from double-blank to double-twelve one domino be drawn, what is the chance that one of the numbers on it is 12 ?

Answer. There are $\frac{13 \cdot 14}{1 \cdot 2}$, or 91 dominoes in the set (*Choice*, Rule X.), and the number twelve appears on 13 of them, since it will appear in combination with *blank* as well as with each of the twelve numbers. Hence there are 91 equally probable events of which 13 will produce the result that a twelve is drawn. Therefore the chance is $\frac{13}{91}$ or $\frac{1}{7}$.

Question 91. The four letters *s, e, n, t* are placed in a row at random : what is the chance of their standing in such order as to form an English word ?

Answer. The four letters can stand in $\lfloor 4$ or twenty-four different orders (*Choice*, Rule III.) : all are equally likely and one must occur. And four of these will produce an English word,

sent,   nest,   nets,   tens.

Hence, by the rule, the required chance is $\frac{4}{24}$ or $\frac{1}{6}$.

Question 92. What is the chance of a year, which is not leap year, having fifty-three Sundays ?

Answer. Such a year consists of fifty-two complete weeks, and one day over. This odd day may be any of the seven days of the week, and there is nothing to render one more likely than another. Only one of them will produce the result that the year should have fifty-three Sundays. Hence (Rule IV.) the chance of the year having fifty-three Sundays is $\frac{1}{7}$.

Question 93. What is the chance that a leap year, selected at random, will contain fifty-three Sundays ?

Answer. Such a year consists of fifty-two complete weeks, and two days over. These two days may be

Sunday and Monday,
Monday and Tuesday,
Tuesday and Wednesday,
Wednesday and Thursday,
Thursday and Friday,
Friday and Saturday,
Saturday and Sunday,

and all these seven are equally likely. Two of them (the first and last) will produce the required result. Hence (Rule IV.) the chance is $\frac{2}{7}$.

Question 94. What is the chance that a year which is known not to be the last year in a century should be leap year ?

Answer. The year may be any of the remaining ninety-nine of any century, and all these are equally likely ; but twenty-four of them are leap years. Therefore (Rule III.) the chance that the year in question is a leap year is $\dfrac{24}{99}$ or $\dfrac{8}{33}$.

Question 95. Three balls are to be drawn from an urn which contains five black, three red, and two white balls. What is the chance of drawing two black balls and one red ?

Answer. Since there are ten balls altogether, three balls can be drawn in $\dfrac{10.9.8}{1.2.3}$, or 120 different ways, all equally likely. Now, two black balls can be selected in $\dfrac{5.4}{1.2}$, or ten ways, and one red in three ways. Hence, two black balls and one red can be drawn in 10×3, or 30 different ways. Thus we have 120 different ways of drawing three balls, whereof 30 ways will give two black and one red. Hence, when three balls are drawn, the chance that they should be two black and one red is (by Rule IV.)

$$\frac{30}{120} \text{ or } \frac{1}{4}.$$

Question 96. If from a lot of thirty tickets, marked 1, 2, 3, &c., four tickets be drawn, what is the chance that those marked 1 and 2 are among them ?

Answer. Four tickets can be drawn out of thirty in $\dfrac{30.29.28.27}{1.2.3.4}$ ways. Four tickets can be drawn, so as to include those marked 1 and 2, in $\dfrac{28.27}{1.2}$ ways. Hence, when four are drawn, the chance that these two are included is

$$\frac{28.27}{1.2} \div \frac{30.29.28.27}{1.2.3.4} = \frac{3.4}{29.30} = \frac{2}{145}.$$

The odds are, therefore, 143 to 2 against the event.

Question 97. *A* has three shares in a lottery where there are three prizes and six blanks. *B* has one share in another, where there is but one prize and two blanks. Shew that *A* has a better chance of winning a prize than *B*, in the ratio of 16 to 7.

Answer. *A* will get a prize unless his three tickets all prove blank. Now, three tickets can be selected in $\frac{9 \cdot 8 \cdot 7}{1 \cdot 2 \cdot 3}$, or 84 ways; and they can be selected so as to be all blank in $\frac{6 \cdot 5 \cdot 4}{1 \cdot 2 \cdot 3}$, or 20 ways. Hence the chance that they should be all blank is $\frac{20}{84}$ or $\frac{5}{21}$; and, therefore, the chance that this should not be so, or that *A* gets at least one prize, is $1 - \frac{5}{21}$, or $\frac{16}{21}$. But it is evident that the chance that *B* gets a prize is (Rule IV.) $\frac{1}{3}$ or $\frac{7}{21}$. Therefore *A* has a better chance than *B* in the ratio of 16 to 7.

Question 98. If four cards be drawn from a pack, what is the chance that there will be one of each suit?

Answer. Four cards can be selected from the pack in $\frac{52 \cdot 51 \cdot 50 \cdot 49}{1 \cdot 2 \cdot 3 \cdot 4}$ or 270725 ways (*Choice*, Rule IX.); but four cards can be selected so as to be one of each suit in only $13 \times 13 \times 13 \times 13$ or 28561 ways (*Choice*, Rule II.). Hence the chance is

$$\frac{28561}{270725} \text{ or a little more than } \frac{1}{10}.$$

Question 99. If four cards be drawn from a pack, what is the chance that they will be marked *one, two, three, four*?

Answer. There are $4 \times 4 \times 4 \times 4$, or 256 ways of drawing four cards thus marked, and 270725 ways of drawing four cards altogether. Hence the chance is

$$\frac{256}{270725},$$

or the odds are more than 1000 to 1 against it.

Question 100. In a bag there are five white and four black balls. If they are drawn out one by one, what is the chance that the first will be white, the second black, and so on alternately?

Answer. The nine balls can be arranged in $\lfloor 9$ ways. But the five white balls can be arranged in the odd places, and the four black balls in the even places in $\lfloor 5 \times \lfloor 4$ ways. Hence the chance that the order will be the alternate order is $\lfloor 5 \times \lfloor 4 \div \lfloor 9$ or $\dfrac{1}{126}$.

Otherwise. The white balls being for the purposes of the question all alike, and the black balls all alike, the total number of orders in which the nine balls can be arranged is (*Choice*, Rule VII.)

$$\frac{\lfloor 9}{\lfloor 4 . \lfloor 5}, \text{ or } 126.$$

The balls are equally likely to be drawn in any of these orders, and one of them is the alternate order required. Therefore the chance is $\dfrac{1}{126}$.

Question 101. In a bag are five red balls, seven white balls, four green balls, and three black balls. If they be drawn one by one, what is the chance that all the red balls should be drawn first, then all the white ones, then all the green ones, and then all the black ones?

Answer. The nineteen balls can be arranged in

$$\frac{\lfloor 19}{\lfloor 5 . \lfloor 7 . \lfloor 4 . \lfloor 3}$$

different orders (*Choice*, Rule VII.). All these are equally likely, and therefore the chance of any particular order is

$$\frac{\lfloor 5 . \lfloor 7 . \lfloor 4 . \lfloor 3}{\lfloor 19}.$$

This will be the chance required; for, all individuality among balls of the same colour having been disregarded, only one of the different arrangements will give the order of colours prescribed in the question.

Question 102. Out of a bag containing 12 balls, 5 are drawn and replaced, and afterwards 6 are drawn. Find the chance that exactly 3 balls were common to the two drawings.

Answer. The second drawing could be made altogether in

$$\frac{\lfloor 12}{\lfloor 6 . \lfloor 6}, \text{ or } 924$$

ways. But it could be made so as to include exactly **3** of the balls contained in the first drawing, in

$$\frac{\underline{5}}{\underline{3}.\underline{2}} \times \frac{\underline{7}}{\underline{3}.\underline{4}}, \text{ or } 350$$

ways; for it must consist of a selection of 3 balls out of the first 5, and a selection of 3 balls out of the remaining 7 (*Choice*, Rules VIII. and II.). Hence, the chance that the second drawing should contain exactly **3** balls common to the first, is $\frac{350}{924}$ or $\frac{25}{66}$.

As the respective probabilities of various throws, with two common dice, are of practical interest, in their bearing upon such games as Backgammon, it may be well to discuss this case with some completeness.

It will be observed that as each die can fall in six ways, the whole number of ways in which the two dice can fall is 6×6 or 36. But these 36 different ways are not practically different throws, since, for example, it makes no difference in practice whether the first die falls *six* and the second *five*, or the first *five* and the second *six*. The number of practically different throws is, in fact, only $\frac{6.7}{1.2}$ or 21; being the number of ways of selecting two numbers out of six numbers when repetitions are allowed (*Choice*, Rule X.). Regarding it in another way, the 36 different ways of the dice falling are made up of six unique ways—

1 and 1,   2 and 2,   3 and 3,   4 and 4,   5 and 5,   6 and 6,

and 30 other ways, consisting of 15 essentially different throws, each repeated twice: thus—

1 and 2,	1 and 3,	1 and 4,	1 and 5,	1 and 6,
2 and 1,	3 and 1,	4 and 1,	5 and 1,	6 and 1,
	2 and 3,	2 and 4,	2 and 5,	2 and 6,
	3 and 2,	4 and 2,	5 and 2,	6 and 2,

$$3 \text{ and } 4, \quad 3 \text{ and } 5, \quad 3 \text{ and } 6,$$
$$4 \text{ and } 3, \quad 5 \text{ and } 3, \quad 6 \text{ and } 3,$$

$$4 \text{ and } 5, \quad 4 \text{ and } 6,$$
$$5 \text{ and } 4, \quad 6 \text{ and } 4,$$

$$5 \text{ and } 6,$$
$$6 \text{ and } 5.$$

Since each die is equally likely to fall in all different ways, the 36 different ways of the two dice falling are all equally likely; and, therefore, when the dice are thrown the probability of any particular way is $\frac{1}{36}$. But it cannot be said that all throws are equally probable, because *six-five* results practically in two ways out of the 36 ways of the dice falling, whereas *six-six* results in only one way. The correct statement is, that the probability of any assigned throw is $\frac{1}{36}$ if that assigned throw be *doublets*; but it is twice as much or $\frac{1}{18}$ if the assigned throw be *not doublets*. Thus the chance of throwing *six-three* is $\frac{1}{18}$, but the chance of throwing *three-three* is $\frac{1}{36}$.

Question 103. When two dice are thrown, what is the chance that the throw will be greater than 8?

Answer. Out of the 36 ways in which the dice can fall there are ten which give a result greater than 8, viz. :

$$3 \text{ and } 6, \quad 4 \text{ and } 5, \quad 4 \text{ and } 6, \quad 5 \text{ and } 6, \quad 5 \text{ and } 5,$$
$$6 \text{ and } 3, \quad 5 \text{ and } 4, \quad 6 \text{ and } 4, \quad 6 \text{ and } 5, \quad 6 \text{ and } 6.$$

Hence the required chance is $\frac{10}{36}$ or $\frac{5}{18}$.

Question 104. What is the chance of throwing at least one ace?

Answer. Of the thirty-six ways in which the dice can fall, eleven give an ace. Hence the chance is $\frac{11}{36}$.

Question 105. What is the chance of making a throw which shall contain neither an ace nor a six?

Answer. Of the thirty-six ways, there are sixteen which involve neither one nor six. Hence the chance is $\frac{16}{36}$ or $\frac{4}{9}$.

This question, as well as the preceding one, may be more conveniently solved by Rule VI.

Question 106. What are the odds against throwing doublets?

Answer. Of the thirty-six ways in which the dice can fall, six give doublets. Therefore the chance for doublets is $\frac{6}{36}$ or $\frac{1}{6}$, and the chance against doublets $\frac{5}{6}$ (Rule III.). Therefore the odds are five to one against doublets.

Or we might reason thus:—However the first die fall, the second die can fall in six ways, of which only one way will give the same number as on the first die. Hence, the odds are five to one against the second die falling the same way as the first, or the odds are five to one against doublets.

Question 107. In one throw with a pair of dice, what is the chance that there is neither an ace nor doublets?

Answer. The dice can fall in thirty-six ways, but in order that there may be neither an ace nor doublets, the first die must fall in one of five ways (viz. 2, 3, 4, 5, 6), and the second, since it may be neither an ace nor the same as the first, may fall in four ways. Hence the number of ways which will produce the required result is 5 × 4 or 20. And, therefore, the chance of this result is $\frac{20}{36}$ or $\frac{5}{9}$.

Question 108. What is the chance of throwing exactly eleven?

Answer. Out of the thirty-six ways, there are two ways which produce eleven; therefore the chance is $\frac{2}{36}$ or $\frac{1}{18}$.

On the principle of the last answer, the reader will have no difficulty in verifying the following statements:

In a single throw with two dice, the odds are—

35	to 1	against throwing	2,
17	to 1	„	„	3,
11	to 1	„	„	4,
8	to 1	„	„	5,
$6\frac{1}{5}$	to 1	„	„	6,
5	to 1	„	„	7,
$6\frac{1}{5}$	to 1	„	„	8,
8	to 1	„	„	9,
11	to 1	„	„	10,
17	to 1	„	„	11,
35	to 1	„	„	12.

Thus the most frequent throw will be *seven*.

In some cases the purpose of a throw is equally answered, whether an assigned number appear on one of the dice, or whether the numbers on the two dice together make it. Let us consider, for example, the chance of throwing five in this way.

The chance of making a throw so that one die shall turn up *five* is $\frac{11}{36}$, and the chance of making a throw which shall amount to *five* is $\frac{4}{36}$. Therefore the chance of throwing *five* in one of these ways is $\frac{11}{36} + \frac{4}{36}$ or $\frac{15}{36}$.

On this principle the following statements may be easily verified:

In a single throw with two dice, when the player is at liberty to count either the sum of the numbers on the two dice, or the number on either die alone, the odds are—

25 to 11, or	$2\frac{3}{11}$	to 1 against throwing	1,
24 to 12, or	2	to 1	,,	,,	2,
23 to 13, or	$1\frac{10}{13}$	to 1	,,	,,	3,
22 to 14, or	$1\frac{4}{7}$	to 1	,,	,,	4,
21 to 15, or	$1\frac{2}{5}$	to 1	,,	,,	5,
20 to 16, or	$1\frac{1}{4}$	to 1	,,	,,	6,
	5	to 1	,,	,,	7,
31 to 5, or	$6\frac{1}{5}$	to 1	,,	,,	8,
	8	to 1	,,	,,	9,
	11	to 1	,,	,,	10,
	17	to 1	,,	,,	11,
	35	to 1	,,	,,	12.

Thus the number which there is the greatest chance of making is *six*.

When three dice are thrown the number of ways in which they can fall is $6 \times 6 \times 6 = 216$, but the number of different throws is only $\frac{6.7.8}{1.2.3}$ or 56 (*Choice*, Rule X.). These 56 throws are made up of

6 triplets each occurring in one way,

30 throws containing a doublet, each throw occurring in 3 ways,

20 throws consisting of three different numbers, each throw occurring in 6 ways.

And the chance of any given triplet (such as 6, 6, 6) is $\frac{1}{216}$.

The chance of any given doublet (such as 6, 6, 5) is $\frac{3}{216}$ or $\frac{1}{72}$.

And the chance of any other given throw (such as 6, 5, 4) is $\frac{6}{216}$ or $\frac{1}{36}$.

Further, the chance of throwing *some* triplet is $\frac{6}{216}$ or $\frac{1}{36}$.

The chance of throwing *some* doublet is $\frac{90}{216}$ or $\frac{5}{12}$.

The chance of throwing neither a triplet nor a doublet is $\frac{120}{216}$ or $\frac{5}{9}$.

EXPECTATION.

The measurement of chance may be approached *ab initio* from the consideration of the price that may reasonably be paid for a gain contingent on some doubtful occurrence. And to many minds this method appears easier than any other. The doubtful occurrence may be of any kind. Simply as a type of it, whatever it may be, we will borrow the proverbial expression " when one's ship comes in." We will assume then that the reader is to receive £1000 if his ship comes in. If the ship fails to arrive he is to receive nothing.

But the reader may wish to part with his right, to transfer it to a neighbour for an equitable sum. The question arises what must this sum be. The mere chance of receiving £1000 is worth something. It is not as good as the certainty of receiving £1000, and therefore it is worth less than £1000. Its fair price must lie somewhere between zero and £1000.

Now there is only one meaning which we can give to the term " fair." The fair price at which the transaction can be made between the two parties must be such that if the transaction were repeated indefinitely say for millions of times there would be no presumption beforehand that either party would be the winner. If for instance the parties had reason to believe that in the long run seven ships out of ten come in, the reader might reasonably ask £700 for his title.

If this particular ship comes in, the other party will have gained £300 by the transaction : but if this ship does not arrive, the reader will have received £700 instead of receiving nothing, that is he will have gained £700. But by hypothesis, on an average, or in the long run, when the transaction is repeated indefinitely, the former event will occur 7 times for 3 occurrences of the latter. Ten millions of ships may be dispatched under the like circumstances, and the same parties may effect the same transaction on each, but there is no presumption that either will gain in the end.

So, if a coin is tossed and I am to receive a shilling if it turn up *head,* my title is worth sixpence.

If a common die is thrown and I am to receive a shilling if it turn up *ace,* my title is worth twopence.

But the appeal to that which would happen *in the long run* is precisely that on which we have founded the doctrine of chance. If 7 ships out of 10 arrive, the odds are 7 to 3 in favour of any particular ship arriving, and the chance of any particular ship arriving is to certainty as 7 to 10. Thus we always have the proportion,—

$$\frac{\text{chance}}{\text{certainty}} = \frac{\text{fair price}}{\text{total stake}}.$$

What we have defined as the fair price is commonly called "the expectation." Strictly it ought to be "the value of the expectation," but the briefer term is convenient. If I am to receive £1000 on the occurrence of an event in favour of which the odds are 7 to 3, it is convenient to say briefly my expectation is £700, though as a matter of fact I expect to receive either £1000 or nothing.

After what we have said the student will have no difficulty in accepting the following Rule.

RULE V.

The expectation from any event is obtained by multiplying the sum to be realized on the event happening, by the chance that the event will happen.

This rule may be illustrated as follows: Suppose a person holds five tickets in a lottery, where the whole number of tickets is twelve: and suppose there be only one prize, and let its value be one shilling.

The person in question gains the prize, if it happen that one of his tickets be drawn. The chance of this event is $\frac{5}{12}$; therefore, according to the rule, the person's expectation is $\frac{5}{12}$ of a shilling, or fivepence. And the correctness of this result may be immediately seen; for we observe, that if the person had bought all the twelve tickets he would have been certain of winning a shilling, and, therefore, he might equitably have given a shilling for the twelve tickets; but all the tickets are of equal value, and are equally valuable whether the same man hold one or more. Hence, each of them is worth a penny, and, therefore, the five in question are worth fivepence (as long as it is unknown which is drawn). Fivepence, therefore, is the sum that might equitably have been given for the assigned person's chance, and, therefore, by the definition this is his *expectation*.

Question 109. A bag contains a £5 note, a £10 note, and six pieces of blank paper. What is the expectation of a man who is allowed to draw out one piece of paper?

Answer. Since there are eight pieces of paper the probability of his drawing the £5 note is $\frac{1}{8}$; therefore, his expectation from the chance of drawing this note is $\frac{1}{8}$ of £5, or $\frac{5}{8}$ of a pound. Similarly, his expectation from the chance of drawing the £10 note is $\frac{1}{8}$ of £10, or $\frac{5}{4}$ of a pound. Therefore his whole expectation is $\frac{15}{8}$ of a pound, or £1. 17s. 6d.

Question 110. What is the expectation of drawing a coin from a bag which contains one sovereign and seven shillings?

Answer. The expectation from the chance of drawing the sovereign is $\frac{1}{8}$ of a sovereign, and the expectation from the chance of drawing a shilling is $\frac{7}{8}$ of a shilling. Hence, the whole expectation is 3s. 4½d.

Question 111. A person is allowed to draw two coins from a purse containing four sovereigns and four shillings. What is the value of his expectation?

Answer. Two coins can be drawn in $\frac{8 \cdot 7}{1 \cdot 2}$ or 28 ways: of these $\frac{4 \cdot 3}{1 \cdot 2}$ or 6 ways will give two sovereigns, 4×4 or 16 ways will give a sovereign and a shilling, and the other 6 ways will give two shillings.

Therefore—

Chance of drawing 40 shillings $= \frac{6}{28}$,

Chance of drawing 21 shillings $= \frac{16}{28}$,

Chance of drawing 2 shillings $= \frac{6}{28}$.

Therefore the expectation is—

from the first chance, $\frac{6}{28} \times 40$, or $\frac{60}{7}$ shillings;

from the second chance, $\frac{16}{28} \times 21$, or 12 shillings;

from the third chance, $\frac{6}{28} \times 2$, or $\frac{3}{7}$ shillings.

Hence the whole expectation is $\frac{60}{7} + 12 + \frac{3}{7}$, or 21 shillings; or one-fourth of the whole sum in the purse.

This result might have been inferred at once from the consideration that, if all the eight coins had been drawn two and two, no drawing could be more likely to exceed in sovereigns than in shillings (the number of sovereigns and shillings being the same). Hence the expectation from each of the four drawings must be the same; and therefore each must be one-fourth of the whole sum to be drawn.

RULE VI.

The chance of two independent events both happening, is the product of the chances of their happening severally.

That is, if the chance of one event happening be $\frac{5}{6}$, and the chance of another independent event happening be $\frac{7}{8}$, the chance that both events should happen is $\frac{5}{6} \times \frac{7}{8}$ or $\frac{35}{48}$.

This may be proved as follows:—

The chance of the first event is the same as the chance of drawing white from a bag containing six balls, of which five are white (Rule IV.).

The chance of the second event is the same as the chance of drawing white from a bag containing eight balls, of which seven are white.

Therefore the chance that both events should happen is the same as the chance that both balls drawn should be white.

But the first ball can be drawn in six ways, and the second in eight ways. Therefore (*Choice*, Rule I.), both can be drawn in 6×8, or 48 ways.

So the first can be *white* in five ways, and the second can be *white* in seven ways. Therefore both can be *white* in 5×7, or 35 ways.

That is, the two balls can be drawn in forty-eight ways (all equally likely), and thirty-five of these ways will give *double-white*. Hence (Rule IV.) the chance of double-white is $\frac{35}{48}$, and therefore the chance of the two given events both happening is $\frac{35}{48}$.

And the same reasoning would apply if the numbers were any others. Hence the rule is true always.

EXAMPLE. Suppose it is estimated that the chance that A can solve a certain problem is $\frac{2}{3}$, and the chance that B can solve it is $\frac{5}{12}$; let us consider what is the chance of the problem being solved when they both try.

The problem will be solved, unless they both fail.

Now the chance that A fails is $\frac{1}{3}$: and the chance that B fails is $\frac{7}{12}$.

Therefore the chance that both fail is

$$\frac{1}{3} \times \frac{7}{12}, \text{ or } \frac{7}{36}.$$

The chance that this should not be so, is

$$1 - \frac{7}{36}, \text{ or } \frac{29}{36}.$$

This is, therefore, the chance that the problem gets solved.

In the case just considered, four results were possible, viz.:—

(1) That A and B should both succeed :

(2)   „ A should succeed and B fail :

(3)   „ A should fail and B succeed :

(4)   „ A and B should both fail.

We may calculate the chance of these four events separately. Thus we have

Chance of A's success $= \dfrac{2}{3}$, of A's failure $= \dfrac{1}{3}$;

„ B's success $= \dfrac{5}{12}$, of B's failure $= \dfrac{7}{12}$.

Therefore, by the rule,

(1) Chance that A and B both succeed $= \dfrac{2}{3} \times \dfrac{5}{12} = \dfrac{10}{36}$:

(2) Chance that A succeeds and B fails $= \dfrac{2}{3} \times \dfrac{7}{12} = \dfrac{14}{36}$:

(3) Chance that A fails and B succeeds $= \dfrac{1}{3} \times \dfrac{5}{12} = \dfrac{5}{36}$:

(4) Chance that A and B both fail $= \dfrac{1}{3} \times \dfrac{7}{12} = \dfrac{7}{36}$.

We observe that

$$\frac{10}{36} + \frac{14}{36} + \frac{5}{36} + \frac{7}{36} = \frac{36}{36} = 1,$$

or the sum of the four probabilities is unity, as it ought to be, since it is certain that one of the four results must happen.

Further, we notice that the problem will be solved if any of the first three events out of (1), (2), (3), and (4) occur. Hence the chance of the problem being solved might have been obtained by adding together the separate probabilities of these three events. Thus—

$$\frac{10}{36} + \frac{14}{36} + \frac{5}{36} = \frac{29}{36},$$

or the probability is $\frac{29}{36}$, as before.

RULE VII.

If there be two events which are not independent, the chance that they should both happen is the product of the chance that the first should happen, and the chance that when the first has happened the second should happen also.

This case differs from the case of Rule VI. by this circumstance,—that the second event, instead of being quite independent of the first, is so related to it that its probability is altered by the first event happening. For example, if two letters are drawn from an alphabet of 20 consonants and six vowels, the chance of the second letter being a vowel, which was originally $\frac{6}{26}$, becomes $\frac{6}{25}$ or $\frac{5}{25}$ according as the first letter was a consonant or a vowel. If however we are to calculate the chance of both being vowels, we have nothing to do with the second drawing except in the case when the first letter was a vowel. Our chance of drawing two vowels is plainly the same as if we had first to draw one from an alphabet of 20 consonants and six vowels, and then independently to draw one from another alphabet of 20 consonants and five vowels. Thus it appears that when the chance of the second event is dependent on the issue of the first, we may treat them as two independent events, if only we take for the second not its original probability but its probability when the first event has happened.

Hence the truth of Rule VII. is manifest.

The result in the particular case just considered, viz., that the chance of drawing two vowels out of an alphabet of 20 consonants and six vowels is

$$\frac{6}{26} \times \frac{5}{25} = \frac{3}{65},$$

is verified by observing that as a drawing of two letters can be made in 26.25 ways, and a drawing of two vowels in 6.5 ways (*Choice*, Rule IV.), the chance of drawing two vowels must be (by Rule III.)

$$\frac{6.5}{26.25} = \frac{3}{65};$$

the same result as is given by the present rule.

Question 112.   One purse contains five sovereigns and four shillings ; another contains five sovereigns and three shillings. One purse is taken at random and a coin drawn out. What is the chance that it be a sovereign ?

Answer.   The chance that the first purse be selected is $\frac{1}{2}$, and if it be selected, the chance that the coin be a sovereign is $\frac{5}{9}$: hence the chance that the coin drawn be one of the sovereigns out of the first purse is

$$\frac{1}{2} \times \frac{5}{9}, \text{ or } \frac{5}{18}.$$

Similarly the chance that it be one of the sovereigns out of the second purse is

$$\frac{1}{2} \times \frac{5}{8}, \text{ or } \frac{5}{16}.$$

Hence the whole chance of drawing a sovereign is

$$\frac{5}{18} + \frac{5}{16}, \text{ or } \frac{85}{144}.$$

Question 113.   What is the expectation from the drawing of the coin in the last question ?

Answer. The chance that it is a sovereign is $\frac{85}{144}$, and therefore the expectation from the chance of drawing a sovereign is $\frac{85}{144}$ of a pound, or $\frac{1700}{144}$ shillings.

If the coin drawn be not a sovereign, it must be a shilling, therefore the chance of drawing a shilling must be $1 - \frac{85}{144}$, or $\frac{59}{144}$ (Rule I.). Hence the expectation from the chance of drawing a shilling is $\frac{59}{144}$ of a shilling. Therefore the whole expectation from the drawing is

$$\frac{1700}{144} + \frac{59}{144}, \text{ or } \frac{1759}{144}$$

shillings, or 12s. $2\frac{7}{12}d$.

Question 114. What would have been the chance of drawing a sovereign if all the coins in the last case had been in one bag; and what would have been the expectation?

Answer. There would have been ten sovereigns and seven shillings in the bag; therefore, the chance of drawing a sovereign would have been $\frac{10}{17}$, and the chance of drawing a shilling $\frac{7}{17}$ (Rule I.). The expectation would therefore have been

$$\frac{200}{17} + \frac{7}{17}, \text{ or } \frac{207}{17}$$

shillings, or 12s. $2\frac{2}{17}d$.

The chance of drawing a sovereign is therefore in this case a little less, and the whole expectation very slightly less than in the former case.

Question 115. What is the chance that in a year named at random Easter should fall on April 25 of the Gregorian Kalendar?

Answer. By reference to the tables at the beginning of the Prayer Book it is seen that this event will occur if the golden number be that affixed to April 18, and if that day be Sunday. The golden number required occurs once in nineteen years, and when it occurs the day is equally likely to be any of the seven days of the week. Therefore the required chance is

$$\frac{1}{19} \times \frac{1}{7} = \frac{1}{133} *.$$

Question 116. There are three parcels of books in another room, and a particular book is in one of them. The odds that it is in one particular parcel are three to two; but if not in that parcel, it is equally likely to be in either of the others. If I send for this parcel, giving a description of it, and the odds that I get the one I describe are two to one, what is my chance of getting the book?

Answer. The chance of getting the parcel described is $\frac{2}{3}$, and the chance that the book is in it is $\frac{3}{5}$; therefore the chance of getting the book in the described parcel is $\frac{2}{3} \times \frac{3}{5}$ or $\frac{6}{15}$.

The chance of getting a parcel not described is $\frac{1}{3}$, and the chance that the book is in it is $\frac{1}{5}$; therefore the chance of getting the book in a parcel not described is $\frac{1}{3} \times \frac{1}{5}$, or $\frac{1}{15}$.

Therefore the whole chance of getting the book at all is $\frac{6}{15} + \frac{1}{15}$, or $\frac{7}{15}$; or the odds are eight to seven against getting it.

Question 117. In a purse are ten coins, of which nine are shillings and one is a sovereign; in another are ten coins, all of which are

---

* Hence on an average Easter will be on April 25 about three times in four centuries. At present, however, and for more than 3000 years to come, it happens about once a century, at intervals of either 57, 68, 84, 95, 152 or 163 years. This excess of frequency is compensated for after the year 4900, when we have three intervals of 220, 1363, and 288 years respectively. The years in which Easter occurs so late as April 25, are

1666	1734	1886	1943	2038	2190	2258	2326	2410
2573	2630	2782	2877	2945	3002	3097	3154	3249
3306	3469	3537	3621	3784	3841	3993	4088	4156
4224	4376	4528	4680	4748	4900	5120	6483	6771
6855	&c.							

shillings.   Nine coins are taken out of the former purse and put into the latter, and then nine coins are taken from the latter and put into the former.   A person may now take whichever purse he pleases ; which should he select ?

Answer.   Since each purse contains the same number of coins, he ought to choose that which is the more likely to contain the sovereign.   Now the sovereign can only be in the second bag, provided *both* the following events have taken place, viz.—

(1)   That the sovereign was among the nine coins taken out of the first bag and put into the second.

(2)   That it was *not* among the nine coins taken out of the second bag and put into the first.

Now the chance of (1) is $\frac{9}{10}$, and when (1) has happened the chance of (2) is $\frac{10}{19}$; therefore the chance of both happening is $\frac{9}{10} \times \frac{10}{19}$, or $\frac{9}{19}$. This, therefore, is the chance that the sovereign is in the second bag, and therefore (Rule I.) the chance that it is in the first is $1 - \frac{9}{19}$ or $\frac{10}{19}$. Hence, the first bag ought to be chosen in preference to the other.

RULE VIII.

The chance that a series of events should all happen is the continued product of the chance that the first should happen, the chance that (when it has happened) then the second should happen, the chance that then the third should happen, and so on.

This is a simple extension of the last rule.   For suppose there be four events, and let $\frac{1}{2}$ be the chance that the first should happen, and when the first has happened, let $\frac{3}{4}$ be the chance that the second should happen, and when these have happened, let $\frac{5}{8}$ be the chance that the third should happen, and when these have happened, let $\frac{1}{4}$ be the chance that the fourth should happen; by Rule VII., the chance that the first and second should both happen is $\frac{1}{2} \times \frac{3}{4}$, or $\frac{3}{8}$. We may now treat this as a single event, and then, again applying the same rule, we get $\frac{3}{8} \times \frac{5}{8}$, or $\frac{15}{64}$ as the chance that the first, second, and third should all happen. Treating this compound event as one event, we can again apply the same rule, and obtain $\frac{15}{64} \times \frac{1}{4}$, or $\frac{15}{256}$ as the chance that all the four events should happen. Thus the chance of all the events is

$$\frac{1}{2} \times \frac{3}{4} \times \frac{5}{8} \times \frac{1}{4},$$

the continued product of all the given chances.

Question 118. There are three independent events whose several chances are $\frac{2}{3}, \frac{3}{5}, \frac{1}{2}$. What is the chance that one of them at least will happen ?

Answer. One at least will happen, unless all fail.

The chance of all failing is $\frac{1}{3} \times \frac{2}{5} \times \frac{1}{2}$, or $\frac{1}{15}$.

Hence the required chance is $1 - \frac{1}{15}$, or $\frac{14}{15}$.

Question 119. There are three independent events whose several chances are $\frac{2}{3}, \frac{3}{5}, \frac{1}{2}$. What is the chance that exactly one of them should happen ?

Answer. The chance that the first should happen and the other fail is

$$\frac{2}{3} \times \frac{2}{5} \times \frac{1}{2}, \text{ or } \frac{4}{30}.$$

So the chance that the second should happen and the others fail is

$$\frac{3}{5} \times \frac{1}{3} \times \frac{1}{2}, \text{ or } \frac{3}{30}.$$

And the chance that the third should happen and the others fail is

$$\frac{1}{2} \times \frac{1}{3} \times \frac{2}{5}, \text{ or } \frac{2}{30}.$$

Hence, the chance that one of these should occur—that is, that *exactly one* of the three events should happen—is

$$\frac{4}{30} + \frac{3}{30} + \frac{2}{30}, \text{ or } \frac{9}{30}, \text{ or } \frac{3}{10}.$$

Question 120. When six coins are tossed, what is the chance that one, and only one, will turn up head?

Answer. The chance that the first should turn up head is $\frac{1}{2}$, and the chance that the others should turn up tail is $\frac{1}{2}$ for each of them. Therefore, the chance that the first should turn up head and the rest tail is

$$\frac{1}{2} \times \frac{1}{2} \times \frac{1}{2} \times \frac{1}{2} \times \frac{1}{2} \times \frac{1}{2}, \text{ or } \frac{1}{64}.$$

And there will be a similar chance that the second should alone turn up head, or that the third should alone turn up head, and so on.

Hence, the whole chance of some one, and only one, turning up head is

$$\frac{1}{64} + \frac{1}{64} + \frac{1}{64} + \frac{1}{64} + \frac{1}{64} + \frac{1}{64}, \text{ or } \frac{6}{64}.$$

Question 121. When six coins are tossed, what is the chance that at least one will turn up head?

Answer. The chance that all should turn up tail is

$$\frac{1}{2} \times \frac{1}{2} \times \frac{1}{2} \times \frac{1}{2} \times \frac{1}{2} \times \frac{1}{2}, \text{ or } \frac{1}{64}.$$

The chance that this should not be so, or that at least one head should turn up, is (Rule I.)

$$1 - \frac{1}{64}, \text{ or } \frac{63}{64}.$$

Question 122. A person throws three dice; what are the respective chances that they should fall all alike, only two alike, or all different?

Answer. The chance that the second should fall the same as the first is $\frac{1}{6}$, and the chance that the third should also fall the same is $\frac{1}{6}$. Hence, the chance that all three fall alike is

$$\frac{1}{6} \times \frac{1}{6}, \text{ or } \frac{1}{36}.$$

The chance that the second should fall as the first, and that the third should fall different, is

$$\frac{1}{6} \times \frac{5}{6}, \text{ or } \frac{5}{36};$$

and there is the same chance that the second and third should be alike and the first different; or that the first and third should be alike, and the second different. Hence, the chance that some two should be alike and the others different, is

$$\frac{5}{36} + \frac{5}{36} + \frac{5}{36}, \text{ or } \frac{15}{36}.$$

The chance that the second should be different from the first is $\frac{5}{6}$ and the chance that the third should be different from either is $\frac{4}{6}$ Hence, the chance that all three are different is

$$\frac{5}{6} \times \frac{4}{6}, \text{ or } \frac{20}{36}.$$

Therefore, the three chances required are $\frac{1}{36}, \frac{15}{36}, \frac{20}{36}$ respectively their sum being unity, since the dice must certainly fall in some one of the three ways.

Question 123. A person throws three dice, and is to receive six shillings if they all turn up alike, four shillings if two only turn up alike, and three shillings if all turn up different; what is his expectation?

Answer. Referring to the last question, the chance of all turning up different is $\frac{1}{36}$; his expectation from this event is therefore $\frac{1}{36}$

six shillings, or two pence. The chance of two only turning up alike is $\frac{15}{36}$ or $\frac{5}{12}$, and his expectation from this event is therefore $\frac{5}{12}$ of four shillings, or twenty pence. The chance of all turning up different is $\frac{20}{36}$ or $\frac{5}{9}$, and his expectation from this event is therefore $\frac{5}{9}$ of three shillings, or twenty pence. Therefore his whole expectation is $2+20+20$, or 42 pence, or three shillings and sixpence.

Question 124. A person goes on throwing a single die until it turns up ace. What is the chance (1) that he will have to make *at least* ten throws; (2) that he will have to make *exactly* ten throws?

Answer. (1) The chance that he fails at any particular trial to throw an ace is $\frac{5}{6}$. The chance that he should fail the first nine times (by Rule VIII.) is $\left(\frac{5}{6}\right)^9$. This, therefore, is the probability that he will have to throw at least ten times.

(2) Since $\left(\frac{5}{6}\right)^9$ is the chance that he fails the first nine times, and $\frac{1}{6}$ the chance that he succeeds the next time, therefore, by Rule VII., $\left(\frac{5}{6}\right)^9 \times \frac{1}{6}$ is the chance that he will have to throw exactly ten times.

Question 125. A die is to be thrown once by each of four persons, A, B, C, D, in order, and the first of them who throws an ace is to receive a prize. Find their respective chances, and the chance that the prize will not be won at all.

Answer. Since A has the first throw, he wins if he throws an ace; his chance is therefore $\frac{1}{6}$.

So B wins provided A fails and he succeeds. The chance of A failing is $\frac{5}{6}$, and of B succeeding is $\frac{1}{6}$. Therefore B's chance of winning is

$$\frac{5}{6} \times \frac{1}{6}, \text{ or } \frac{5}{36}.$$

So C wins provided A and B both fail, and he succeeds. The chance of A and B both failing is $\frac{5}{6} \times \frac{5}{6}$, or $\frac{25}{36}$; and then the chance of C succeeding is $\frac{1}{6}$. Therefore C's chance of winning is

$$\frac{25}{36} \times \frac{1}{6}, \text{ or } \frac{25}{216}.$$

So D wins provided A, B, and C all fail, and he succeeds. The chance of A, B, and C all failing is $\frac{5}{6} \times \frac{5}{6} \times \frac{5}{6}$, or $\frac{125}{216}$; and then the chance of D succeeding is $\frac{1}{6}$. Therefore D's chance of winning is

$$\frac{125}{216} \times \frac{1}{6}, \text{ or } \frac{125}{1296}.$$

The prize is not won at all, provided all four fail to throw an ace. The chance that this should be the case is

$$\frac{5}{6} \times \frac{5}{6} \times \frac{5}{6} \times \frac{5}{6}, \text{ or } \frac{625}{1296}.$$

Question 126. Two persons, A and B, throw alternately with a single die, and he who first throws an ace is to receive a prize of £1. What are their respective expectations?

Answer. The chance that the prize should be won

at the first throw, is $\frac{1}{6}$:

at the second throw, is $\frac{5}{6} \times \frac{1}{6}$:

at the third throw, is $\left(\frac{5}{6}\right)^2 \times \frac{1}{6}$:

at the fourth throw, is $\left(\frac{5}{6}\right)^3 \times \frac{1}{6}$:

at the fifth throw, is $\left(\frac{5}{6}\right)^4 \times \frac{1}{6}$:

at the sixth throw, is $\left(\frac{5}{6}\right)^5 \times \frac{1}{6}$:

and so on.

But the first, third, and fifth, &c., throws belong to A, and the second, fourth, sixth, &c., belong to B. Hence A's chance of winning is

$$\frac{1}{6} + \left(\frac{5}{6}\right)^2 \cdot \frac{1}{6} + \left(\frac{5}{6}\right)^4 \cdot \frac{1}{6} + \&c. \ ;$$

and B's chance is

$$\frac{5}{6} \cdot \frac{1}{6} + \left(\frac{5}{6}\right)^3 \cdot \frac{1}{6} + \left(\frac{5}{6}\right)^5 \cdot \frac{1}{6} + \&c. \ ;$$

that is, B's chance is equal to A's multiplied by $\frac{5}{6}$. Hence B's expectation is $\frac{5}{6}$ of A's, or B's is to A's in the ratio of five to six. But their expectations must together amount to £1. Hence A's expectation is $\frac{6}{11}$ of a pound, and B's $\frac{5}{11}$ of a pound.

Question 127. What is the chance that a person with two dice will throw aces exactly four times in six trials?

Answer. The chance of throwing aces at any particular trial is $\frac{1}{36}$, and the chance of failing is $\frac{35}{36}$. Hence the chance of succeeding at four assigned trials and failing at the other two is $\left(\frac{1}{36}\right)^4 \times \left(\frac{35}{36}\right)^2$. But aces will be thrown *exactly four times* if they be thrown at any set of four trials which might be assigned out of the six trials, and if they fail at the remaining two. And (*Choice*, Rule IX.) it is possible to assign four out of six in $\frac{6 \cdot 5 \cdot 4 \cdot 3}{1 \cdot 2 \cdot 3 \cdot 4}$, or fifteen ways. Hence the chance required is fifteen times the chance of succeeding in four *assigned* trials, and failing at the other two. Therefore it is

$$\left(\frac{1}{36}\right)^4 \times \left(\frac{35}{36}\right)^2 \times 15, \text{ or } \frac{6125}{725594112} :$$

therefore the odds are more than 100,000 to 1 against the event.

Question 128. If on an average nine ships out of ten return safe to port, what is the chance that out of five ships expected, at least three will arrive?

Answer. The chance that any particular ship returns is $\frac{9}{10}$. The chance that any particular set of three ships should all arrive is $\left(\dfrac{9}{10}\right)^3$, and the chance that the other two should not arrive is $\left(\dfrac{1}{10}\right)^2$. Therefore the chance that a particular set of three should alone arrive is $\left(\dfrac{9}{10}\right)^3 \times \left(\dfrac{1}{10}\right)^2$, or $\dfrac{729}{100000}$. And out of five ships a set of three can be selected in $\dfrac{5 \cdot 4 \cdot 3}{1 \cdot 2 \cdot 3}$ or 10 ways. Hence the chance that some one of these sets of three should alone arrive is

$$\frac{729}{100000} \times 10, \text{ or } \frac{729}{10000}.$$

This is therefore the chance that *exactly three* ships should arrive.

Similarly the chance that any particular set of four should alone arrive is $\left(\dfrac{9}{10}\right)^4 \times \dfrac{1}{10}$, or $\dfrac{6561}{100000}$; and the chance that some one of the five possible sets of four should alone arrive is $\dfrac{6561}{100000} \times 5$, or $\dfrac{32805}{100000}$. This is therefore the chance that *exactly four* ships should arrive.

And the chance that all the five should arrive is $\left(\dfrac{9}{10}\right)^5$, or $\dfrac{59049}{100000}$.

But the chance that *at least three* should arrive is the chance that either *three exactly*, or *four exactly*, or *five exactly* should arrive: and is therefore the sum of the several chances of these exact numbers arriving: that is, the required chance is

$$\frac{7290}{100000} + \frac{32805}{100000} + \frac{59049}{100000}, \text{ or } \frac{99144}{100000}, \text{ or } \frac{12393}{12500}.$$

Question 129. *A* and *B* play at a game which cannot be drawn and on an average *A* wins three games out of five. What is the chance that *A* should win at least three games out of the first five?

Answer. The chance that *A* wins three assigned games, and *B* the other two, is $\left(\dfrac{3}{5}\right)^3 \cdot \left(\dfrac{2}{5}\right)^2$, or $\dfrac{108}{3125}$. But the three may be assigned in $\dfrac{5 \cdot 4 \cdot 3}{1 \cdot 2 \cdot 3}$, or 10 ways (*Choice*, Rule IX.). Hence the chance that *A* should win some three games and *B* the other two is

$$\frac{108}{3125} \times 10, \text{ or } \frac{1080}{3125}.$$

Similarly the chance that A should win some four games and B the other one is

$$\frac{162}{3125} \times 5, \text{ or } \frac{810}{3125}.$$

And the chance that A should win all five games is

$$\left(\frac{3}{5}\right)^5, \text{ or } \frac{243}{3125}.$$

Therefore the chance that A wins either three, or four, or all out of the first five games is

$$\frac{1080}{3125} + \frac{810}{3125} + \frac{243}{3125} = \frac{2133}{3125},$$

or the odds are rather more than two to one in A's favour.

EXPECTATION OF LIFE.

The next four questions are based on some results of Vital Statistics. It will be assumed that out of 400 persons born, 57 die in their first year, 20 in their second, 11 in their third, and so on, according to the subjoined table, until at the age of 90, only 4 survive.

And we shall further assume that of 100 persons arriving at the age of 90, 19 die in the next year, 17 in the next, 15 in the next, and so on in arithmetical progression, until at the end of the 100th year all are dead.

The following approximate results of the table are easily remembered.

Out of 400 persons born

100 die before the age of 5 years,

100 more (accurately 101) die before the age of 50,

100 more (accurately 99) die before the age of 70,

100 survive 70 years.

Again:

120 (accurately 122) die in the first 20 years,

120 (accurately 121) die in the next 40 years,

120 die in the next 20 years,

leaving 40 (accurately 37) to survive the age of 80.

A	D	R	A	D	R	A	D	R	A	D	R	A	D	R
1	57	343	21	2	276	41	3	229	61	5	152	81	5	32
2	20	323	22	2	274	42	3	226	62	5	147	82	5	27
3	11	312	23	2	272	43	3	223	63	5	142	83	4	23
4	7	305	24	2	270	44	3	220	64	6	136	84	4	19
5	5	300	25	2	268	45	3	217	65	6	130	85	4	15
6	3	297	26	2	266	46	3	214	66	6	124	86	3	12
7	2	295	27	2	264	47	3	211	67	6	118	87	3	9
8	2	293	28	2	262	48	4	207	68	6	112	88	2	7
9	2	291	29	2	260	49	4	203	69	6	106	89	2	5
10	1	290	30	2	258	50	4	199	70	6	100	90	1	4
11	1	289	31	2	256	51	4	195	71	7	93	91	·76	3·24
12	1	288	32	2	254	52	4	191	72	7	86	92	·68	2·56
13	1	287	33	2	252	53	4	187	73	7	79	93	·6	1·96
14	1	286	34	2	250	54	4	183	74	7	72	94	·52	1·44
15	1	285	35	3	247	55	4	179	75	6	66	95	·44	1
16	1	284	36	3	244	56	4	175	76	6	60	96	·36	·64
17	1	283	37	3	241	57	4	171	77	6	54	97	·28	·36
18	1	282	38	3	238	58	4	167	78	6	48	98	·2	·16
19	2	280	39	3	235	59	5	162	79	6	42	99	·12	·04
20	2	278	40	3	232	60	5	157	80	5	37	100	·04	0

The column D gives the number of deaths in each year, the column R the number remaining alive at the end of the year.

Question 130. What is the chance of a person aged 30 living till he is 60 ?

Answer. Out of 400 persons born simultaneously with him 142 die in the first 30 years, and 258 survive. Of these 101 die in the next

30 years and 157 survive. The chance that the man in question is one of the survivors is therefore $\dfrac{157}{258}$.

Question 131. What are the odds against a person aged 40 living for 30 years?

Answer. Out of 232 persons surviving to the age of 40 there will be 132 deaths in the next 30 years, and 100 will then survive. The odds are therefore 132 to 100 or 33 to 25 against the person living to seventy.

Question 132. What is the expectation of life of a person on his 90th birthday?

Answer. The chance that he dies the first year is $\dfrac{19}{100}$, the second year $\dfrac{17}{100}$, and so on, in arithmetical progression. But if he dies the first year (since he may equally die in any part of it) his expectation of life is only $\dfrac{1}{2}$ year. So if he die in the second year his expectation is $\dfrac{3}{2}$ years. If he die in the third year it is $\dfrac{5}{2}$ years, and so on. Hence his whole expectation is

$$\frac{19.1 + 17.3 + 15.5 + 13.7 + \ldots \quad + 3.17 + 1.19}{200},$$

which will be found to amount to $3\dfrac{7}{20}$.

Question 133. What is the expectation of life of a person on his 81st birthday?

Answer. The chance that he dies the first year is $\dfrac{5}{32}$, the second, third and fourth each $\dfrac{4}{32}$, the fifth and sixth each $\dfrac{3}{32}$, the seventh and eighth each $\dfrac{2}{32}$, the ninth $\dfrac{1}{32}$, and the chance that he survives this, *i.e.*, that he reaches his 90th year, is $\dfrac{4}{32}$. His expectation of life prior to the completion of the 90th year is therefore

$$\frac{5.1 + 4(3+5+7) + 3(9+11) + 2(13+15) + 17}{64} = \frac{99}{32}.$$

And his expectation subsequent to his 90th year is

$$\frac{4}{32}\left(9+3\frac{7}{20}\right)=\frac{247}{160},$$

the nine years being added to the result of the previous question.

Hence his whole expectation is

$$\frac{99}{32}+\frac{247}{160}=\frac{742}{160}=4\frac{51}{80}.$$

RULE IX.

If a doubtful event can happen in a number of different ways, any accession of knowledge concerning the event which changes the probability of its happening will change, in the same ratio, the probability of any particular way of its happening.

It follows from the axiom that the probability of the event happening at all must be equal to the sum of the probabilities of its happening in the several ways.

First, suppose for simplicity that all the ways are equally likely. Let there be seven ways, and let the chance of each one severally occurring be $\frac{1}{10}$: then the chance of the event happening at all is seven times this, or $\frac{7}{10}$.

But suppose that our knowledge is increased by the information that the event happens nine times out of ten, or by such other information as brings our estimate of its probability up to $\frac{9}{10}$ instead of $\frac{7}{10}$, thus increasing the probability in the ratio of seven to nine.

It is still true that there are only seven ways of the event happening, all of which are equally likely : hence the probability of the event happening in any particular one of these ways is $\frac{1}{7}$ of $\frac{9}{10}$, or $\frac{9}{70}$, with our new information. Hence our information concerning the event has increased the chance of its happening in an assigned way from $\frac{1}{10}$ or $\frac{7}{70}$ to $\frac{9}{70}$, that is, it has increased it in the ratio of seven to nine, the same ratio in which the probability of the event itself was increased.

And the same argument would hold if the numbers were any others, and therefore the rule is true, provided all the ways of the event happening are equally probable.

Secondly, suppose the ways are not equally probable. We may in this case regard them as groups of subsidiary ways, which would be equally probable. Then, as we have shewn, the chance of each one of the subsidiary ways would be increased (or decreased) in the same ratio as the chance of the event itself, and therefore the sum of the chances of any group of these subsidiary ways would be changed in the same ratio.

For instance, if the event could happen in any one of three ways, whose respective chances were $\frac{1}{3}$, $\frac{1}{6}$, $\frac{1}{4}$, or $\frac{4}{12}$, $\frac{2}{12}$, $\frac{3}{12}$, we might divide the first of these ways into four subsidiary ways, the next into two ways, and the other into three ways, and the chance of each of these subsidiary ways would be $\frac{1}{12}$. If therefore, by an accession of knowledge, the chance of the whole event were diminished in the ratio of three to two, each subsidiary way of the event's happening would have a diminished probability of $\frac{2}{3}$ of $\frac{1}{12}$, or $\frac{1}{18}$, and the probabilities of the three given ways would become respectively $\frac{4}{18}$, $\frac{2}{18}$, $\frac{3}{18}$, or $\frac{2}{9}$, $\frac{1}{9}$, $\frac{1}{6}$: that is, they would be diminished in the same ratio as the chance of the event itself.

Thus we see that the rule is true always.

Question 134. A bag contains five balls, which are known to be either all black or all white—and both these are equally probable. A white ball is dropped into the bag, and then a ball is drawn out at random and found to be white. What is now the chance that the original balls were all white?

Answer. The probabilities are here affected by the observed event that a ball drawn out at random proved to be white.

We will first calculate the probabilities before this event was observed (which we will call *à priori* probabilities), and then consider how they are affected by the accession of knowledge produced by the observation of the event. (Probabilities modified by this knowledge may be distinguished as *à posteriori* probabilities.)

The event might happen in two ways; either by the balls having been all white, and any one of them being drawn, or by the five original balls having been black, the new one alone white, and this one drawn.

The *à priori* probability that all are white is $\frac{1}{2}$, and then the chance of drawing a white ball is 1 (or certainty). Hence the chance of the event happening in this way is $\frac{1}{2} \times 1$, or $\frac{1}{2}$.

So the *à priori* probability that the first five were black is $\frac{1}{2}$, and then the chance of drawing a white ball is $\frac{1}{6}$. Hence the chance of the event happening in this way is $\frac{1}{2} \times \frac{1}{6}$, or $\frac{1}{12}$.

Therefore the whole *à priori* chance of the event happening is

$$\frac{1}{2} + \frac{1}{12}, \text{ or } \frac{7}{12}.$$

But when the ball is drawn and observed to be white, this knowledge immediately increases the chance from $\frac{7}{12}$ to 1 (or certainty):

that is, it increases the chance in the ratio of 7 to 12. Therefore, by Rule IX., the chances of the event happening in the several ways are increased in the same ratio.

Hence the *à posteriori* chance of the event having happened in the first way is $\frac{1}{2} \times \frac{12}{7}$, or $\frac{6}{7}$; and the *à posteriori* chance of its having happened in the second way is $\frac{1}{12} \times \frac{12}{7}$, or $\frac{1}{7}$. Or the chance of the original balls having been all white is now $\frac{6}{7}$, and of their having been all black $\frac{1}{7}$.

Question 135. In a parcel of 1000 dice there is one that has every face marked six: all the rest are correctly marked. A die taken at random out of the parcel is thrown four times and always turns up *six*. What is the chance that this is the false die?

Answer. The die is either false or true: and the respective chances of these two cases *à priori* are $\frac{1}{1000}$ and $\frac{999}{1000}$. In the first case the chance that *six* should turn up four times in succession is unity; in the second case it is $\left(\frac{1}{6}\right)^4$, or $\frac{1}{1296}$. Therefore we have *à priori*,—

(1) the chance that the die should be false, and *six* should turn up four times, is $\frac{1}{1000}$:

(2) the chance that the die should be true, and *six* should turn up four times, is $\frac{37}{48000}$:

and the chance that from one or other the same result should happen is

$$\frac{1}{1000} + \frac{37}{48000} = \frac{17}{9600}.$$

But after our knowledge is augmented by the observation of the fact that the die turns up *six* four times in succession, this latter chance becomes unity, that is, it becomes multiplied by $\frac{9600}{17}$. Hence (Rule IX.) the chances (1) and (2) become multiplied in the same ratio. Therefore *à posteriori*, the chance that the die should be false and *six* have turned up four times is $\frac{1}{1000} \times \frac{9600}{17} = \frac{48}{85}$. This is the required chance.

Question 136. A purse contains ten coins, each of which is either a sovereign or a shilling : a coin is drawn and found to be a sovereign, what is the chance that this is the only sovereign ?

Answer. A priori, the coin drawn was equally likely to be a sovereign or a shilling*, therefore the chance of its being a sovereign was $\frac{1}{2}$.

A posteriori, the chance of its being a sovereign is unity : or the chance is *doubled* by the observation of the event. Therefore (Rule IX.) the chance of any particular way in which a sovereign might be drawn is also doubled.

Now the chance that there was only one sovereign was *à priori*

$$\frac{10}{2^{10}} \text{ or } \frac{10}{1024} \, ;$$

and in this case the chance of drawing a sovereign was $\frac{1}{10}$.

Hence the chance that there should be only one sovereign, and that it should be drawn, was *à priori*

$$\frac{10}{1024} \times \frac{1}{10}, \text{ or } \frac{1}{1024}.$$

And the *à posteriori* chance that a sovereign should be drawn in this way is the double of this : *i.e.* $\frac{2}{1024}$ or $\frac{1}{512}$; which is therefore the required chance.

* In the statement of this question the words "each of which" implies that the purse has been filled in such a way that each coin separately is equally likely to be a sovereign or a shilling. For instance each coin may have been taken from either of two bags at random, one containing sovereigns and the other shillings. The case is carefully marked off from that of Qn. 137. Mr Venn in his strictures on this solution (*Logic of Chance*, Second Edition, pp. 166, 167) appears to overlook the significance of the words "each of which," and implies that the solution of Qn. 137 would have been applicable to Qn. 136.

Question 137. A purse contains ten coins, which are either sovereigns or shillings, and all possible numbers of each are equally likely : a coin is drawn and found to be a sovereign, what is the chance that this is the only sovereign ?

Answer. *A priori*, the coin drawn was equally likely to be a sovereign or a shilling, therefore the chance of its being a sovereign was $\frac{1}{2}$.

A posteriori, the chance of its being a sovereign is unity : or the chance is doubled by the observation of the event.

Therefore (Rule IX.) the chance of any particular way in which a sovereign might be drawn is also doubled.

Now, *à priori*, eleven cases were equally probable, viz. that there should be

0, 1, 2, 3, 4, 5, 6, 7, 8, 9, 10 sovereigns.

10, 9, 8, 7, 6, 5, 4, 3, 2, 1, 0 shillings.

Therefore the chance of there being exactly one sovereign was $\frac{1}{11}$, and in this case the chance of drawing a sovereign was $\frac{1}{10}$.

Hence the chance that there should be only one sovereign, and that it should be drawn was, *à priori*,

$$\frac{1}{11} \times \frac{1}{10}, \text{ or } \frac{1}{110}.$$

And the *à posteriori* chance that a sovereign should be drawn in this way is the double of this, that is, $\frac{2}{110}$ or $\frac{1}{55}$, which is, therefore, the chance required.

Question 138. *A, B, C* were entered for a race, and their respective chances of winning were estimated at $\frac{2}{11}, \frac{4}{11}, \frac{5}{11}$. But circumstances come to our knowledge in favour of A, which raise his chance to $\frac{1}{2}$; what are now the chances in favour of B and C respectively ?

Answer. A could lose in two ways, viz. either by B winning or by C winning, and the respective chances of his losing in these ways were *à priori* $\frac{4}{11}$ and $\frac{5}{11}$, and the chance of his losing at all was $\frac{9}{11}$. But after our accession of knowledge the chance of his losing at all becomes $\frac{1}{2}$, that is, it becomes diminished in the ratio of 18 : 11. Hence the chance of either way in which he might lose is diminished in the same ratio. Therefore the chance of B winning is now

$$\frac{4}{11} \times \frac{11}{18}, \text{ or } \frac{4}{18};$$

and of C winning

$$\frac{5}{11} \times \frac{11}{18}, \text{ or } \frac{5}{18}.$$

These are therefore the required chances.

Question 139. One of a pack of fifty-two cards has been removed; from the remainder of the pack two cards are drawn and are found to be spades; find the chance that the missing card is a spade.

Answer. A priori, the chance of the missing card being a spade is $\frac{1}{4}$, and the chance that then two cards drawn at random should be both spades is $\frac{12 \cdot 11}{51 \cdot 50}$, or $\frac{132}{2550}$. Hence the chance that the missing card should be a spade, and two spades be drawn, is

$$\frac{1}{4} \times \frac{132}{2550}, \text{ or } \frac{11}{850}.$$

The chance of the missing card being not a spade is $\frac{3}{4}$, and the chance that then two spades should be drawn is $\frac{13 \cdot 12}{51 \cdot 50}$, or $\frac{156}{2550}$. Hence the chance that the missing card should be not a spade, and two spades be drawn, is

$$\frac{3}{4} \times \frac{156}{2550}, \text{ or } \frac{39}{850}.$$

Therefore the chance that in one way or the other two spades should be drawn is

$$\frac{11}{850} + \frac{39}{850}, \text{ or } \frac{50}{850}, \text{ or } \frac{1}{17}.$$

But after the observation of the event this chance becomes certainty, or becomes multiplied by 17. Therefore the chance of either way from which the result might occur is increased in the same ratio.

So the chance that the given card was a spade becomes *à posteriori*,

$$\frac{11}{850} \times 17, \text{ or } \frac{11}{50}.$$

Question 140. There are four dice, two of which are true and two are so loaded that with either the chance of throwing *six* is $\frac{1}{3}$. Two of them at random are thrown and turn up *sixes*. Find the chance (*a*) that both are loaded; (*b*) that one only is loaded; (*c*) that neither is loaded.

Answer. The *à priori* chances are

$$(a) \ \frac{1}{6}, \quad (b) \ \frac{4}{6}, \quad (c) \ \frac{1}{6};$$

and the chance of throwing *sixes* in each case

$$(a) \ \frac{1}{9}, \quad (b) \ \frac{1}{18}, \quad (c) \ \frac{1}{36}.$$

Therefore the whole *à priori* chance of throwing *sixes* is

$$\frac{1}{54} + \frac{1}{27} + \frac{1}{216} = \frac{13}{216}.$$

A posteriori this is unity, therefore the chances of the three hypotheses having produced the result are multiplied *à posteriori* by $\frac{216}{13}$. Thus they are

$$(a) \ \frac{4}{13}, \quad (b) \ \frac{8}{13}, \quad (c) \ \frac{1}{13}.$$

Questions as to the credibility of the testimony of witnesses will depend for their solution upon the last rule, and may be answered in a manner similar to that of the questions just considered. In most questions of this class, the testimony given, or the assertions made, constitute a phenomenon which might have occurred whether the event reported occurred or not, or in whatsoever manner it occurred. We may first investigate the *à priori* probabilities of such testimony being given, on the several hypotheses possible with respect to the occurrence of the event, and by summing them we may deduce the *à priori* probability of the testimony being given at all. If we then take into consideration the fact that the testimony has been given, this accession of knowledge raises the last probability into certainty, and therefore increases it in a definite ratio, which can be calculated. In the same ratio (by Rule IX.) must the probabilities be increased of the several ways in which the testimony may have been generated, or in which the event in question may have happened. Thus we obtain the *à posteriori* and final probability of any assigned manner in which the event could possibly have occurred. A few examples will fully illustrate this.

Question 141. *A* speaks truth three times out of four, *B* four times out of five ; they agree in asserting that from a bag containing nine balls, all of different colours, a white ball has been drawn ; shew that the probability that this is true is $\frac{96}{97}$.

Answer. We will consider those chances as *à priori*, which are independent of the knowledge that *A* and *B* make the report in question, and those as *à posteriori* which are subsequent to this knowledge.

The *à priori* chance that a white ball should be drawn is $\frac{1}{9}$, and in this case the chance that *A* and *B* should both assert it, is $\frac{3}{4} \times \frac{4}{5}$; hence the chance that *A* and *B* should both truly assert a white ball to be drawn, is *à priori*,

$$\frac{1}{9} \times \frac{3}{4} \times \frac{4}{5}, \text{ or } \frac{1}{15}.$$

The *à priori* chance that a white ball should not be drawn is $\frac{8}{9}$; the chance that *A* should make a false report is $\frac{1}{4}$, and that he should select the white ball out of the eight which might be falsely asserted to have come up is $\frac{1}{8}$; hence in this case the chance that he asserts that the white is drawn is $\frac{1}{8} \times \frac{1}{4}$, and the chance that B should make the same assertion is $\frac{1}{8} \times \frac{1}{5}$; therefore the chance that A and B should both falsely assert a white ball to be drawn is

$$\frac{8}{9} \times \frac{1}{8} \times \frac{1}{4} \times \frac{1}{8} \times \frac{1}{5}, \text{ or } \frac{1}{1440}.$$

Consequently the *à priori* chance that they both assert (either truly or falsely) that a white ball should be drawn is

$$\frac{1}{15} + \frac{1}{1440}, \text{ or } \frac{97}{1440}.$$

But *à posteriori* this chance becomes certainty, or it becomes multiplied by $\frac{1440}{97}$. Hence the chance of each way in which they may make the assertion, is multiplied in the same ratio. Therefore, *à posteriori*, the chance that they make the assertion truly is

$$\frac{1}{15} \times \frac{1440}{97}, \text{ or } \frac{96}{97};$$

and the chance that they make it falsely is

$$\frac{1}{1440} \times \frac{1440}{97}, \text{ or } \frac{1}{97}.$$

Question 142. *A* gives a true report four times out of five, *B* three times out of five, and *C* five times out of seven. If *B* and *C* agree in reporting that an experiment failed which *A* reports to have succeeded, what is the chance that the experiment succeeded ?

Answer. The chance that the given reports should be made upon the experiment having succeeded is

$$\frac{1}{2} \times \frac{4}{5} \times \frac{2}{5} \times \frac{2}{7}, \text{ or } \frac{16}{350}.$$

The chance that the given reports should be made on the experiment having failed is

$$\frac{1}{2} \times \frac{1}{5} \times \frac{3}{5} \times \frac{5}{7}, \text{ or } \frac{15}{350}.$$

The *à priori* chance that in one way or other the given reports should be made is

$$\frac{16}{350} + \frac{15}{350}, \text{ or } \frac{31}{350}.$$

But, *à posteriori*, this is certain, or the chance is multiplied by $\frac{350}{31}$. Hence, also, the chance of each way in which the reports could be made is multiplied by $\frac{350}{31}$.

Therefore, *à posteriori*, the chance that the experiment succeeded is

$$\frac{16}{350} \times \frac{350}{31}, \text{ or } \frac{16}{31}.$$

We will conclude this chapter with some illustrations of the principles of probability, drawn from the game of whist.

This game is played with a pack of fifty-two cards, consisting of four suits of thirteen cards, marked differently. The cards are all dealt out to four players, of whom two and two are partners, so that each has thirteen cards. One of the dealer's cards is turned up, and the suit to which this card belongs is called trumps. Four particular cards in this suit —the ace, king, queen, and knave—are called honours.

It follows, from Rule IV., that the chance that the turned up card is an honour is $\frac{4}{13}$, and that it is not an honour is $\frac{9}{13}$.

Question 143. What is the chance that each party in the game should have two honours?

Answer. Besides the turned up card, there are fifty-one cards, of which twenty-five belong to the dealer and his partner, and twenty-six to their adversaries.

First,—Suppose the turned up card is an honour. The chance of this is $\frac{4}{13}$. Then the chance that one other honour should be among the twenty-five, and the remaining two among the twenty-six, is

$$3 \cdot \frac{25}{51} \cdot \frac{26}{50} \cdot \frac{25}{49};$$

therefore the chance that the turned up card should be an honour, and the honours equally divided, is

$$3 \cdot \frac{25}{51} \cdot \frac{26}{50} \cdot \frac{25}{49} \cdot \frac{4}{13}, \text{ or } \frac{100}{833}.$$

Secondly,—Suppose the turned up card is not an honour. The chance of this is $\frac{9}{13}$. Then the chance that two of the honours should be among the twenty-five, and the remaining two among the twenty-six, is

$$\frac{4 \cdot 3}{1 \cdot 2} \cdot \frac{25}{51} \cdot \frac{24}{50} \cdot \frac{26}{49} \cdot \frac{25}{48};$$

therefore the chance that the turned up card should not be an honour, and the honours be equally divided, is

$$6 \cdot \frac{25}{51} \cdot \frac{24}{50} \cdot \frac{26}{49} \cdot \frac{25}{48} \cdot \frac{9}{13}, \text{ or } \frac{225}{833}.$$

Hence the whole chance that the honours should be equally divided is

$$\frac{100}{833} + \frac{225}{833}, \text{ or } \frac{325}{833}.$$

In the same manner we may write down almost at sight the chances of the occurrence of other arrangements of the cards. We give a few examples:

1. If an honour turns up, the respective chances that the dealer and his partner have between them exactly *one, two, three,* or *four* honours are

$$\frac{26 \cdot 25 \cdot 24}{51 \cdot 50 \cdot 49}, \quad 3 \cdot \frac{25 \cdot 26 \cdot 25}{51 \cdot 50 \cdot 49}, \quad 3 \cdot \frac{25 \cdot 24 \cdot 26}{51 \cdot 50 \cdot 49}, \quad \frac{25 \cdot 24 \cdot 23}{51 \cdot 50 \cdot 49};$$

or $\quad \frac{312}{2499}, \quad \frac{975}{2499}, \quad \frac{936}{2499}, \quad \frac{276}{2499}.$

The sum of these fractions is unity, for one of the four cases must certainly occur ; and their ratios are nearly as

$$8 \; : \; 25 \; : \; 24 \; : \; 7.$$

2. If an honour does not turn up, the respective chances that the dealer and his partner have *none*, or exactly *one, two, three,* or *four* honours are

$$\frac{26.25.24.23}{51.50.49.48}, \quad 4 \cdot \frac{25.26.25.24}{51.50.49.48}, \quad 6 \cdot \frac{25.24.26.25}{51.50.49.48},$$

$$4 \cdot \frac{25.24.23.26}{51.50.49.48}, \quad \frac{25.24.23.22}{51.50.49.48};$$

or

$$\frac{299}{4998}, \quad \frac{1300}{4998}, \quad \frac{1950}{4998}, \quad \frac{1196}{4998}, \quad \frac{253}{4998}.$$

The sum of these fractions is unity, for one of the five cases must certainly occur ; and their ratios are nearly as

$$6 \; : \; 26 \; : \; 39 \; : \; 24 \; : \; 5.$$

3. Before it is known whether an honour will turn up, the respective chances that the dealer and his partner have between them *none*, or exactly *one, two, three,* or *four* honours are

$$\frac{207}{4998}, \quad \frac{1092}{4998}, \quad \frac{1950}{4998}, \quad \frac{1404}{4998}, \quad \frac{345}{4998};$$

the sum of the fractions being unity.

Hence, speaking approximately, we may expect that on the average, for every *one hundred* times the cards are dealt, the dealer and his partner will have four honours *seven* times, and the other players *four* times. The dealer and his partner will have three honours *twenty-eight* times, and the other players *twenty-two* times. And each party will have two honours the remaining *thirty-nine* times.

4. The chance that each of the four players should have one honour is not affected by the turning up of the last card. For we get equivalent expressions for the chance, whether an honour be turned up or not, the expressions being respectively

$$\frac{\lfloor 3 . 13^3}{51.50.49} \quad \text{and} \quad \frac{\lfloor 4 . 12 . 13^3}{51.50.49.48},$$

and each of these is equal to

$$\frac{2197}{20825}, \text{ or very nearly } \frac{5}{48}.$$

5. If an honour turns up, the respective chances that the dealer should hold exactly *one, two, three,* or *four* honours are

$$\frac{39.38.37}{51.50.49}, \quad \frac{3}{1} \times \frac{12.39.38}{51.50.49}, \quad \frac{3}{1} \times \frac{12.11.39}{51.50.49}, \quad \frac{12.11.10}{51.50.49};$$

or
$$\frac{9139}{20825}, \quad \frac{8892}{20825}, \quad \frac{2574}{20825}, \quad \frac{220}{20825}.$$

The sum of these fractions is unity, it being certain that the dealer has at least one honour ; and their ratios are approximately as

$$125 : 121 : 35 : 3.$$

6. If an honour does not turn up, the respective chances that the dealer should hold *none*, or exactly *one, two, three,* or *four* honours are

$$\frac{39.38.37.36}{51.50.49.48}, \quad 4.\frac{12.39.38.37}{51.50.49.48}, \quad 6.\frac{12.11.39.38}{51.50.49.48},$$

$$4.\frac{12.11.10.39}{51.50.49.48}, \quad \frac{12.11.10.9}{51.50.49.48};$$

or
$$\frac{27417}{83300}, \quad \frac{36556}{83300}, \quad \frac{16302}{83300}, \quad \frac{2860}{83300}, \quad \frac{165}{83300}.$$

The sum of these fractions is unity, and their ratios are approximately as

$$332 : 443 : 198 : 35 : 2.$$

7. Before it is known whether an honour will turn up, the respective chances that the dealer should hold *none*, or exactly *one*, or *two*, or *three*, or *four* honours, are

$$\frac{18981}{83300}, \quad \frac{36556}{83300}, \quad \frac{22230}{83300}, \quad \frac{5148}{83300}, \quad \frac{385}{83300};$$

the sum of these fractions being unity, and their ratios approximately as

$$148 : 284 : 173 : 40 : 3.$$

8. If an honour turns up, the respective chances that a player, who is not the dealer, should hold no honour, or exactly *one*, or *two*, or *three* honours, are

$$\frac{38 \cdot 37 \cdot 36}{51 \cdot 50 \cdot 49}, \quad 3 \cdot \frac{13 \cdot 38 \cdot 37}{51 \cdot 50 \cdot 49}, \quad 3 \cdot \frac{13 \cdot 12 \cdot 28}{51 \cdot 50 \cdot 49}, \quad \frac{13 \cdot 12 \cdot 11}{51 \cdot 50 \cdot 49};$$

or

$$\frac{8436}{20825}, \quad \frac{9139}{20825}, \quad \frac{2964}{20825}, \quad \frac{286}{20825};$$

the sum of these fractions being unity, and their ratios approximately as

$$59 : 64 : 21 : 2.$$

9. If an honour does not turn up, the respective chances that a player, who is not the dealer, should hold *none*, or *one*, or *two*, or *three*, or *four* honours are

$$\frac{38 \cdot 37 \cdot 36 \cdot 35}{51 \cdot 50 \cdot 49 \cdot 48}, \quad 4 \cdot \frac{13 \cdot 38 \cdot 37 \cdot 36}{51 \cdot 50 \cdot 49 \cdot 48}, \quad 6 \cdot \frac{13 \cdot 12 \cdot 38 \cdot 37}{51 \cdot 50 \cdot 49 \cdot 48}$$

$$4 \cdot \frac{13 \cdot 12 \cdot 11 \cdot 38}{51 \cdot 50 \cdot 49 \cdot 48}, \quad \frac{13 \cdot 12 \cdot 11 \cdot 10}{51 \cdot 50 \cdot 49 \cdot 48};$$

or

$$\frac{73815}{249900}, \quad \frac{109668}{249900}, \quad \frac{54834}{249900}, \quad \frac{10868}{249900}, \quad \frac{715}{249900};$$

the sum of these fractions being unity, and their ratios approximately as

$$103 : 153 : 77 : 15 : 1.$$

10. Before it is known whether an honour will turn up, the respective chances that a player, who is not the dealer, should hold *none*, or *one*, or *two*, or *three*, or *four* honours are the same as are the dealer's chances in the case when the card turned up is not an honour, viz. (as in case 6),

$$\frac{27417}{83300}, \quad \frac{36556}{83300}, \quad \frac{16302}{83300}, \quad \frac{2860}{83300}, \quad \frac{165}{83300}.$$

CHAPTER VII.

THE PRINCIPLES OF CHANCE EXHIBITED ALGEBRAICALLY.

For convenience of reference we shall now cast into algebraical form the nine rules established in the preceding chapter, referring the student to that chapter for the arguments by which each theorem is proved.

We must commence with the axiom (page 125) that *the probability of an event happening is the sum of the several probabilities of its happening in whatever several ways it can happen.*

From the convention that probability shall be expressed in terms of certainty as a unit we immediately obtain :—

PROPOSITION XL.

If p be the probability of an event happening, the probability of its not happening is $1-p$. (Rule I., page 125.)

PROPOSITION XLI.

If the odds be n to m against an event, the chance of the event happening is $\dfrac{m}{m+n}$, *and the chance of its not happening is* $\dfrac{n}{m+n}$. (Rule II., page 127.)

From the axiom stated above the next proposition immediately follows:—

PROPOSITION XLII.

If an event can happen in m ways and fail in n ways, all these ways being equally likely and such that not more than one can occur, the odds are n to m against the event, and the respective probabilities of its happening or not happening are as in the last proposition. (Rule III., page 128.)

By regarding the "ways" of this proposition as *events* in themselves, and the "event" of the proposition as a *result* which may follow, we transform the proposition into the following:—

PROPOSITION XLIII.

If there be m + n equally probable events one of which must happen and only one can happen, and if any one of m of these events will produce a certain result which cannot otherwise be produced, the probability of this result is $\dfrac{m}{m+n}$. (Rule IV., page 130.)

From the definition of the term expectation (page 141) we deduce the next proposition:—

PROPOSITION XLIV.

If p be the probability of an event by which a person will gain a prize of value V, the value of his expectation is pV. (Rule V., page 142.)

COROLLARY I. If p_1, p_2, p_3, ... be the probabilities of several events, by which prizes V_1, V_2, V_3, ... respectively would be gained, the whole expectation is

$$p_1 V_1 + p_2 V_2 + p_3 V_3 + \ldots.$$

COROLLARY II. If p_1 be the chance of a quantity being V_1 and if p_2 be the chance of its being V_2 and if p_3 be the chance of its being V_3 and so on, the average magnitude of the quantity will be $p_1 V_1 + p_2 V_2 + p_3 V_3 + \ldots.$

This may be taken as the definition of *average*.

PROPOSITION XLV.

If p and q be the respective chances of two independent events, the chance that both will happen is pq. (Rule VI., p. 144.)

For let p and q be written as proper fractions; thus:

$$p = \frac{M}{M + N}, \qquad q = \frac{m}{m + n},$$

where M, N, m, n are integers*. Then the chance of the first event is the same as the chance of success in an experiment which can succeed in M ways and fail in N ways, all the $M + N$ ways being equally likely (Prop. XLIII.); and

---

* It is here assumed that p and q are commensurable ratios. If this be not the case the theorem will still be true. For, if possible, let the chance of the two events be $pq + x$ instead of pq. Then we may take two commensurable quantities p', q' greater than p, q, but as near as we please to them. Take them so near that their product is less than $pq + x$. Then the chance of the two given events is less than the chance of two events whose separate chances are p', q'. That is (since the proposition is true for commensurable quantities), it is less than $p'q'$ and à fortiori less than $pq + x$. But by hypothesis it is equal to $pq + x$, which is impossible. And in the same way we can shew that the chance cannot be $pq - x$. Hence the proposition is true in the case when the chances are incommensurable quantities.

the chance of the second is the same as the chance of success in an experiment which can succeed in m ways and fail in n ways. Therefore the chance of the two events is the same as the chance of both experiments succeeding. But both experiments can turn out in $(M + N)(m + n)$ ways all of which are equally likely, and both experiments can succeed in Mm ways (Prop. I.). Therefore the chance of both experiments succeeding is (Prop. XLIII.)

$$\frac{Mm}{(M + N)(m + n)},$$

which is equal to pq. This therefore is the probability that both the events will happen.   Q. E. D.

COROLLARY. The chance that neither event happens will be $(1 - p)(1 - q)$, or $1 - p - q + pq$.

The chance that at least one happens will be $p + q - pq$.

The chance that the first happens without the second will be $p - pq$.

The chance that the second happens without the first will be $q - pq$.

The chance that one and only one happens will be $p + q - 2pq$.

The reasoning of the last proposition will equally apply when the events are not independent, provided q or $\frac{m}{m + n}$ be the chance of the second event happening *when the first has happened*, so that the number of ways of both experiments turning out may still (by Prop. I.) be $(M + N)(m + n)$, and the number of ways of both succeeding be Mm. Hence we have the following :—

PROPOSITION XLVI.

If p be the chance of an event happening, and when it has happened q be the chance of a dependent event happening, then the chance that both should happen is pq. (Rule VII., page 147.)

PROPOSITION XLVII.

If p be the probability of an event A ; and when A has happened, q be the probability of another event B; and when A and B have happened, r be the probability of a third event C ; and so on, to any number of events ; the chance of all happening is the continued product of all the several chances, p, q, r.... (Rule VIII., page 151.)

For (by Prop. XLV. or XLVI., as the case may be), the chance of the first and second is pq: taking these two as one compound event, the chance of this and the third event is (by the same proposition) $pq \times r$ or pqr: and so we may extend the reasoning to any number of events.

PROPOSITION XLVIII.

If a doubtful event P may happen in any one of a series of ways A, B, C... and if a, b, c... be the chances of A, B, C... respectively, so that the chance of the event is $a + b + c + ... = p < 1$, and if some accession of knowledge independent of A, B, C... increase the probability of the event P in any ratio $(1 : \mu$, suppose), the probabilities of A, B, C... will be severally increased in the same ratio. (Rule IX., page 162.)

For let θ be the G.C.M.* of $a, b, c...$ so that $\dfrac{a}{\theta}, \dfrac{b}{\theta}, \dfrac{c}{\theta}$ ... are

---

* It should be noted that the G.C.M. of a series of fractions (all in their lowest terms) is the fraction having for its numerator the G.C.M. of the numerators, and for its denominator the L.C.M. of the denominators.

integers. Then we may regard the way A as made up of the aggregation of a number $\frac{a}{\theta}$ of subsidiary ways each of which has the probability θ. So, for B, C, &c. Then the event P can happen in $\frac{a}{\theta} + \frac{b}{\theta} + \frac{c}{\theta} + \ldots = \frac{p}{\theta}$ different ways, all equally likely. Now the accession of knowledge which changes the probability of the event from p to μp must affect the probability of the several ways so that their sum may be now μp instead of p. But since the ways were equally probable and the accession of knowledge has no particular relation to any of them they must remain equally probable. Hence the probability of each of them must be $\mu\theta$. But A is made up of an aggregation of $\frac{a}{\theta}$ of such ways, therefore the probability of A is μa. Similarly the probability of B is μb and of C is μc, &c.

COROLLARY I. If (as is very commonly the case) the accession of knowledge be the knowledge that P has happened, we must have $\mu = 1 \div (a + b + c + \ldots)$, and the à *posteriori* chances of A, B, C, &c. become

$$\frac{a}{a + b + c + \ldots}, \qquad \frac{b}{a + b + c + \ldots}, \qquad \frac{c}{a + b + c + \ldots}, \text{ &c.}$$

COROLLARY II. If A be a cause which *may* produce the event P, and α be the probability that when A has happened it will produce P; and similarly if β, γ, ... be the respective chances that when B, C, ... have happened P will be produced; then the first "way" of P happening is made up of the compound contingency,

    (1)   that A shall happen,

    (2)   that A having happened shall produce P,

and the chance of this is $a\alpha$. Similarly $b\beta$, $c\gamma$, ... are the chances of P happening in the other ways. Therefore we have to substitute $a\alpha$, $b\beta$, $c\gamma$, ... for the a, b, c, ... of the proposition. And if (as in Cor. I.) P is *à posteriori* certain, the *à posteriori* chances of A, B, C, ... become

$$\frac{a\alpha}{a\alpha + b\beta + c\gamma + \ldots}, \quad \frac{b\beta}{a\alpha + b\beta + c\gamma + \ldots}, \quad \frac{c\gamma}{a\alpha + b\beta + c\gamma + \ldots}, \&\text{c.}$$

The term Inverse Probability is used by many writers to denote those cases in which the *à priori* probability of a cause is modified by the observation of some effect due to the cause.

But there seems no reason to regard these cases as belonging to a special category. All probability is based on the limitation of our knowledge, and every accession of knowledge in regard to a contingent event alters the probability (to us) of the event. It makes no difference whether the event be past or future. The past event of which we have no certain knowledge is as much a subject of probability as a future possible event. And the observation of any result which may have been produced by the event in question is simply an accession of knowledge with regard to the event.

Suppose that a purse contains seven coins, and we are told that they are either six sovereigns and a shilling or six shillings and a sovereign. Moreover let the conditions be such that either of these conditions was equally probable. The composition of the purse is a past event, but to us it is a subject of probability. The value of the contents is either £6. 1*s.* or £1. 6*s.*, and with our present knowledge the expectation of the value is $3\frac{1}{2}$ guineas.

But a coin is drawn at random and replaced, and is seen to be a sovereign. This observation throws some additional

light on the composition of the purse. Its value is still
either £6. 1s. or £1. 6s., but we immediately feel that it is
more likely that it contains six sovereigns than one. Upon
this accession of knowledge we are ready to give more than
3½ guineas for the purse. But no new principle is here
introduced. It is simply the fact that more evidence has
come to light regarding the composition of the purse, and
on the larger evidence we form a new estimate of its value.
The term "Inverse Probability" appears to be unnecessary
and misleading.

NOTES ON POPULATION, AND EXPECTATION OF LIFE.

1. Let $\delta_1, \delta_2, \delta_3 \ldots$ be the respective chances that a
person die in the 1st, 2nd, 3rd … year of his life.

The arithmetical values of these constants have been
already given in the table on page 160, the entries in Column
D being the numerators to denominator 400. That is,

$$\delta_1 = \frac{57}{400}, \quad \delta_2 = \frac{20}{400}, \quad \delta_3 = \frac{11}{400}, \quad \delta_4 = \frac{7}{400}, \&c.$$

2. Out of N persons born in a given place in the course
of a year, let $\theta_0 N$ be the number who die in the same year,
$\theta_1 N$ the number who die in the next year, $\theta_2 N$ in the next,
and so on.

It is plain that if all the births took place at the first
moment of the year we should have

$$\theta_0 = \delta_1, \quad \theta_1 = \delta_2, \quad \theta_2 = \delta_3, \quad \theta_3 = \delta_4, \&c.$$

And if all the births took place in the last moment of the
year we should have

$$\theta_0 = 0, \quad \theta_1 = \delta_1, \quad \theta_2 = \delta_2, \quad \theta_3 = \delta_3, \&c.$$

The births being actually spread over the whole year, we take as a sufficient approximation the mean between the foregoing.   Hence

$$\theta_0 = \frac{\delta_1}{2}, \quad \theta_1 = \frac{\delta_1 + \delta_2}{2}, \quad \theta_2 = \frac{\delta_2 + \delta_3}{2}, \quad \theta_3 = \frac{\delta_3 + \delta_4}{2},$$

and so on.   The values of δ being known from the table on page 160, the values of θ are now known.

3.   Excluding the consideration of immigration and emigration, if B be the number of births in a year, and D the number of deaths in a year, in a population which numbered N at the beginning of the year, the population at the end of the year will number $N + B - D$.

In other words the population will be multiplied in a year by

$$1 + \frac{B}{N} - \frac{D}{N} = \mu \text{ suppose.}$$

We may take the births and deaths in a year to be proportional to the population at the beginning of the year, so that μ may be treated as a constant.

4.   Since the population is multiplied every year by μ, if B and D be the respective numbers of births and deaths in any year, $\dfrac{B}{\mu}$ and $\dfrac{D}{\mu}$ will be the numbers in the previous year, $\dfrac{B}{\mu^2}$ and $\dfrac{D}{\mu^2}$ in the year before that, and so on.

The deaths D in a given year must be composed of the following :—

$\theta_0 B$ deaths of persons born in the year,

$\theta_1 \dfrac{B}{\mu}$ „   „   „   the previous year,

$\theta_2 \dfrac{B}{\mu^2}$ „   „   „   the year before that, and so on.   Hence

$$D = B \left\{ \theta_0 + \frac{\theta_1}{\mu} + \frac{\theta_2}{\mu^2} + \frac{\theta_3}{\mu^3} + \ldots \right\} = B \frac{\mu + 1}{2} \left\{ \frac{\delta_1}{\mu} + \frac{\delta_2}{\mu^2} + \frac{\delta_3}{\mu^3} + \ldots \right\}.$$

But (Art. 3) $\dfrac{D}{N} = \dfrac{B}{N} - (\mu - 1)$.

$$\therefore \frac{B}{N} = \cfrac{\mu - 1}{1 - \cfrac{\mu + 1}{2} \left\{ \cfrac{\delta_1}{\mu} + \cfrac{\delta_2}{\mu^2} + \cfrac{\delta_3}{\mu^3} + \ldots \right\}}.$$

Thus we have two equations connecting the birth-rate, the death-rate, and the annual multiplier of population, so that when any one of these three is given, the other two are determinate, on the basis of such a table of mortality as is given on page 160.

5.   Let R_1, R_2, R_3 ... represent the remainders of the series $\delta_1 + \delta_2 + \delta_3 + \ldots$ after $1, 2, 3, \ldots$ terms respectively have been taken, so that $R_x = \delta_{x+1} + \delta_{x+2} + \delta_{x+3} + \ldots$.   Then out of N persons born, $N R_x$ will be the number who survive the age of x years; and the chance of a person aged m years living for at least n years more will be $R_{m+n} \div R_m$.

6.   Observing that $\delta_x = R_{x-1} - R_x$, and $R_0 = 1$, the last equation of Art. 4 becomes

$$\frac{B}{N} = \cfrac{2\mu}{1 + (\mu + 1) \left\{ \cfrac{R_1}{\mu} + \cfrac{R_2}{\mu^2} + \cfrac{R_3}{\mu^3} + \ldots \right\}}.$$

7.   Let E_0, E_1, E_2 ... be the expectations of life of persons aged 0, 1, 2, ... years respectively.   We may suppose the deaths in each year to be equally distributed over the year, so that if a man is to die in his first year his expectation of life is half a year; if he is to die in his second year his expectation is a year and a half, and so on.   Then

$$E_x = \tfrac{1}{2} \cdot \frac{\delta_{x+1}}{R_x} + \left(1 - \frac{\delta_{x+1}}{R_x} \right) (1 + E_{x+1}),$$

for a man aged x years has the chance $\delta_{x+1} \div R_x$ of dying in his first year, and the complementary chance of surviving his first year.   In the one event he has an expectation $\frac{1}{2}$, and in the other an expectation E_{x+1} *dating from a year hence*, or $1 + E_{x+1}$ from the present date.

Since $\delta_{x+1} = R_x - R_{x+1}$ the last equation reduces to

$$R_x (E_x - \tfrac{1}{2}) = R_{x+1} (E_{x+1} + \tfrac{1}{2}),$$

a formula by which it is easy to calculate successive values of E.

8.   *To find the chance that M who is aged m years, will survive N who is aged n years.*

The chance that M should die in a year subsequent to N is easily seen to be

$$\frac{\delta_{n+1}R_{m+1} + \delta_{n+2}R_{m+2} + \dots}{R_m R_n},$$

to $s - n$ terms, where s is the extreme age to which any one can live; and the chance that they die in the same year is

$$\frac{\delta_{n+1}\delta_{m+1} + \delta_{n+2}\delta_{m+2} + \dots}{R_m R_n}.$$

In the latter case the chance that M survives N is $\frac{1}{2}$. Therefore the whole chance of M surviving N is

$$\frac{\delta_{n+1}(R_{m+1} + \frac{1}{2}\delta_{m+1}) + \delta_{n+2}(R_{m+2} + \frac{1}{2}\delta_{m+2}) + \&c.}{R_m R_n}.$$

Or (observing that $2R_{m+1} + \delta_{m+1} = R_m + R_{m+1}$, and that $\delta_{n+1} = R_n - R_{n+1}$),

$$\frac{(R_m + R_{m+1})(R_n - R_{n+1}) + (R_{m+1} + R_{m+2})(R_{n+1} - R_{n+2}) + \&c.}{2R_m R_n},$$

which is

$$\frac{R_m R_n + (R_{m+1}R_n - R_m R_{n+1}) + (R_{m+2}R_{n+1} - R_{m+1}R_{n+2}) + \&c.}{2R_m R_n}.$$

CHAPTER VIII.

THE RULE OF SUCCESSION (SO-CALLED).

IN some treatises on probability the following rule is stated :—

If the probability of an event is entirely unknown, and it has been observed to happen n times in succession, the chance that it happens the next time is $(n+1)/(n+2)$.

The rule thus drafted has been subject to much adverse criticism. In some quarters the discredit cast upon it has been so absolute as to imply that it contains no element of truth. The validity of the rule, or its fallacy, depends upon the interpretation of the words "entirely unknown." We have shewn that probability always implies ignorance, it is a function of the limitation of our knowledge; but it is not very easy to conceive the event concerning the probability of which our mind presents an absolute blank until certain repetitions of it give us ground to expect that it will happen again.

The event to which the rule refers must evidently be of the nature of an experiment which may either succeed or fail. It is plain that if the experiment be repeated a number of times, and we observe that it succeeds much more frequently than it fails, we are acquiring certain data which will affect our expectation of success at any particular trial. If we estimate that before our observation began the experiment was equally likely to succeed or fail, it is certain that every occasion of success will raise the estimate while a preponderance of failures will depress it. But that we should estimate the event as equally likely to occur or fail is not the same thing as that we are entirely ignorant concerning it. The rule does not apply.

But however ignorant we may be of the probability of the experiment succeeding, we know at least that this probability lies between the limits represented by zero and unity. If we may assume that *all values between these limits are equally likely,* we are establishing the condition which the rule connotes by the term "entirely unknown." But the assumption must be recognized as arbitrary. In many cases it would be at least as reasonable to suppose that mean values are more likely than extreme ones.

The condition of things contemplated in the rule may be mechanically approached as follows.

Let *m* be some very large number. (In order to actually arrive at the required conditions we shall have to make *m* infinite.)

Let a die of *m* faces be thrown and let a number of black balls equal to the number turned up be placed in a bag, and white balls added till the total number is *m* + 1.

Let the bag thus composed be presented to a stranger who knows the process by which it has been prepared, but does not know what was the number turned up. Let him be invited to draw a ball and to replace it. The proportion of black balls in the bag may be said to be entirely unknown, and the chance of drawing a black ball (as far as his knowledge goes) may be anything between zero and unity, represented by a fraction having the denominator $m + 1$ and for numerator any integer from 1 to m. And *in consequence of the mode in which the bag has been composed* all the values

$$\frac{1}{m+1}, \quad \frac{2}{m+1}, \quad \frac{3}{m+1}, \ldots \frac{m}{m+1}$$

are equally likely. In this case if m be indefinitely large the rule will apply, and if the first n drawings each give a black ball, the chance of the $(n+1)th$ drawing being black, will be $(n+1)/(n+2)$.

But the bag might have been composed by a different method; for instance each ball placed in the bag might have been equally likely to be black or white, and then the Rule of Succession would have failed.

It is necessary therefore to avoid the vague expression "entirely unknown" and draft the rule with greater precision. In the form in which we proceed to state it it is capable of rigid proof as follows.

RULE.

If the probability of an experiment succeeding is so far unknown that all possible probabilities may be deemed equally likely: and if the experiment is then found to succeed n times in succession, the chance that it succeeds the next time is $(n + 1)/(n + 2)$.

Let the probability of success be x/m, where x is equally likely to have any of the values 0, 1, 2,... m.

The chance that the first n trials should be all successful is

$$\frac{1}{m+1} \left\{ \left(\frac{1}{m}\right)^n + \left(\frac{2}{m}\right)^n + \left(\frac{3}{m}\right)^n + \ldots + \left(\frac{m}{m}\right)^n \right\} = \frac{1}{N} \text{ suppose.}$$

When this event is observed to have taken place, it is plain that x cannot be zero, and the respective probabilities that x has the values $1, 2, \ldots m$ become

$$\frac{N}{m+1}\left(\frac{1}{m}\right)^n, \quad \frac{N}{m+1}\left(\frac{2}{m}\right)^n, \quad \frac{N}{m+1}\left(\frac{3}{m}\right)^n, \ldots \frac{N}{m+1}\left(\frac{m}{m}\right)^n,$$

and the chance of success at the $(n+1)th$ trial is therefore

$$\frac{N}{m+1}\left\{\left(\frac{1}{m}\right)^{n+1} + \left(\frac{2}{m}\right)^{n+1} + \left(\frac{3}{m}\right)^{n+1} + \ldots + \left(\frac{m}{m}\right)^{n+1}\right\}$$

$$= \frac{\left(\frac{1}{m}\right)^{n+1} + \left(\frac{2}{m}\right)^{n+1} + \left(\frac{3}{m}\right)^{n+1} + \ldots + \left(\frac{m}{m}\right)^{n+1}}{\left(\frac{1}{m}\right)^{n} + \left(\frac{2}{m}\right)^{n} + \left(\frac{3}{m}\right)^{n} + \ldots + \left(\frac{m}{m}\right)^{n}}.$$

If we divide numerator and denominator each by m, and then increase m indefinitely, the numerator and denominator ultimately become $\frac{1}{n+2}$ and $\frac{1}{n+1}$ respectively [Note A at the end of the Chapter]. Hence the chance of success at the $(n+1th)$ trial is $(n+1)/(n+2)$. Q. E. D.

It is plain that the Rule of Succession thus established is only a particular case of a more general rule. In the cases in which it is applicable it expresses the inference and expectation as to the $(n+1)th$ trial, derived from the observation of the first n trials, when these n trials have been all successful. But there must equally be an inference to be drawn when the n observed trials have eventuated in some successes and some failures: say in p successes and $n-p$ failures. We proceed to state and prove the rule in its more general form.

GENERALISATION OF THE RULE.

*If the probability of an experiment succeeding is so far
unknown that all possible probabilities may be deemed equally
likely: and if the experiment is then found to succeed p times
in n successive trials the chance that it succeeds at the next
trial is $(p+1)/(n+2)$.*

As before let the probability of success be x/m where x is
equally likely to have any of the values $0, 1, 2, \ldots m$.

The chance that in the first n trials there should be
exactly p successes is

$$\frac{1}{m+1}\left\{\left(\frac{1}{m}\right)^p\left(\frac{m-1}{m}\right)^{n-p} + \left(\frac{2}{m}\right)^p\left(\frac{m-2}{m}\right)^{n-p} + \ldots \right.$$
$$\left. + \left(\frac{m-1}{m}\right)^p\left(\frac{1}{m}\right)^{n-p}\right\} = \frac{1}{N} \text{ suppose.}$$

When this event is observed to have taken place, it is
plain that x can have neither of the values 0 and m, and the
respective probabilities that x has the values $1, 2, 3, \ldots (m-1)$
become

$$\frac{N}{m+1}\left(\frac{1}{m}\right)^p\left(\frac{m-1}{m}\right)^{n-p}, \quad \frac{N}{m+1}\left(\frac{2}{m}\right)^p\left(\frac{m-2}{m}\right)^{n-p},$$
$$\frac{N}{m+1}\left(\frac{3}{m}\right)^p\left(\frac{m-3}{m}\right)^{n-p}, \text{ &c.}$$

and the chance of success at the $(n+1)th$ trial therefore
becomes

$$\frac{\left(\frac{1}{m}\right)^{p+1}\left(\frac{m-1}{m}\right)^{n-p} + \left(\frac{2}{m}\right)^{p+1}\left(\frac{m-2}{m}\right)^{n-p} + \left(\frac{3}{m}\right)^{p+1}\left(\frac{m-3}{m}\right)^{n-p} + \ldots + \left(\frac{m-1}{m}\right)^{p+1}\left(\frac{1}{m}\right)^{n-p}}{\left(\frac{1}{m}\right)^{p}\left(\frac{m-1}{m}\right)^{n-p} + \left(\frac{2}{m}\right)^{p}\left(\frac{m-2}{m}\right)^{n-p} + \left(\frac{3}{m}\right)^{p}\left(\frac{m-3}{m}\right)^{n-p} + \ldots + \left(\frac{m-1}{m}\right)^{p}\left(\frac{1}{m}\right)^{n-p}}$$

If we divide numerator and denominator each by m, and then increase m indefinitely, the numerator and denominator ultimately become $1 \div C_{p+1}^{n+1}(n+2)$ and $1 \div C_p^n(n+1)$ [Note B at the end of the Chapter]. Hence the chance of success at the $(n+1)th$ trial is $(p+1)/(n+2)$.   Q. E. D.

NOTE. If $p = \frac{1}{2}N$ the chance becomes $\frac{1}{2}$, the obvious result since the evidence equally favours success or failure.

Though the cases are very rare in which the radical assumption of the Rule of Succession is strictly justified, the rule may be taken to afford a rough and ready estimate in many cases in which the assumption is approximately justified.

If two absolutely unknown players sit down to play chess, and if A wins 5 games, while B wins 3, we should conclude that A is the better player; and if we were to bet on the issue of the next game we should give odds in favour of A. At first sight we might be disposed to say that their skill is presumably as 5 to 3, and that these odds should be given on the next game; but this principle is seen to be false if we apply it after one game only has been played. It would lead to the conclusion that the winner of the first game is certain to win the rest. The Rule of Succession is not liable to any such *reductio ad absurdum* and the conclusions to which it leads in regard to games of chess or other trials of skill are reasonable enough. If we apply it to the case before us it gives the odds 3 to 2 in favour of A winning the next game; but if the number of games played be increased the odds approximate to the ratio of the number of games won by each player. If for example A wins 500 and B wins 300 games the odds in favour of A winning the next game are 501 to 301. This is entirely in harmony with what we should intuitively expect.

NOTE A.

We know that

$$1^2 + 2^2 + 3^2 + \ldots + m^2 = \frac{m^3}{3} + \frac{m^2}{2} + \ldots,$$

$$1^3 + 2^3 + 3^3 + \ldots + m^3 = \frac{m^4}{4} + \frac{m^3}{2} + \ldots.$$

It is very easy to extend this by elementary algebra and to shew that

$$1^n + 2^n + 3^n + \ldots + m^n = \frac{m^{n+1}}{n+1} + \frac{m^n}{2} + \ldots.$$

Hence we have

$$\frac{1^n + 2^n + 3^n + \ldots + m^n}{m^{n+1}} = \frac{1}{n+1} + \text{negative powers of } m.$$

And therefore if m be indefinitely increased we have ultimately

$$\frac{1^n + 2^n + 3^n + \ldots + m^n}{m^{n+1}} = \frac{1}{n+1}.$$

NOTE B.

Again, we know that

$$1(m-1) + 2(m-2) + 3(m-3) + \ldots + (m-1)1 = \frac{m^3}{6} - \frac{m}{6},$$

$$1(m-1)^2 + 2(m-2)^2 + \ldots + (m-1)1^2 = \frac{m^4}{12} - \frac{m^2}{12},$$

$$1(m-1)^3 + 2(m-2)^3 + \ldots + (m-1)1^3 = \frac{m^5}{20} - \&c.,$$

and generally

$$1\,(m-1)^{n-1}+2\,(m-2)^{n-2}+\ldots+(m-1)\,1^{n-2}=\frac{m^{n+1}}{n\,(n+1)}$$

$$\text{ - lower powers of } m,$$

$$1^2\,(m-1)^{n-2}+2^2\,(m-2)^{n-2}+\ldots+(m-1)^2\,1^{n-2}$$

$$=\frac{1\,.\,2\,.\,m^{n+1}}{(n-1)\,n\,(n+1)}-\&\text{c.,}$$

$$1^3\,(m-1)^{n-3}+2^3\,(m-2)^{n-3}+\ldots+(m-1)^3\,1^{n-3}$$

$$=\frac{1\,.\,2\,.\,3\,.\,m^{n+1}}{(n-2)\,(n-1)\,n\,(n+1)}-\&\text{c.,}$$

and so on.

$$1^p\,(m-1)^{n-p}+2^p\,(m-2)^{n-p}+\ldots+(m-1)^p\,1^{n-p}$$

$$=\frac{m^{n+1}}{C_p^n\,(n+1)}-\&\text{c.}$$

Therefore if m be indefinitely increased we have ultimately

$$\frac{1^p\,(m-1)^{n-p}+2^p\,(m-2)^{n-p}+\ldots+(m-1)^p\,1^{n-p}}{m^{n+1}}=\frac{1}{C_p^n\,(n+1)}.$$

CHAPTER IX.

SUCCESSIVE TRIALS.

IF it be our object to give accuracy to popular estimates of chance and expectations in cases when the event is capable of experimental repetition, we shall be best understood if we measure the probability of the event by defining the number of times that the experiment would have to be repeated *on an average* before success is reached.

In the case of a simple event of which the chance of success at any experiment is always the same, the average number of trials required for success is the reciprocal of the chance of succeeding at any trial. If it be the question of throwing doublets with a pair of dice, the chance of success at any trial is $\frac{1}{6}$, and, on an average, 6 trials will be required in order to succeed. Of course the operator may succeed at the first trial, or he may fail for 6 or 60 or 600 trials; but if the player go on indefinitely, always counting the number of the throws he has had to make in trying to throw doublets, he will find that on an average six throws were wanted to attain success.

And the statement that an average of six throws will be required in order to throw doublets must not be confounded with the statement of the number of throws required in order that success may be more likely than failure. As a matter of fact, if the operator make only four throws he is more likely to throw doublets than not, (the odds being 671 to 625 in favour of success); and yet it is obvious that in the long run success will occur once in six trials, and that in an indefinite period of play, there will be on an average six throws for every success.

In questions in which the chance of success at any experiment is not always the same, but depends (for instance) on the result of the previous trial, the average number of trials required for success is no longer the reciprocal of the chance of succeeding at the first trial. To this class will belong questions respecting sequences of results. For example: if it be required to throw doublets twice in succession the chance of succeeding immediately is $\frac{1}{36}$, but the average number of throws required for success is 42 (*infra*, Prop. LIV.). So the odds against throwing sixes three times consecutively are 46655 to 1, but the average number of throws required for success will be 47988.

The rarity of long sequences of heads or tails in tossing a coin cannot be better exhibited than in the statement that on an average we shall have to toss $2(2^n - 1)$ times to get a sequence of n heads. Thus if we make 10 tosses per minute we must expect to work 13 hours and 39 minutes to get a sequence of 12 heads; and 218 hours and 27 minutes to get a sequence of 16 heads.

The term *Expectation* is usually limited to cases in which a person is to receive a sum of money contingent on the issue of some doubtful event. (See the definition, page 141.) Thus if a showman receives a penny for every shot at "Aunt Sally," and gives a cocoanut for every successful shot, and if a player succeeds once in seven shots, the showman's expectation as a return for each cocoanut is sevenpence: and the player's expectation is the value of a cocoanut *minus seven-*

pence. But we may well speak of expectation independently of money, and say that the player has an expectation of seven shots. Similarly if a man tosses a coin till he gets a sequence of 4 heads we may say that his expectation is 30 tosses.

PROPOSITION XLIX.

If on an average success be attained in s trials, then will
$$s = 1 + f_1 + f_2 + f_3 + \ldots,$$
where f_r denotes the chance of failing in the first r trials.

For if μ_1 be the chance of succeeding at the first trial; and after the first has failed, μ_2 be *then* the chance of succeeding at the second trial; and after the first and second have both failed, μ_3 be *then* the chance of succeeding at the third trial, and so on, we shall have (Prop. XLIV. Cor. 2)

$$s = \mu_1 + 2f_1\mu_2 + 3f_2\mu_3 + 4f_3\mu_4 + \ldots.$$

But $\mu_r = 1 - \dfrac{f_r}{f_{r-1}}$ for all values of r: therefore

$$s = 1 + 2f_1 + 3f_2 + 4f_3 + \ldots - (f_1 + 2f_2 + 3f_3 + \ldots)$$
$$= 1 + f_1 + f_2 + f_2 + \ldots. \quad \text{Q. E. D.}$$

NOTE. The series will be continued to infinity unless in the nature of the case success within (say) r trials is certain. In this case $f_r, f_{r+1}, \ldots$ will each be zero.

COROLLARY. If the chance of failing at *any* trial be f, then

$$f_1 = f, \ f_2 = f^2, \ f_3 = f^3, \ \&c.$$

and $$s = 1 + f + f^2 + f^3 + \ldots \text{ to infinity}$$

$$= \frac{1}{1-f} = \frac{1}{\mu},$$

where μ is the chance of succeeding at any trial.

The result in this particular case might have been anticipated. It simply expresses the fact that if the chance of success is $\dfrac{1}{n}$, success will occur on an average once in n trials.

EXAMPLE. To draw double-blank from a set of 28 dominoes will require on an average 28 trials if the dominoes drawn be replaced, but only an average of $14\frac{1}{2}$ trials if they be not replaced. For by the Corollary, we have in the former case

$$s = 1 \div \left(1 - \frac{27}{28}\right) = 28,$$

and in the latter, by the Proposition,

$$s = 1 + \frac{27}{28} + \frac{26}{28} + \frac{25}{28} + \dots \text{ to 28 terms} = \frac{29}{2}.$$

PROPOSITION L.

If an experiment succeed on an average once in n trials, the chance that it fails throughout n given trials is never greater than $\dfrac{1}{e}$; *and if n be large this chance is approximately* $\dfrac{1}{e}$.

For the chance of failing in any trial is $1 - \dfrac{1}{n}$, and the chance of failing in all the n trials is $\left(1 - \dfrac{1}{n}\right)^n$. But by expansion, $\left(1 - \dfrac{1}{n}\right)^{-n}$ is seen to be greater than e, and therefore $\left(1 - \dfrac{1}{n}\right)^n < \dfrac{1}{e}$; and, as n is increased indefinitely, $\left(1 - \dfrac{1}{n}\right)^n = \dfrac{1}{e}$. Therefore &c. Q. E. D.

NOTE.   The value of the reciprocal of e is ·367879.   The values of the chance are as follows:

When $n =$ 10,   Chance   = ·34867,

   „ $n =$ 20,   „   = ·35848,

   „ $n =$ 30,   „   = ·36162,

   „ $n =$ 50,   „   = ·36417,

   „ $n =$ 100,   „   = ·36604,

   „ $n = 1000$,   „   = ·36771.

PROPOSITION LI.

If an event happen at random on an average once in time t, the chance of its not happening in a given period τ is $e^{-\frac{\tau}{t}}$.

Divide each unit of time into an indefinitely large number n of small instants.   Then in the periods t, τ there will be nt, $n\tau$ respectively of such instants.   By making n large enough we may make the instants so short that the event may be said to happen at one such instant.   Since it happens on an average once in nt instants, the chance of its happening at any particular instant is $\dfrac{1}{nt}$, and the chance of its not happening in the given period of $n\tau$ instants is

$$\left(1 - \frac{1}{nt}\right)^{n\tau} = \left[\left(1 - \frac{1}{nt}\right)^{nt}\right]^{\frac{\tau}{t}}.$$

But when n is indefinitely large,

$$\left(1 - \frac{1}{nt}\right)^{nt} \text{ ultimately} = \frac{1}{e}.$$

Therefore the required chance is $\left(\dfrac{1}{e}\right)^{\frac{\tau}{t}}$, or $e^{-\frac{\tau}{t}}$.   Q. E. D.

EXAMPLE. If an earthquake happens on an average once a year, the chance that in a given year there should not be an earthquake is $\dfrac{1}{e}$.

PROPOSITION LII.

If an experiment succeed m times and fail n times, the chance that among the m + n trials there are nowhere k consecutive successes is the coefficient of x^m in the expansion of

$$\frac{\lfloor m \rfloor \lfloor n}{\lfloor m+n} \cdot \left(\frac{1-x^k}{1-x} \right)^{n+1}.$$

For all the trials being equally likely to succeed all possible arrangements of the m successes and n failures must be equally likely to occur. Now the arrangements without k consecutive successes may be made by regarding the n failures as standing in a row and then distributing into the $n+1$ spaces between them (inclusive of the ends of the row) the m successes so that no parcel may have more than $k-1$. By Prop. XXVIII. (writing m for n and putting $q = 0$, $z = k$, $r = n + 1$) the number of arrangements thus made is the coefficient of x^m in the expansion of

$$\left(\frac{1-x^k}{1-x} \right)^{n+1}.$$

And the total number of arrangements is $\lfloor m + n \div \lfloor m \lfloor n$. Whence the truth of the proposition is evident.

PROPOSITION LIII.

If μ be the chance of an operation succeeding in any trial, and $\nu = 1 - \mu$ the chance of its failing, the chance that in n *trials there shall not be k consecutive successes is the coefficient of x^n in*

$$\frac{1 - \mu^k x^k}{1 - x + \mu^k \nu x^{k+1}}.$$

For the chance that there should be exactly r successes among the n trials is

$$\frac{\lfloor n}{\lfloor r \lfloor n - r} \mu^r \nu^{n-r}.$$

And if there are r successes and $n - r$ failures the chance that there should not be k consecutive successes is, by the last proposition, the coefficient of x^r in the expansion of

$$\frac{\lfloor r \lfloor n - r}{\lfloor n} X^{n-r+1}, \text{ where } X = \frac{1 - x^k}{1 - x}.$$

Hence the chance of there being exactly r successes but not k consecutive successes is the coefficient of x^r in the expansion of $\mu^r \nu^{n-r} X^{n-r+1}$, which is the coefficient of x^n in the expansion of $\mu^r \nu^{n-r} x^{n-r} X^{n-r+1}$.

Now the whole chance required will be obtained by giving r all its possible values (from 0 to n inclusive) and adding. Hence the chance will be the coefficient of x^n in the expansion of

$$\mu^n X \left\{ 1 + \left(\frac{\nu}{\mu}\right) xX + \left(\frac{\nu}{\mu}\right)^2 x^2 X^2 + \left(\frac{\nu}{\mu}\right)^3 x^3 X^3 + \dots + \left(\frac{\nu}{\mu}\right)^n x^n X^n \right\}.$$

And the series within the brackets may be continued to infinity if we please, since the terms thus added contain only higher powers of x and cannot affect the coefficient of x^n. Hence the chance required is the coefficient of x^n in

$$\frac{\mu^n X}{1 - \left(\frac{\nu}{\mu}\right) xX}, \text{ or } \frac{\mu^n (1 - x^k)}{1 - \frac{x}{\mu} + \left(\frac{\nu}{\mu}\right) x^{k+1}}.$$

But the coefficient of x^n in any function is not altered if we write μx for x in the function, and then divide by μ^n. Therefore the chance is the coefficient of x^n in

$$\frac{1 - \mu^k x^k}{1 - x + \mu^k \nu x^{k+1}}. \quad \text{Q.E.D.}$$

NOTE. By actual division, we find that the first k coefficients are all unity, a result which corresponds to the fact that if $n < k$ there cannot possibly be k consecutive successes.

PROPOSITION LIV.

If μ be the chance of an operation succeeding at any trial, and ν the chance of its failing, on an average $(\mu^{-k} - 1)/\nu$ trials must be made in order to obtain k consecutive successes.

For if s be the average number of trials we have (Prop. XLIX.)
$$s = 1 + F_1 + F_2 + F_3 + ...,$$

where (Prop. LIII.) $F_r =$ the coefficient of x^r in the expansion of

$$\frac{1 - \mu^k x^k}{1 - x + \mu^k \nu x^{k+1}}.$$

Therefore

$s =$ the sum of the coefficients in the same expansion.

But the sum of the coefficients in any function of x is obtained by writing unity for x in the function; therefore

$$s = \frac{1 - \mu^k}{\mu^k \nu} = \frac{\mu^{-k} - 1}{\nu}. \quad \text{Q.E.D.}$$

NOTE. A direct proof of this proposition from elementary considerations is suggested in Exercises 831 and 832, at the end of the volume.

COROLLARY. If s' be the average number of trials in order to get k consecutive failures, then

$$s' = \frac{\nu^{-k} - 1}{\mu}.$$

But if A happen once in m trials, and B happen once in n of the same trials, one or other will happen on an average $m + n$ times in mn trials, or once in $\dfrac{mn}{m+n}$ trials. Hence if σ be the average number of trials in order to get k consecutive successes *or* failures, then

$$\sigma = \frac{ss'}{s+s'} = \frac{(1-\mu^k)(1-\nu^k)}{\mu\nu - (\mu - \mu^k)(\nu - \nu^k)}.$$

EXAMPLES. If we toss a coin till we get 3 consecutive heads the average number of tosses required will be 14. (For we have $\mu = \frac{1}{2}$, $k = 3$.)

If we throw a die until we get 3 consecutive aces, the average number of throws required will be 258. (For we have $\mu = \frac{1}{6}$, $k = 3$.)

If A plays chess twice as well as B, they must on an average play more than 7 games before A wins a sequence of 3 consecutive games; they must play more than 31 games before A wins a sequence of 6; and nearly 170 games before A wins a sequence of 10.

Also, they must play on an average 39 games before B wins a sequence of 3; 1092 games before B wins a sequence of 6; and 88572 games before B wins a sequence of 10.

But if they stop playing as soon as *either* has won a sequence of 3, the average number of games will be slightly over 6, and if they play for a sequence of 6, the average number will be slightly over 30.

CHAPTER X.

EXPECTATION OF PARTS.

WHEN a magnitude is broken into several parts, questions may be asked as to the value not merely of one share taken at random, but possibly as to the value of the largest share or the smallest share, or some other not indifferent share. Or if the magnitude to be divided be geometrical, such as a line of varying density, or an area or a solid, there may be questions as to the linear dimensions of parts which are not indifferent. Some such questions will be considered in the present chapter.

We use the symbol $\mathcal{E}(x)$ to denote the expectation or mean value of a variable magnitude x, the variation depending upon chance.

It should be noted that
$$\mathcal{E}(x) + \mathcal{E}(y) = \mathcal{E}(x + y),$$
and if a is constant
$$\mathcal{E}(ax) = a\mathcal{E}(x).$$

But $\mathcal{E}(x) \times \mathcal{E}(y)$ is not the same thing as $\mathcal{E}(xy)$ unless x and y are quite independent, so that every value of x can occur with any value of y, and every value of y with any value of x.

For example if x and y are the sides of a rectangle, and if x is equally likely to take any value from 0 to a, while y is equally likely to take any value from 0 to b, we shall have

$$\mathcal{E}(x) = \tfrac{1}{2}a, \quad \mathcal{E}(y) = \tfrac{1}{2}b, \quad \mathcal{E}(xy) = \mathcal{E}(x) \times \mathcal{E}(y) = \tfrac{1}{4}ab.$$

But if x and y are so connected that they are always in the ratio $a : b$, we shall still have $\mathcal{E}(x) = \tfrac{1}{2}a$ and $\mathcal{E}(y) = \tfrac{1}{2}b$; but we shall find $\mathcal{E}(xy) = \tfrac{1}{3}ab$, and the rule of multiplication does not hold good. Equally, it will not hold good if $x = y$. That is, $\mathcal{E}(x^2)$ is not the square of $\mathcal{E}(x)$.

Of course it may happen that though x and y are not equal their expectations may be equal: as for instance when x varies equably between the values 0 and $a + b$, and y equably between the values a and b. But though $\mathcal{E}(x) = \mathcal{E}(y)$ we may not assume that $\mathcal{E}(x^2) = \mathcal{E}(y^2)$, nor yet that $\mathcal{E}(xz) = \mathcal{E}(yz)$, where z is another variable quantity. The latter equation would however be obviously true if z were constant.

To divide a given magnitude s into n parts is obviously the same thing as to take n magnitudes subject only to the condition that their sum is s. It is plain that as the magnitudes are indifferent and their sum is s, the expectation of each one must be s/n.

But it has sometimes been questioned whether the placing of $n-1$ points at random on a finite line is the same thing as dividing the line into n parts at random. It does not seem that we have any right à *priori* to assume that the expectation of either extreme segment is necessarily the same as the expectation of a segment between two of the random points. Two different proofs of the equality of these expectations are given in DCC EXERCISES, 497; but the following consideration seems sufficient to establish the proposition.

Suppose $n - 1$ black points and one white point are to be marked at random on a finite line. All orders of the points are equally likely. Therefore the white point is equally likely to fall on any of the n segments into which the black points divide the line. Hence these n segments must be of equal expectation.

PROPOSITION LV.

If n random magnitudes α, β, γ, ... be subject only to the condition

$$a\alpha + b\beta + c\gamma + \ldots = s,$$

then $\qquad \mathcal{E}(\alpha) = \dfrac{s}{an}, \quad \mathcal{E}(\beta) = \dfrac{s}{bn}, \quad \mathcal{E}(\gamma) = \dfrac{s}{cn}$, &c.

For $a\alpha$, $b\beta$, $c\gamma$, ... are themselves random quantities subject only to the condition that their sum is s. Therefore (page 206) they are of equal expectation. That is

$$\mathcal{E}(a\alpha) = s/n ;$$

whence $\qquad \mathcal{E}(\alpha) = s/an,$

and similarly $\quad \mathcal{E}(\beta) = s/bn, \ \mathcal{E}(\gamma) = s/cn$, &c.

PROPOSITION LVI.

If a magnitude s be divided at random into n parts, and these parts be arranged in order of magnitude beginning with the least, their respective expectations will be

$$\frac{s}{n} \cdot \frac{1}{n}$$

$$\frac{s}{n} \left\{ \frac{1}{n} + \frac{1}{n-1} \right\}$$

$$\frac{s}{n} \left\{ \frac{1}{n} + \frac{1}{n-1} + \frac{1}{n-2} \right\},$$

and so on.

Let α denote the smallest part; β the excess of the second over the first; γ the excess of the third over the second; and so on. Then the parts are

$$\alpha, \ \alpha + \beta, \ \alpha + \beta + \gamma, \text{ and so on.}$$

Now $\alpha, \beta, \gamma, \ldots$ are n random quantities subject only to the condition that

$$n\alpha + (n - 1)\beta + (n - 2)\gamma + \ldots = s.$$

Therefore by Prop. LV.

$$\mathcal{E}(\alpha) = \frac{s}{n^2}, \ \mathcal{E}(\beta) = \frac{s}{n(n-1)}, \ \mathcal{E}(\gamma) = \frac{s}{n(n-2)},$$

and so on. Hence the expectations of the several parts are as enunciated.

NOTE. The case when $n = 3$ is proved independently by a consideration of Trilinear Coordinates in DCC EXERCISES, 680. The general case is also proved by the Integral Calculus in DCC EXERCISES, page 235.

We now approach a theorem of very great interest and importance. We shall prove it first for some simple cases and pass step by step to the general case.

PROPOSITION LVII.

If n random magnitudes $\alpha, \beta, \gamma, \ldots$ be subject only to the condition

$$a\alpha + b\beta + c\gamma + \ldots = s,$$

then every term in the expansion of $(a\alpha + b\beta + c\gamma + \ldots)^m$ is of equal expectation, m being any positive integer.

And since the number of terms in the expansion is R_m^n, the expectation of each term is $s^n \div R_m^n$.

Or which is the same thing

$$\mathcal{E}\left(\alpha^p\beta^q\gamma^r\ldots\right) = \frac{s^{p+q+r+\cdots}\,\underline{|n-1}\,\underline{|p}\,\underline{|q}\,\underline{|r}\ldots}{a^pb^qc^r\ldots\,\underline{|n-1+p+q+r+\ldots}}.$$

CASE I. *To shew that if* $\alpha + \beta + \gamma + \ldots = s$,

$$\mathcal{E}\left(\alpha^2\right) = \frac{2s^2}{n\,(n+1)}, \quad \mathcal{E}\left(\alpha^3\right) = \frac{6s^3}{n(n+1)(n+2)},$$

and generally $\mathcal{E}\left(\alpha^m\right) = s^m \div R_m^n$.

We may think of the magnitudes as segments of a straight line $AB = s$.

Let α denote the extreme segment at A.

Let a new point of section be introduced at random so as to divide the line into $n + 1$ segments.

The chance that the new point lies on α is α/s and in this case the expectation of the extreme segment is $\frac{1}{2}\alpha$.

The chance that the new point is *not* on α is $(s - \alpha)/s$ and in this case the extreme segment remains α. Hence the total expectation of the extreme segment is

$$\mathcal{E}\left\{\frac{\alpha}{s}\cdot\frac{\alpha}{2} + \frac{s-\alpha}{s}\cdot\alpha\right\} = \mathcal{E}\left\{\alpha - \frac{\alpha^2}{2s}\right\} = \frac{s}{n} - \frac{1}{2s}\mathcal{E}\left(\alpha^2\right).$$

But since the line is now divided into $n + 1$ parts, this expectation must be $s/(n+1)$,

$$\therefore \frac{s}{n+1} = \frac{s}{n} - \frac{1}{2s}\mathcal{E}\left(\alpha^2\right); \text{ whence } \mathcal{E}\left(\alpha^2\right) = \frac{2s^2}{n\,(n+1)}.$$

So the proposition is true for $\mathcal{E}\left(\alpha^2\right)$. We shall now shew that if it is true for $\mathcal{E}\left(\alpha^p\right)$ it is true for $\mathcal{E}\left(\alpha^{p+1}\right)$, where p is any integer.

Introduce a new point of section, then the total expectation of the pth power of the extreme segment is

$$\mathcal{E}\left\{\frac{\alpha}{s}\cdot\frac{\alpha^p}{p+1}+\frac{s-\alpha}{s}\cdot\alpha^p\right\}=\mathcal{E}\left\{\alpha^p-\frac{p}{p+1}\cdot\frac{\alpha^{p+1}}{s}\right\}$$

$$=\frac{s^p}{R_p^n}-\frac{p}{s(p+1)}\mathcal{E}(\alpha^{p+1}).$$

But since the line is divided into $n+1$ parts this expectation must be s^p/R_p^{n+1}. Equating we obtain

$$\mathcal{E}(\alpha^{p+1})=s^{p+1}\left\{\frac{1}{R_p^n}-\frac{1}{R_p^{n+1}}\right\}\frac{p+1}{p}=\frac{s^{p+1}}{R_{p+1}^n}.$$

Therefore if the proposition be true for α^p, it is true for α^{p+1}. Hence it holds for all positive integral powers of α. That is

$$\mathcal{E}(\alpha^m)=s^m\div R_m^n.$$

CASE II. *To shew that if $\alpha+\beta+\gamma+\ldots=s$,*

$$\mathcal{E}(\alpha^{m-1}\beta)=s^m\div mR_m^n.$$

We have $\qquad\qquad \alpha+\beta+\gamma+\ldots=s,$

$$\therefore \alpha^m+\alpha^{m-1}\beta+\alpha^{m-1}\gamma+\ldots=s\alpha^{m-1},$$

whence $\qquad \mathcal{E}(\alpha^m)+(n-1)\mathcal{E}(\alpha^{m-1}\beta)=s\mathcal{E}(\alpha^{m-1}),$

and as $\mathcal{E}(\alpha^m)$ and $\mathcal{E}(\alpha^{m-1})$ are known we obtain $\mathcal{E}(\alpha^{m-1}\beta)$.

COROLLARY. When $m=2$ we have

$$\mathcal{E}(\alpha^2)=\frac{2s^2}{n(n+1)}\text{ and }\mathcal{E}(\alpha\beta)=\frac{s^2}{n(n+1)},$$

and when $m=3$ we have

$$\mathcal{E}(\alpha^3)=\frac{6s^3}{n(n+1)(n+2)},\ \mathcal{E}(\alpha^2\beta)=\frac{2s^3}{n(n+1)(n+2)},$$

$$\mathcal{E}(\alpha\beta\gamma)=\frac{s^3}{n(n+1)(n+2)},$$

where the value of $\mathcal{E}(\alpha\beta\gamma)$ is written down from the consideration that $\mathcal{E}(\alpha + \beta + \gamma)^3 = s^3$, the expectations of the other terms in the expansion being already known.

CASE III. *If a magnitude s be divided at random into two parts α, β, then*

$$\mathcal{E}(\alpha^p\beta^q) = s^{p+q}\,\lfloor p\,\lfloor q \div \lfloor p + q + 1,$$

where p and q are positive integers.

By Case II. Cor. we know that the theorem is true when $p + q = 2$ or $p + q = 3$. It will therefore suffice to shew that if it is true when $p + q = m$ it will be true when $p + q = m + 1$.

Let $p + q = m$, then the theorem may be written

$$C_p^m \mathcal{E}(\alpha^p\beta^{m-p}) = s^m \div (m + 1),$$

where p may have any value from 0 to m,

$$\therefore \mathcal{E}(\alpha^m) = C_1^m \mathcal{E}(\alpha^{m-1}\beta) = C_2^m \mathcal{E}(\alpha^{m-2}\beta^2) = \ldots = s^m \div (m + 1).$$

Multiplying throughout by $\alpha + \beta = s$ we obtain

$$\mathcal{E}(\alpha^{m+1}) + \mathcal{E}(\alpha^m\beta) = s^{m+1} \div (m + 1) \ldots\ldots\ldots\ldots(i),$$

$$C_1^m \{\mathcal{E}(\alpha^m\beta) + \mathcal{E}(\alpha^{m-1}\beta^2)\} = s^{m+1} \div (m + 1)\ldots\ldots\ldots\ldots(ii),$$

$$C_2^m \{\mathcal{E}(\alpha^{m-1}\beta^2) + \mathcal{E}(\alpha^{m-2}\beta^3)\} = s^{m+1} \div (m + 1) \ldots\ldots\ldots(iii),$$

and so on.

But we know (Case II.) that $\mathcal{E}(\alpha^{m+1}) = s^{m+1} \div (m + 2)$,

$\therefore$ equation (i) gives us $C_1^{m+1} \mathcal{E}(\alpha^m\beta) = s^{m+1} \div (m + 2)$,

equation (ii) gives us $\quad C_2^{m+1} \mathcal{E}(\alpha^{m-1}\beta^2) = s^{m+1} \div (m + 2)$,

equation (iii) gives us $\quad C_3^{m+1} \mathcal{E}(\alpha^{m-2}\beta^3) = s^{m+1} \div (m + 2)$,

and so on.

Therefore the theorem is true when $p + q = m + 1$.

Therefore it is true generally.

CASE IV.   *If a magnitude s be divided at random into n parts α, β, γ,..., then*

$$\mathcal{E}\left(\alpha^p\beta^q\gamma^r...\right) = s^{p+q+r+\cdots}\frac{\lfloor n-1 \rfloor \lfloor p \rfloor \lfloor q \rfloor \lfloor r \rfloor \cdots}{\lfloor n-1+p+q+r+\cdots \rfloor},$$

where each of the indices p, q, r, ... is zero or a positive integer.

We have seen (Case III.) that this is true when the magnitude is divided into 2 parts. It will therefore suffice to shew that if it is true when there are n parts it will be true when there are $n+1$ parts.

Assuming it true for n parts, let a new point of partition be introduced. Suppose that it falls on α so that the $n+1$ parts are now $\alpha, \beta, \gamma, \dots \xi$. The chance that it thus falls is α/s; and by Case III. we have

$$\mathcal{E}\left(\alpha_1^p\xi^x\right) = \alpha^{p+x}\lfloor p \rfloor \lfloor x \rfloor \div \lfloor p+x+1 \rfloor.$$

That is, the substitution of $\alpha_1^p\xi^x$ for α^{p+x} multiplies the expectation of the continued product in the ratio $\lfloor p \rfloor \lfloor x \rfloor : \lfloor p+x+1 \rfloor$. Hence if $\mathcal{E}_{n+1}$ denote expectation when there are $n+1$ parts, α/s is the chance that the expectation $\mathcal{E}_{n+1}(\alpha^p\beta^q\gamma^r \dots \xi^x)$ should be $\lfloor p \rfloor \lfloor x \rfloor : \lfloor p+x+1 \rfloor$ times the known expectation $\mathcal{E}\left(\alpha^{p+x}\beta^q\gamma^r...\right)$.

Similarly β/s is the chance that it should be

$$\lfloor q \rfloor \lfloor x \rfloor : \lfloor q+x+1 \rfloor$$

times the known expectation $\mathcal{E}\left(\alpha^p\beta^{q+x}\gamma^r...\right)$; and so on.

Hence

$$\mathcal{E}_{n+1}\left(\alpha^p\beta^q\gamma^r... \xi^x\right) = \frac{\lfloor p \rfloor \lfloor x \rfloor}{s\lfloor p+x+1 \rfloor}\mathcal{E}\left(\alpha^{p+x+1}\beta^q\gamma^r...\right)$$

$$+ \frac{\lfloor q \rfloor \lfloor x \rfloor}{s\lfloor q+x+1 \rfloor}\mathcal{E}\left(\alpha^p\beta^{q+x+1}\gamma^r...\right) + \&c.$$

But since the theorem is true for n parts, each of the n terms in the second member of this equation is

$$\frac{\lfloor n-1 \rfloor \lfloor p \rfloor \lfloor q \rfloor \lfloor r \ldots \lfloor x}{\lfloor n+p+q+r+\ldots+x} s^{p+q+r+\ldots+x},$$

and the sum of the n terms is n times this.

That is

$$\mathcal{E}_{n+1}(\alpha^p \beta^q \gamma^r \ldots \xi^x) = \frac{\lfloor n \rfloor \lfloor p \rfloor \lfloor q \rfloor \lfloor r \ldots \lfloor x}{\lfloor n+p+q+r+\ldots+x} s^{p+q+r+\ldots+x}.$$

Therefore if the theorem is true for n parts it is true for $n+1$ parts.

Therefore it is true generally.

GENERAL CASE. If we write $a\alpha$, $b\beta$, $c\gamma, \ldots$ for α, β, $\gamma, \ldots$ respectively, we obtain the general theorem.

Thus Prop. LVII. is completely proved.

PROPOSITION LVIII.

If a magnitude s be divided at random into n parts α, β, $\gamma, \ldots$ and if r be an integer not greater than n, and m any integer whatever, then

$$\mathcal{E}\left\{(\alpha + \beta + \gamma + \ldots \text{ to } r \text{ terms})^m\right\}$$

$$= s^m \cdot \frac{r(r+1)(r+2)\ldots \text{ to } m \text{ factors}}{n(n+1)(n+2)\ldots \text{ to } m \text{ factors}},$$

$$= s^m \cdot \frac{r(r+1)(r+2)\ldots \text{ to } n-r \text{ factors}}{(r+m)(r+1+m)(r+2+m)\ldots \text{ to } n-r \text{ factors}}.$$

Let σ denote the sum of the r magnitudes α, β, $\gamma, \ldots$. Then by Prop. LV. whatever be σ

$$\mathcal{E}(\alpha^m) = \sigma^m \div R_m^r.$$

Since this is true for all values of σ we have

$$\mathcal{E}(\alpha^m) = \mathcal{E}(\sigma^m) \div R_m^n,$$

or
$$\mathcal{E}(\sigma^m) = R_m^r \mathcal{E}(\alpha^m)$$

$$= s^m R_m^r \div R_m^n,$$

or $\mathcal{E}\{(\alpha + \beta + \dots \text{ to } r \text{ terms})^m\} = s^m \dfrac{r(r+1)\dots(r+m-1)}{n(n+1)\dots(n+m-1)}.$

NOTE. The result is represented geometrically as follows:

$$\overline{O \qquad P_1 \qquad P_2 \qquad P_3 \dots P_n.}$$

Let $OP_n = s$ denote the undivided magnitude, $P_1, P_2, P_3, \dots$ in order, the points of partition, then

$$\mathcal{E}(OP_r^m)$$

$$= OP_n^m \cdot \frac{r(r+1)(r+2)\dots \text{ to } n-r \text{ factors}}{(r+m)(r+1+m)(r+2+m)\dots \text{ to } n-r \text{ factors}}.$$

PROPOSITION LIX.

If n magnitudes be taken at random, the expectation of the mth power of their sum is R_m^n times the expectation of the mth power of one of them.

In the proof of Prop. LVIII. we found

$$\mathcal{E}(\sigma^m) = R_m^r \mathcal{E}(\alpha^m).$$

This result is altogether independent of n, and will therefore be unaffected if n become infinite. But to select r magnitudes out of an infinite number of magnitudes is the same thing as to take r magnitudes at random. Therefore we need not think of the r magnitudes as selected out of n magnitudes, but we may consider them random quantities arbitrarily taken.

Writing n for r we have

$$\mathcal{E}\{(\alpha + \beta + \gamma + \ldots)^m\} = R_m^n \mathcal{E}(\alpha^m). \qquad \text{Q. E. D.}$$

LINES OF VARIABLE DENSITY. AREAS. VOLUMES.

If a point taken at random on a line is more likely to fall at one point than at another, it is convenient to think of the line as having a density at any point proportional to the chance of the random point falling there. We may conceive the line as the geometrical limit of a string of varying thickness, when the thickness is diminished indefinitely but the ratio of the thicknesses at different points remains ultimately unchanged,—the string being such that the random point is equally likely to fall at any point within the mass of the string.

It will be observed that the argument immediately preceding Prop. LV. applies equally to the string of variable density, provided we regard as equal segments not those of equal length but those of equal mass. We may therefore assume the truth of the following proposition :—

PROPOSITION LX.

If points be taken at random on a finite line of varying density, they will divide the line into masses of equal expectation.

The cases of most common occurrence are those in which the density varies as the distance, or as the square of the distance, from one extremity of the line.

A line in which the density at any point varies as the distance of the point from one extremity of the line may be regarded as a sector of a circle of indefinitely small angle. Moreover if we are only concerned with distances measured along radii of the circle it is not even necessary that the angle of the sector should be indefinitely small: we may apply our conclusions to a sector of finite angle.

Hence if $n - 1$ points be taken at random on the sector of a circle, and circles concentric with the original circle be drawn through them, the sector will be divided into n areas of equal expectation.

In this generalisation the line in which the density varies as the distance from one extremity is conceived as the condensation along one radius of a series of concentric circular annuli, the sector closing up like a fan.

But it is not necessary that the annuli should be circular provided their boundaries be all similar and have the extremity of the line as the centre of similitude. We therefore arrive at the following general theorem :—

PROPOSITION LXI.

If $n - 1$ points be taken at random within any closed figure, and if with any fixed point as centre of similitude, $n - 1$ figures similar and similarly situated to the original figure be drawn, passing one through each of the random points, the original area will be divided into n areas of equal expectation.

If we consider a line in which the density varies as the square of the distance from the extremity, we may think of it as the condensation into one radius of the volume of a cone. By precisely the same steps as we have followed in the former case, we arrive at the following theorem :—

PROPOSITION LXII.

If $n-1$ points be taken at random within any closed surface in space, and if with any fixed point as centre of similitude, $n-1$ surfaces similar and similarly situated to the original surface be constructed, passing one through each of the random points, the original volume will be divided into n volumes of equal expectation.

In the statement of Prop. LVIII. m was taken to be any integer whatever, and the first form in which the result was given would be nugatory unless m were integral. The alternative form however into which the result was cast is equally intelligible when m is a fraction. The question therefore arises, Is the theorem true when m is a fraction or even when m is negative? Answer:—Yes, but unfortunately we cannot prove it by elementary algebra. The following proof by the Integral Calculus is however simple.

PROPOSITION LXIII.

If a magnitude s be divided at random into n parts $\alpha, \beta, \gamma, \ldots$, and if r be an integer not greater than n, and m any number positive or negative, fractional or integral, then

$$E\left\{(\alpha+\beta+\gamma+\ldots \text{ to } r \text{ terms})^m\right\}$$

$$= s^m \frac{r(r+1)(r+2)\ldots \text{ to } n-r \text{ factors}}{(r+m)(r+1+m)(r+2+m)\ldots \text{ to } n-r \text{ factors}}.$$

With the geometrical representation of the Note to Prop. LVIII., let $OP_r = xs$.

Then $r-1$ points of partition must fall on $OP_r = xs$.

And $n-r-1$ points of partition on $P_r P_n = (1-x)s$.

The chance is proportional to $x^{r-1}(1-x)^{n-r-1}\,dx$.

Hence

$$\mathcal{E}(x^m) = \int_0^1 x^{m+r-1}(1-x)^{n-r-1}\,dx \div \int_0^1 x^{r-1}(1-x)^{n-r-1}\,dx$$

$$= \frac{\Gamma(m+r)}{\Gamma(m+n)} \div \frac{\Gamma(r)}{\Gamma(n)} = \frac{r(r+1)(r+2)\dots(n-1)}{(m+r)(m+r+1)\dots(m+n-1)},$$

$$\therefore \mathcal{E}(OP_r^m) = s^m \cdot \frac{r(r+1)(r+2)\dots \text{ to } n-r \text{ factors}}{(m+r)(m+r+1)\dots \text{ to } n-r \text{ factors}},$$

where there is no restriction on the value of m.

PROPOSITION LXIV.

If $P_1, P_2, P_3, \dots P_{n-1}$ be random points on a line $OP_n = s$ in which the density varies as the distance from O, to find $\mathcal{E}(OP_r^m)$.

The masses $OP_1, P_1P_2, P_2P_3, \dots$ are quantities into which the mass OP_n has been divided at random. Therefore by Prop. LVIII.

$$\mathcal{E}\{(\text{mass } OP_r)^m\} = (\text{mass } OP_n)^m \cdot \frac{r(r+1)(r+2)\dots}{(m+r)(m+r+1)\dots}.$$

But by Prop. LXIII. m may be fractional. We may therefore write $\tfrac{1}{2}m$ for m. At the same time note that

$$\text{mass } OP_r : \text{mass } OP_n = OP_r^2 : s^2.$$

Thus we get

$$\mathcal{E}(OP_r^m)$$

$$= s^m \frac{r(r+1)(r+2)\dots \text{ to } n-r \text{ factors}}{(\tfrac{1}{2}m+r)(\tfrac{1}{2}m+r+1)(\tfrac{1}{2}m+r+2)\dots \text{ to } n-r \text{ factors}}$$

NOTE. If $m=2$ we get the obvious result

$$\mathcal{E}(OP_r^2) = s^2 r/m.$$

The case when $m = 1$ is important:—

$$\mathcal{E}(OP_r) = s \frac{(2r)(2r+2)(2r+4)\ldots \text{ to } n-r \text{ factors}}{(2r+1)(2r+3)(2r+5)\ldots \text{ to } n-r \text{ factors}},$$

and
$$\mathcal{E}(P_{r-1}P_r) = \mathcal{E}(OP_r) \div (2r-1),$$

and when $r = 1$

$$\mathcal{E}(OP_1) = s \cdot \frac{2.4.6\ldots(2n-2)}{3.5.7\ldots(2n-1)}.$$

PROPOSITION LXV.

If P_1, P_2, P_3, ... P_{n-1} be random points on a line $OP_n = s$, in which the density varies as the square of the distance from O, to find $\mathcal{E}(OP_r^m)$.

Following the steps of the last proof we obtain

$$\mathcal{E}(OP_r^m)$$
$$= s^m \cdot \frac{r(r+1)(r+2)\ldots \text{ to } n-r \text{ factors}}{(\frac{1}{3}m+r)(\frac{1}{3}m+r+1)(\frac{1}{3}m+r+2)\ldots \text{ to } n-r \text{ factors}}.$$

NOTE. If $m = 3$ we get the obvious result

$$\mathcal{E}(OP_r^3) = s^3 r/n.$$

The last two propositions are of very wide application; the one in plane and the other in solid geometry. For instance we can write down at sight such results as the following:—

(1) If 3 points be taken at random within a triangle the expectation of the distance of the nearest one from the base is one-seventh of the altitude.

(2) If 3 points be taken at random within a pyramid or cone the expectation of the distance of the nearest one from the base is one-tenth of the altitude.

CHAPTER XI.

ON THE DISADVANTAGE OF GAMBLING.

A "fair" bet is one in which each person's stake is proportional to his mathematical chance of winning; as when a man bets 5 to 1 against a die turning up ace.

An "even" bet is one in which each person stakes the same sum. If an "even" bet is also a "fair" bet, the mathematical chances of the contingent events must be equal, as when a man bets a penny to a penny that a coin will turn up "head."

A fair bet satisfies the criterion that if it be repeated an indefinite number of times there is no presumption that either party rather than the other should be the gainer. If a die be thrown 600 times and a man bet on every throw 5 to 1 against ace turning up, the expectation of the number of *not-aces* is 5 times as great as the expectation of the number of aces, and there is no presumption in favour of the man either winning or losing. This may be taken as a typical case of an uneven but fair bet.

The hypothesis however implies that the two players are equally free from limitations. If any condition were introduced that the play must stop when a certain position is reached, and if that position is more favourable to one player than to the other, the latter is at a disadvantage

And such a condition is sometimes introduced by the very nature of the case. If two boys play pitch and toss for pennies, one possessing 30 pence and the other 3 pence, the gains and losses may be expected to fluctuate; but if a point is ever reached at which the first boy has made a net gain of 3d., the play necessarily stops, for the second boy has nothing to stake, and it stops at the point most disadvantageous to this boy. He may in the course of the play have won 10 pence or 20 pence but there was nothing to make him stop at so favourable a point. Unless he were so lucky as to make a gain of 30 before his adversary made a gain of 3 there was nothing to stop him at a favourable point, and though each toss was fair he was at a disadvantage in the series. The following facts about the case are easily demonstrated :—

1. Chance that in the long run one or other should be ruined = 1 (i.e. certainty).

2. On an average this will occur in 90 throws.

3. The odds are 10 to 1 that the one ruined is the poorer one. (See Prop. LXVI.)

The following is another example illustrative of the fact that a series of wagers, each individual wager being perfectly fair, may be rendered unfair if there be an implied contract to stop at a stage that unequally affects the two parties. A man owes me a pound : he proposes to toss up for "double or quits," that is, if I win, his debt to me becomes £2 ; if I lose, it is cancelled altogether. Suppose I win : he now owes me £2, and he again proposes "double or quits": I win again and he owes me £4 : again he proposes "double or quits" and I win again : he owes me £8 : again he proposes "double or quits" and I lose : the debt is now cancelled, and we cease to play.

It is evident that in this case my winning the first three times was no advantage to me; it did not matter in the least how soon I lost.   Unless I could go on winning *always* the result must inevitably be the cancelling of the debt. The condition that we were to stop play as soon as the debt was cancelled was unfair to me, and though each individual wager was fair, the series of wagers *subject to this condition* was unfair.

Gambling is the act of exchanging something small and certain for something large and uncertain.   It makes no difference in principle whether the thing exchanged is itself of positive or negative value.   It may be that a small and certain gain is bartered for the chance of a larger gain; or that a small and certain loss is bartered for the chance of a larger loss.   In either case the person who exchanges the small certainty for the large uncertainty is gambling.   The following two examples may be compared.

(1)   A party of twelve persons dine at an hotel at a charge of five shillings each.   Instead of each person paying his own account, they agree to draw lots as to who shall pay the whole amount.

(2)   An article worth £3 is to be disposed of by raffle each of twelve persons paying five shillings for a ticket, and determining by lot who is to possess the article.

It will be observed that in the first case a certain disbursement of five shillings is exchanged for a chance $\left(= \frac{1}{12} \right)$ of a larger disbursement of sixty shillings.   In the second case a certain possession of five shillings is given up in exchange for a chance $\left(= \frac{1}{12} \right)$ of a larger possession of sixty shillings.   Both transactions are perfectly fair: but, as we shall shew, inexpedient and disadvantageous.

In discussing the disadvantage of gambling we need scarcely consider any but fair bets. For it is clear that if there be a disadvantage in a fair bet, an unfair bet must *à fortiori* be disadvantageous to the party against whom it is unfair. On the other hand no one can doubt that a sufficiently unfair wager must be advantageous to the party in whose favour it is unfair.

Whether a single fair bet, regarded by itself and without consideration of its being repeated, can be said to be disadvantageous is a question open to argument. It resolves itself into the enquiry whether a small and certain sum is more advantageous to a man than the uncertain prospect of a larger sum, the mathematical expectations being equal. If the sums in question are inconsiderable compared with the man's property it will generally be said that there is no appreciable advantage or disadvantage. But if we consider the operation on a larger scale, in the case in which a man's whole property or the greater part of it is at stake, we shall scarcely hesitate as to our decision. We feel that it is better for a man to possess £100 for certain, than to decide by the toss of a coin whether he shall have £200 or nothing at all. Or, not to take quite the extreme case : suppose that having £100 he is invited to hazard £50 on fair and even terms. We feel that it is more advantageous to have £100 for certain than to have an equal chance of £150 or £50. The benefit of winning is not so great as the injury of losing. If he lose he halves his property but if he gains he does not double it.

We have not however to discuss this as a matter of sentiment. Putting it mathematically we say that the winning of an even wager increases a man's property in a less ratio than that in which the losing of the wager decreases it. If he stake the nth part of his property, winning will increase his property as n to $n+1$, while losing will decrease it as n to $n-1$. If he perform the operation twice, each time staking the nth part of what he holds, and if he gain once and lose once, his property is decreased as n^2 to n^2-1.

But in truth the advantage or disadvantage of a venture must be judged by its effect in the long run when the operation is indefinitely repeated. If it is advantageous to perform the operation once it must be advantageous to perform it again. Its tendency is seen in the ultimate result.

It must be noted that the repeating of a venture may be understood in two different ways. A man possessed of £100 makes an even bet of £1. The bet may be regarded as absolute in amount, and repetition may mean that he goes on making bets of £1. Or it may be regarded relatively to what he possesses; and repetition will then mean that he goes on always staking the 100*th* part of what he holds. We call the first the *absolute* and the second the *relative* repetition of the wager.

I. ABSOLUTE REPETITION. If this test be applied, every player is necessarily at a disadvantage unless his means are infinite. If indeed I were restricted to play with a single opponent our gambling could only end in one of us being ruined, and if I had the ampler means the odds would be in favour of my ruining my opponent. But in practice I am not restricted to playing with one person. When one opponent is ruined I can find another to play with: and if I play sufficiently long my own turn must come to be ruined. If I gamble I practically gamble with society whose resources are unlimited, while my own resources are limited *. And

* Mr Venn (*Logic of Chance*, Second Edition, p. 413) objects that we have here overlooked the fact that the adversaries with whom the gambler plays

the limit of my own resources results in my disadvantage. If I begin with a thousand pounds, even if I gain a million I may lose it all again; but if I once reach a net loss of a thousand I can never retrieve it, for I have nothing more to stake. This is the basis of the disadvantage of gambling: there is (as it were) a pendulum swinging between gain and loss with oscillations of .varying amplitude: the pendulum oscillates fairly enough between gain and loss, but when once it reaches a certain degree of loss *it is held there* and swings no more. This stop, existing only on the side of loss with no compensating stop upon the side of gain, is the "disadvantage" of gambling.

II. RELATIVE REPETITION. It is clear that in this case the gamester can never lose absolutely all, but the disadvantage of his operation is even more obvious than in the former case. Suppose he always stake one nth of what he holds in an even venture. He can only hope to succeed m times for m times that he fails, and the $2m$ operations will then multiply his holding by

$$\left(1 + \frac{1}{n}\right)^m \left(1 - \frac{1}{n}\right)^m = \left(1 - \frac{1}{n^2}\right)^m,$$

which is less than unity. Or if the venture be uneven but fair. Let the odds be $\alpha : \beta$, where $\alpha + \beta = 1$, on the event

"are not one body with a common purse like the bank in a gambling establishment." But this does not in the least affect our argument. The habitual gambler is practically playing with the gambling public. One particular adversary may be ruined, but the gambler can still find some one to play with. The gambling public is never exhausted. There is a prospect that the gambler's operations may be forcibly terminated to his disadvantage, through his having nothing more to stake; but there is no prospect that they will compulsorily terminate to his advantage through the exhaustion of the resources of the gambling world. Every one who gambles is therefore carrying on an unequal warfare: he is ranged with a restricted capital against an adversary whose means are infinite.

which he supports and let him wager α/n of his holding against β/n. He can only hope to succeed αm times for βm times that he fails, and the m operations multiply his holding by

$$\left(1+\frac{\beta}{n}\right)^{\alpha m}\left(1-\frac{\alpha}{n}\right)^{\beta m} = \left(1-\frac{\alpha\beta}{2n^2}+\&c.\right)^m,$$

which again is less than unity.

[An alternative form of this proof is given as Prop. LXVIII.]

But, it may be said, how can gambling be thus disadvantageous to every one when it can only cause money to pass from hand to hand, but cannot diminish the total amount of money in the hands of those who engage in it? We do not deny that some one must eventually be the gainer. If a thousand people wager among themselves on fair terms, until one of them has gained all their aggregate property, we do not deny that this man has reaped an advantage. If all began on equal terms he is 1000 times as rich as he was at first. But we may deny that, when the odds were 999 to 1 in favour of his being absolutely ruined, it was worth his while to run the risk. The fact that he would be compelled to stop at the moment most disadvantageous to himself was left out of consideration when his venture was deemed to be of neutral advantage or disadvantage to him. We shall presently consider the compensation required when this element of disadvantage is taken into account.

When however it is said that gambling is disadvantageous it must be remembered that under certain circumstances the making of a bet is not of the nature of gambling but the reverse. One venture may neutralise another and may thus tend to substitute a small certainty for a large contingency.

If we have made a bet against an event, another bet in favour of the event will reduce or possibly annihilate our risk.   But the original risk need not be the result of a bet, it may exist in the very circumstances of life.   The liability to fire may put me under the risk of losing £1000 if my house is burnt down.   If I pay £1 to insure myself against this risk for a year I am accepting a small certain loss of £1 in place of a contingent loss of £1000.   The transaction is of the nature of a bet, but on my part it is the reverse of gambling.

The Insurance Company, if it took my risk and no other, would indeed be gambling, but by collection of risks much of the risk is eliminated.   This will be better understood by a simpler case.

In the examples cited on page 222 it will be observed that the risks incurred by the persons at the hotel or by the purchasers of the raffle-tickets are entirely due to the division of interest among the different persons.   If the twelve persons at the hotel were all in partnership, or had agreed at the end of the day to divide their profits, it would be indifferent who should pay the bill : and in like manner if the twelve raffle-tickets all passed into one ownership there would no longer be any risk or venture. The collecting together of the various risks neutralises the risks.

When the party at the hotel have agreed to draw lots for the payment of the whole bill, one of the party may feel that it would be very inconvenient for him to have to pay £3, though he could easily pay the five shillings which is the value of his risk.   It may be that he would rather pay down even something more than five shillings, rather than run the risk of having to pay £3. He offers say five shillings and three pence to any one who will relieve him of his risk; and finding an independent person who makes it his business to take up such risks he strikes the bargain and pays his five shillings and three pence. Possibly, upon reflection, the other members of the party perceive the disadvantage of gambling and transfer their risk on the same terms to the same person. What has now happened? The risks have all been neutralised: the person who has taken them up has received 63 shillings and has to pay the bill of 60 shillings, making three shillings profit for himself. His business is Insurance. But it must be observed that his profit depends entirely upon the disadvantage of gambling, the disadvantage which induced each person to give 5s. 3d. instead of 5s. to be freed from his venture.

Again, suppose that out of every twenty ships which make a particular voyage one is lost, and the remaining nineteen come safely to port. And suppose there is one ship making this voyage which with its cargo is worth £20,000. The value of the owner's expectation is just £19,000. But, according to the hypothesis which we are illustrating, it would be expedient for the owner to take a less sum than this for his expectation, say £19,000 − x. He may in consequence prudently pay £1000 + x to an Insurance Company in return for a guarantee that his £20,000 shall be secured him in full. And the Insurance Company, collecting together a great number of such risks, may profitably accept the bargain, their profit being entirely dependent on the fact that the shipowner is ready to accept for his contingent prospect an uncontingent sum, *which is less than his mathematical expectation.* For if the Insurance Company were to insure all the ships, securing to each owner his mathematical expectation (*i.e.* if they charged only £1000 premium instead of £1000 + *x*), their own mathematical expectation of profit would be zero. They could only hope that the premiums received would in the long run balance the claims upon them, without leaving any profit to remunerate them for their trouble. Thus, the continued existence of Insurance Companies commercially successful is a standing witness to the fact, that a prudent man will commute a contingent prospect of value for less than the sum measured by his mathematical expectation.

To the community, gambling is disadvantageous because its tendency is opposed to the equable distribution of wealth. It tends to accumulate property in a few hands, making the rich richer and the poor poorer. This tendency speculation introduces into trade. Insurance, as far as it goes, diminishes risk and limits the speculative element in the ventures of trade. The consent of the civilised world to the proposition that Insurance is expedient is an eloquent acknowledgment of the truth that gambling is inexpedient. For Insurance is the reverse of gambling and can only be wise in that gambling is foolish.

The manner in which contingencies may be so collected together as to eliminate the element of chance is illustrated by the following example.

Suppose *n* horses are entered for a race, and at some epoch before the race let the published odds be

$a - 1$ to 1 against the first,

$b - 1$ to 1 against the second,

$c - 1$ to 1 against the third,

and so on.

Now suppose a man bets, at the prices quoted,

$$\frac{a-1}{a} \text{ to } \frac{1}{a} \text{ against the first,}$$

$$\frac{b-1}{b} \text{ to } \frac{1}{b} \text{ against the second,}$$

$$\frac{c-1}{c} \text{ to } \frac{1}{c} \text{ against the third,}$$

and so on.

It is easily seen that whatever horse wins, his gains are represented algebraically by

$$\left(\frac{1}{a} + \frac{1}{b} + \frac{1}{c} + \ldots\right) - 1.$$

If this expression be positive, he gains the same sum whatever horse wins. If it be negative, he loses the same sum whatever horse wins. (In this case if he betted *on* instead of *against* every horse he would win the same sum.) If the estimated chances of the several horses winning happen to fulfil the condition of true chances we shall have

$$\frac{1}{a} + \frac{1}{b} + \frac{1}{c} + \ldots = 1,$$

and the man will neither gain nor lose. But in any case if he make the bets we have defined, the result is absolutely certain. He has collected together a series of ventures and in their aggregate there is no venture.

We now proceed to establish on the strictest mathematical principles the disadvantage of gambling, and to shew how the disadvantage may be measured.

PROPOSITION LXVI.

If A has m pounds, and B has n pounds, and if A repeatedly stake a pound against a pound staked by B, in a fair wager, one of them must eventually win all the stakes, and their respective chances of winning all are as m to n.

Let f_x represent the prospect of all being ultimately won by one who has x pounds, while the other has $m + n - x$.

Then since after the next wager this player must have either $x - 1$ or $x + 1$, and the chance of each of these is $\frac{1}{2}$, we have

$$f_x = \frac{1}{2} f_{x-1} + \frac{1}{2} f_{x+1}$$

for all values of x; which shews that f_0, f_1, $f_2 \ldots$ are in arithmetical progression.

But it is plain that $f_0 = 0$ and $f_{m+n} = 1$, therefore the common difference is $\dfrac{1}{m + n}$, and therefore

$$f_x = \frac{x}{m + n}.$$

Therefore the respective chances at first of A and B winning the whole stakes are

$$f_m = \frac{m}{m + n} \text{ and } f_n = \frac{n}{m + n},$$

which are as m to n. And their sum is unity, which shews that it is certain that one or other will eventually win all. Q.E.D.

NOTE. A's chance of being ruined is $1 - \dfrac{m}{m + n}$, which when n is indefinitely increased differs from unity by less

than any assignable fraction. But when n is infinite we have
the case in which A is gaming not with an antagonist of
limited means but with society in general. Hence we have
the following corollary.

COROLLARY. *If a man with limited means repeatedly
stake a pound against a pound, in a fair wager, the chance
of his not being ultimately ruined is less than any assignable chance.*

The foregoing corollary shews that, on the strictest
mathematical principles, a man who continues to stake a
constant sum in a fair wager must expect to be ruined in
the end. Such a course of gambling—unregulated by any
consideration of the gambler's disposable fund, until the
absolute exhaustion of the fund places a peremptory limit on
his play—is therefore manifestly inexpedient. And if it be
inexpedient in the long run, it cannot be expedient even
when carried to any limited extent.

For any limited extent of play which may be thought
to be expedient, must leave the gambler either poorer or
richer than he was at first. If it leave him poorer, it cannot
be expedient. If it leave him richer, the same course of
gambling which was expedient at first, cannot be less expedient now; and, therefore, it cannot be expedient for him
to stop. Hence, no play, which can be resolved into simple
repetitions of the same venture, which is proved to be inexpedient in the long run, can be expedient when confined
to any assignable extent.

We have spoken of fair wagers. And if a fair wager be
inexpedient, an unfair wager must be *à fortiori* inexpedient
to the party against whom are the odds, though it may be
sufficiently unfair to be advantageous to the other party.
The position is illustrated by the following proposition.

PROPOSITION LXVII.

If A has m pounds, and B has n pounds, and if A repeatedly stake a pound against a pound staked by B in a wager in which the odds are $\mu : 1$ in A's favour, what are their respective chances of winning the whole?

Let A_x represent A's chance of winning all when he has x pounds, and B has $m + n - x$.

And let B_x represent B's chance of winning all when he has x pounds, and A has $m + n - x$. Then we shall have

$$A_x = \frac{1}{1 + \mu} A_{x-1} + \frac{\mu}{\mu + 1} A_{x+1},$$

or

$$A_x - A_{x-1} = \mu \left(A_{x+1} - A_x \right).$$

Giving x successive values from 1 to x, we get

$$A_1 - A_0 = \mu \left(A_2 - A_1 \right),$$
$$A_2 - A_1 = \mu \left(A_3 - A_2 \right),$$
$$\&c. = \&c. ;$$

and by continued multiplication

$$A_1 - A_0 = \mu^{x-1} \left(A_x - A_{x-1} \right),$$

or

$$A_x - A_{x-1} = \left(A_1 - A_0 \right) \frac{1}{\mu^{x-1}}.$$

Give x successive values from 1 to x and add: then

$$A_x - A_0 = \left(A_1 - A_0 \right) \left(1 + \frac{1}{\mu} + \frac{1}{\mu^2} + \dots + \frac{1}{\mu^{x-1}} \right).$$

But $A_0 = 0$; therefore

$$A_x = A_1 \left(1 - \frac{1}{\mu^x} \right) \div \left(1 - \frac{1}{\mu} \right).$$

But $A_{m+n} = 1$; therefore, putting $x = m + n$,

$$1 = A_1 \left(1 - \frac{1}{\mu^{m+n}} \right) \div \left(1 - \frac{1}{\mu} \right);$$

whence

$$A_x = \frac{1 - \mu^{-x}}{1 - \mu^{-(m+n)}};$$

similarly

$$B_x = \frac{\mu^x - 1}{\mu^{m+n} - 1}.$$

Therefore A's and B's original chances are

$$A_m = \frac{\mu^{m+n} - \mu^n}{\mu^{m+n} - 1}, \text{ and } B_n = \frac{\mu^n - 1}{\mu^{m+n} - 1},$$

and the sum of these is unity, shewing that one or other must in time win all.

NOTE. B's chance of winning all may be written

$$B_n = \frac{1}{\mu^m} \cdot \frac{1 - \dfrac{1}{\mu^n}}{1 - \dfrac{1}{\mu^{m+n}}},$$

and when n is infinite (μ being greater than unity), this becomes $\dfrac{1}{\mu^m}$, which is therefore A's chance of being ruined when his antagonist's funds are unlimited. Therefore we have the following corollary.

COROLLARY. *If a man with limited funds (m pounds) repeatedly stake a pound against a pound in a wager in which the odds on every venture are $\mu : 1$ in his favour (his antagonist's funds not being limited), the chance that he is ultimately ruined is $\dfrac{1}{\mu^m}$.*

PROPOSITION LXVIII.

A man constantly stakes a fixed proportion of his property in a fair wager, in which if he wins he will increase his property by $\frac{1}{m}$th part, and if he loses he will decrease it by $\frac{1}{n}$th part. To shew that in the long run he will lose.

Let μ be the chance of his winning each wager. Then, since the wager is fair,

$$\mu\left(1+\frac{1}{m}\right)+(1-\mu)\left(1-\frac{1}{n}\right)=1,$$

whence $\qquad \mu=\dfrac{m}{m+n}, \quad \text{and} \quad 1-\mu=\dfrac{n}{m+n}.$

Therefore, on the average, out of $m+n$ wagers he will win m times, and lose n times.

Therefore, on the average, in $m+n$ wagers he will multiply his property by

$$\left(1+\frac{1}{m}\right)^{m}\left(1-\frac{1}{n}\right)^{n}.$$

But by expansion, it is seen that

$$\left(1+\frac{1}{m}\right)^{m}<e \quad \text{and} \quad \left(1-\frac{1}{n}\right)^{-n}>e,$$

or $\qquad \left(1+\dfrac{1}{m}\right)^{m}<e \quad \text{and} \quad \left(1-\dfrac{1}{n}\right)^{n}<\dfrac{1}{e};$

therefore $\qquad \left(1+\dfrac{1}{m}\right)^{m}\left(1-\dfrac{1}{n}\right)^{n}<1.$

Hence the average multiplier is less than unity, or the general tendency of the man's operation is to decrease his funds. Q.E.D.

But however inexpedient it may be for a man to exchange a small certainty for the chance of a large uncertainty of equal expectant value, there must be some smaller sum which it might be expedient for him to give for the chance. Or conversely, if a man have a chance, however small, of receiving a property of value, he will not relinquish his title to it without receiving something in return, even though it be advantageous to him to accept less than the value of his expectation as given in Prop. XLIV.

And on the principle that the advantage of any speculation is to be judged by the effect in the long run of indefinitely repeating the operation on a scale proportioned to the funds then possessed, it is easy to calculate what sum may be advantageously given for any venture.

It is not necessary to regard the fund in possession as representing the whole of the speculator's property. It may be taken as that portion of his property which he thinks he is able to speculate with. We therefore speak of his "available" funds, designating thereby the funds (whether the whole or the part of his property) which he considers available for the purposes of speculation.

PROPOSITION LXIX.

There are m tickets in a lottery for one prize of value a. To determine what price may be paid for a ticket by a man whose available fund is n, so that by repeating his operation an average number of gains may balance an average number of losses.

"Repeating his operation" will here mean that when the first venture is decided the man will purchase a ticket in another lottery in which the prize is to the amount of the fund which he *then* holds in the ratio of a to n.

Suppose x the sum which he may pay for a ticket. Then every unsuccessful venture multiplies his fund by $1 - \dfrac{x}{n}$ and every successful venture multiplies it by $1 + \dfrac{a}{n} - \dfrac{x}{n}$. But in the long run he will have $m - 1$ unsuccessful issues for one successful one. Therefore the average multiplier for m ventures will be

$$\left(1 + \frac{a}{n} - \frac{x}{n}\right)\left(1 - \frac{x}{n}\right)^{m-1}.$$

This must be unity, since the gains, on the average, balance the losses. Therefore,

$$1 + \frac{a}{n} - \frac{x}{n} = \left(1 - \frac{x}{n}\right)^{-(m-1)},$$

an equation to determine x.

If n be a large number (as is usually the case) we may obtain an approximate solution, by neglecting terms which involve $\dfrac{1}{n^3}$, $\dfrac{1}{n^4}$, &c. Thus

$$1 + \frac{a}{n} - \frac{x}{n} = 1 + \frac{(m-1)\,x}{n} + \frac{(m^2 - m)\,x^2}{2n^2} + \&c.,$$

whence $\qquad (m^2 - m)\,x^2 + 2mnx = 2an,$

which gives approximately

$$x = \frac{a}{m}\left\{1 - \left(1 - \frac{1}{m}\right)\frac{a}{2n}\right\}.$$

This is therefore the price which a man with funds n may prudently give for the chance $\dfrac{1}{m}$ of a prize a.

COROLLARY. If he buy two tickets in the same lottery his chance of a prize is $\frac{2}{m}$. Hence writing $\frac{m}{2}$ for m in the result of the proposition we obtain the price he may pay for two tickets, viz.

$$\frac{2a}{m}\left\{1 - \left(1 - \frac{2}{m}\right)\frac{a}{2n}\right\},$$

or he may pay for each of them

$$\frac{a}{m}\left\{1 - \left(1 - \frac{2}{m}\right)\frac{a}{2n}\right\}.$$

So if he purchase r tickets, he may pay for each of them

$$\frac{a}{m}\left\{1 - \left(1 - \frac{r}{m}\right)\frac{a}{2n}\right\};$$

or if he purchase all the m tickets, he may pay for each its full mathematical value, $\frac{a}{m}$.

PROPOSITION LXX.

There are $a + b + c + \ldots = m$ tickets in a lottery, and there are a blanks, b prizes each worth β, c prizes each worth γ, and so on. To determine what price a man whose available fund is n may pay for a ticket.

Let ω be the absolute value of each ticket, so that

$$m\omega = b\beta + c\gamma + \ldots = \text{the sum of the prizes.}$$

Also let

$$m\Omega = b\beta^2 + c\gamma^2 + \ldots$$

and let x be the price which the man in question ought to pay for the ticket.

Then if we proceed as in the last Proposition we find the average multiplier for m ventures, viz.

$$\left(1 - \frac{x}{n}\right)^a \left(1 + \frac{\beta}{n} - \frac{x}{n}\right)^b \left(1 + \frac{\gamma}{n} - \frac{x}{n}\right)^c \cdots$$

This must be equal to unity.   Therefore, expanding,

$$0 = \frac{mx - m\omega}{n} + \frac{mx^2 - 2m\omega x + m\Omega}{2n^2} + \cdots$$

from which equation x is to be found.   If, as is usually the case, the amount at stake is small compared with the speculator's whole funds, n must be a very large number; therefore we shall obtain an approximate value of x, by neglecting the terms involving high negative powers of n, in our equation.   Therefore

$$x = \omega - \frac{\Omega - \omega^2}{2n},$$

which is therefore the price which a man with funds n may prudently give for the ticket whose mathematical value is ω.

COROLLARY.   *The price which a man whose available fund is n pounds may pay for a share in a speculation in which p_1 will be his chance of winning P_1, p_2 his chance of winning P_2, and so on (where $p_1 + p_2 + \ldots = 1$) will be*

$$\Sigma(pP) - \frac{\Sigma(pP^2) - \{\Sigma(pP)\}^2}{2n}.$$

EXAMPLES.   Having n shillings, what may one pay to be entitled to a number of shillings equal to the number turned up at a single throw of a die?

$$\text{Here } \Sigma(pP) = \frac{1}{6}(1+2+3+4+5+6) = \frac{7}{2},$$

$$\Sigma(pP^2) = \frac{1}{6}(1+4+9+16+25+36) = \frac{91}{6}.$$

And the required number of shillings is approximately

$$\frac{7}{2}\left(1-\frac{5}{12n}\right).$$

Again. If the throw be made with two dice, we shall have (see page 139)

$$\Sigma(pP)=7, \qquad \Sigma(pP^2)=329\div6.$$

And the required number of shillings will be approximately

$$7\left(1-\frac{5}{12n}\right).$$

It must be remembered that the results of the two foregoing propositions and the corollary are only obtained on the hypothesis that n is very large compared with $\Sigma(pP)$ and with $\Sigma(pP^2)\div\Sigma(pP)$. This requires that the man's original fund should be very large compared not only with the amount which he stakes, but also with the amount which he has a chance (though it may be a very small chance) of winning.

In all practical cases the former conditions will be fulfilled, as no one would think of staking, in any single venture, his whole property, or a sum bearing any considerable ratio to his whole property. But cases will be likely to arise in which the latter condition is not satisfied, as when a man may purchase, for a sum comparatively small compared with his means, a ticket in a lottery in which there is a prize very many times larger than his whole property. In this case, the approximate results obtained above cannot be applied, and we must have recourse to the original equation in the form in which it was presented before we introduced the approximations which are now inadmissible. We may, however, still approximate, in virtue of the condition that the stake must be small compared with the speculator's whole funds. Thus:—

PROPOSITION LXXI.

To find an approximate formula for the sum which a speculator may pay for any defined expectation, without assuming that his funds are necessarily large compared with the value of the prizes.

Let X (small compared with n, though not necessarily small compared with P) be the sum which a man whose available fund is n may pay for the chances p_1, p_2, p_3 ... of receiving prizes worth P_1, P_2, P_3, ... respectively, as in the last corollary.

Then the rigorous equation to determine X is

$$\left(1 + \frac{P_1}{n} - \frac{X}{n}\right)^{p_1} \left(1 + \frac{P_2}{n} - \frac{X}{n}\right)^{p_2} \left(1 + \frac{P_3}{n} - \frac{X}{n}\right)^{p_3} \dots = 1,$$

from which, since X is small compared with n, we obtain

$$X = \frac{\left(1 + \frac{P_1}{n}\right)^{p_1} \left(1 + \frac{P_2}{n}\right)^{p_2} \left(1 + \frac{P_3}{n}\right)^{p_3} \dots - 1}{\dfrac{p_1}{n + P_1} + \dfrac{p_2}{n + P_2} + \dfrac{p_3}{n + P_3} + \dots}.$$

This formula is equally applicable when there is a possibility of not receiving any prize, as the failure to receive a prize may be treated as the receiving of a prize of zero value: *i.e.* one of the quantities P_1, P_2, P_3 ... will be in this case zero.

COROLLARY. In the case when there is a single prize P, and the chance of gaining it is p, the formula becomes

$$X = \frac{\left(1 + \frac{P}{n}\right)^p - 1}{\dfrac{p}{n + P} + \dfrac{1 - p}{n}} = \frac{n(n + P)}{n + (1 - p)P} \left\{\left(1 + \frac{P}{n}\right)^p - 1\right\}.$$

EXAMPLES. A man possessing a pound is offered a ticket in a lottery, in which there are 99 blanks, and one prize worth 100 pounds. What may he pay for the ticket?

Here $\qquad n=1, \quad P=100, \quad p=\dfrac{1}{100}.$

$$X=\frac{101}{100}\left(\sqrt[100]{101}-1\right)=\frac{101}{100}\times \cdot 0472 = \cdot 0519.$$

Hence he can only afford to pay about a shilling for the ticket.

Again. How much may a man with 10 pounds pay for the same ticket?

Here $\qquad n=10, \quad P=100, \quad p=\dfrac{1}{100}.$

$$X=\frac{1100}{109}\left(\sqrt[100]{11}-1\right)=\frac{1100}{109}\times \cdot 0242 = \cdot 244.$$

Hence he can afford to pay about 4s. $10\frac{1}{2}d$. for the ticket.

Again. How much may a man with 100 pounds pay for the same ticket?

Here $\qquad n=100, \quad P=100, \quad p=\dfrac{1}{100}.$

$$X=\frac{20000}{199}\left(\sqrt[100]{2}-1\right)=\frac{20000}{199}\times \cdot 0069 = \cdot 693.$$

Hence he may pay nearly 14 shillings for the ticket.

Again. Suppose the man has 1000 pounds. This sum is large compared with the value of the prize. Hence we may apply the simpler formula given in Proposition LXX. (Cor.), which leads to the result

$$1-\frac{1}{2000}\left(100-1\right)=1-\frac{99}{2000}= \cdot 9505.$$

Hence he may pay 19 shillings for the ticket.

If we had applied to this last case the formula of the present corollary we should have obtained the slightly more correct result ·9507, the difference between the two results being nearly one-fifth of a farthing.

The formula of Proposition LXXI. is applicable in the case of the Petersburg problem, a problem of some intrinsic interest, but chiefly of importance on account of its having been repeatedly made the ground of objections to the mathematical theory of probability. This celebrated problem may be stated as follows:—

(PROP. LXXII.) THE PETERSBURG PROBLEM.

A coin is tossed again and again until a head falls. The player is to receive a florin if head falls the first time: two florins if it falls the second time, and not before: four florins if it falls the third time, and not before: and so on, doubling every time. To determine what the player might advantageously give for the expectation.

The absolute value of the expectation is easily seen to be infinite. Thus—

The chance of winning the florin at the first throw is $\frac{1}{2}$: the value of the expectation is therefore half a florin.

The chance of failing at the first throw and winning the two florins at the second throw is $\frac{1}{4}$: the value of the expectation is therefore $\frac{1}{4}$ of two florins, or half a florin.

So, the chance of winning the four florins at the third throw is $\frac{1}{8}$: the value of the expectation is therefore $\frac{1}{8}$ of four florins, or half a florin, and so on.

Hence the value of the expectation attaching to each throw to which there is a possibility of the play extending is half a florin. If the play were limited to $2n$ throws the expectation would be n florins. But the play may extend to a number of throws larger than any assignable number. Therefore the whole expectation is worth a number of florins larger than any assignable number : that is, it is infinitely great.

But here a difficulty is raised. The mathematical expectation has been found to be of infinite value, and yet (it is objected) no one in his senses would give even such a moderate sum as £50 for the prospect defined in the problem.

The fallacy of this objection has been pointed out already. A man who is playing for even limited stakes is at a disadvantage from the risk of his limited means terminating his operations at an unfavourable epoch. Much more is he at a disadvantage when the interests at stake are (as in this case) very large or even infinite. The absolute value of a mathematical expectation is not the prize which a man of limited means ought to pay for the prospect. It expresses the value of the expectation to a man who is able to repeat the venture indefinitely without the risk of his operations being ever terminated by lack of means. The speculator's fund, to begin with, must be infinite in comparison with the stakes involved, before he may venture to give the absolute value of the mathematical expectation for any contingent prospect which he may desire to purchase. In the Petersburg problem the mathematical expectation is infinite : but if one is to give an infinite sum for the venture one must take care to hold funds *infinite in comparison with this infinity.* In other words, the speculation on these terms is only proper for one with respect to whose funds the infinite stake is inconsiderable. The stake which he lays down may be ∞, provided that his funds are $\infty \times \infty$.

But to find the sum which a man of limited means may pay for the expectation defined in our statement of the problem we may apply the result of Proposition LXXI. Thus if n be the number of florins which the man possesses, the formula to determine the sum which he may pay may be written as follows:—

$$X = \frac{\left(1 + \frac{1}{n}\right)^{\frac{1}{2}} \left(1 + \frac{2}{n}\right)^{\frac{1}{4}} \left(1 + \frac{4}{n}\right)^{\frac{1}{8}} \ldots - 1}{\frac{1}{2(n+1)} + \frac{1}{4(n+2)} + \frac{1}{8(n+4)} + \ldots},$$

and observing that

$$n^{\frac{1}{2} + \frac{1}{4} + \frac{1}{8} + \ldots} = n,$$

and that

$$2^{\frac{1}{4}} \cdot 4^{\frac{1}{8}} \cdot 8^{\frac{1}{16}} \ldots = 2^{\frac{1}{4} + \frac{2}{8} + \frac{3}{16} + \ldots} = 2,$$

we get

$$X = \frac{\frac{4}{n}\left(1 + \frac{n}{1}\right)^{\frac{1}{2}} \left(1 + \frac{n}{2}\right)^{\frac{1}{4}} \left(1 + \frac{n}{4}\right)^{\frac{1}{8}} \left(1 + \frac{n}{8}\right)^{\frac{1}{16}} \ldots - 2}{\frac{1}{n+1} + \frac{1}{2(n+2)} + \frac{1}{4(n+4)} + \frac{1}{8(n+8)} + \ldots}.$$

If n be any power of 2 we can put the result into a form free from infinite series. Thus, if θ and ϕ are constants, viz.

$$\theta = (1+1)^{\frac{1}{2}} \left(1 + \frac{1}{2}\right)^{\frac{1}{4}} \left(1 + \frac{1}{4}\right)^{\frac{1}{8}} \ldots ad \ inf. = 1 \cdot 6253 \ldots$$

and

$$\phi = \frac{1}{1+1} + \frac{1}{2(1+2)} + \frac{1}{4(1+4)} + \ldots ad \ inf. = \cdot 7355 \ldots$$

we shall have

$$X = \frac{\frac{4}{n}(3\theta)^{\frac{1}{n}}(1+4)^{\frac{2}{n}}(1+8)^{\frac{4}{n}} \ldots (1+n)^{\frac{1}{2}} - 2}{\frac{1}{n+1} + \frac{1}{2(n+2)} + \frac{1}{4(n+4)} + \ldots + \frac{1}{\frac{1}{2}n(n+\frac{1}{2}n)} + \frac{\phi}{n^2}}.$$

The result when n is given is easily evaluated by the aid of a table of logarithms.

For instance, if $n = 8$, the numerator is ·7342 and the denominator is ·1934. Hence $X = 3·796$. Therefore if the speculator possesses 8 florins he may give nearly $3\frac{4}{5}$ for the venture.

If $n = 32$, the numerator is ·2297, and the denominator is ·0570. Hence $X = 4·025$. Therefore if the speculator have 32 florins he may give rather more than 4 for the venture.

If $n = 1024$ the numerator is ·012, and the denominator is ·001943. Therefore if the speculator have 1024 florins he may give very little more than 6 florins for the venture.

The result at which we have arrived is not to be classed with the arbitrary methods which have been again and again propounded to evade the difficulty of the Petersburg problem and other problems of a similar character. Formulæ have often been proposed, which have possessed the one virtue of presenting a finite result in the case of this famous problem, but they have often had no intelligible basis to rest upon, or, if they have been established on sound principles, sufficient care has not been taken to draw a distinguishing line between the significance of the result obtained, and the different result arrived at when the mathematical expectation is calculated.

We have not assigned any new value to the mathematical expectation; we have not substituted a new expression for the old; but we have deduced a separate result, which without disturbing the mathematical expectation has a definite meaning of its own. We have found not the fair price at which a contingent prospect may be transferred from one man to another, but the value which such a prospect has to a man in given circumstances. We have simply determined the terms at which a man may purchase a contingent

prospect of advantage, so that by repeating the operation—
each time on a scale proportionate to his funds at that time—
he may be left neither richer nor poorer when each issue of
the venture shall have occurred its own average number of
times. By continuing the operation indefinitely, the re-
currences of each issue will tend to be proportional to their
respective probabilities, and, therefore, the condition we have
taken is equivalent to the condition that *in the long run* the
man may expect to be neither richer nor poorer.

It would be a great mistake to suppose that the price
which one man may prudently give for a venture is the price
which the man with whom he is dealing may prudently take
for it, or that it is a fair price at which to make the compact.
The price which the man may prudently give is not even
the price which the same man may prudently take if he
change sides with his fellow gambler. *The sum in consideration of which a man possessed of n pounds may accept
a position in which p_1 is the chance of his having to pay
P_1, p_2 the chance of his having to pay P_2, and so on (where
$\Sigma p = 1$) must be obtained by changing the algebraical
signs of X, P_1, P_2...in the formulæ of Propositions LXX.
(Cor.) and LXXI.*

Thus on the hypothesis of Proposition LXX. (Cor.) we
shall have

$$X = \Sigma\,(pP) + \frac{1}{2n}\left[\Sigma\,(pP^2) - \{\Sigma\,(pP)\}^2\right],$$

and in the more general case dealt with in Proposition LXXI.
we shall have

$$X = \frac{1 - \left(1 - \dfrac{P_1}{n}\right)^{p_1}\left(1 - \dfrac{P_2}{n}\right)^{p_2}\left(1 - \dfrac{P_3}{n}\right)^{p_3}\cdots}{\dfrac{p_1}{n - P_1} + \dfrac{p_2}{n - P_2} + \dfrac{p_3}{n - P_3} + \cdots}.$$

CHAPTER XII.

THE GEOMETRICAL REPRESENTATION OF CHANCES.

It is often convenient to represent or depict chances by a geometrical figure. As every chance expressed in terms of certainty is a proper fraction, or a ratio of lesser inequality, it may be represented by the ratio of a smaller length to a larger length, or a smaller area to a larger area, or (in solid geometry) a smaller volume to a larger volume. Especially it is often convenient to represent it as the ratio of a *part* of a line (or area or volume) to the *whole* line (or area or volume). And in this case the complementary chance is at the same time represented by the ratio of the *remainder* to the *whole,* and the odds are represented by the ratio of the part to the remainder. Thus if $\frac{AB}{AC}$ (figure 1) represent the chance of a given event happening, $\frac{BC}{AC}$ will be the chance of its not happening, and $AB : BC$ the odds in favour of its happening.

Figure 1.

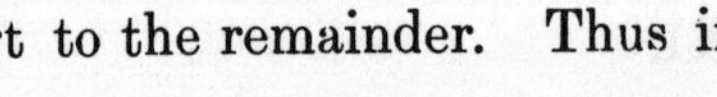

Sometimes the question under consideration is geometrical in its character, and the result comes out naturally in a geometrical form. For instance, a chain AC (figure 1)

consists of a length AB of iron and a length BC of brass: required the chance that a link taken at random will be iron. The chance is evidently $AB \div AC$.

So, if a point be taken at random in an area (or volume) a, the chance that it will be within a smaller *interior* area (or volume) b is expressed by the ratio of the areas, and is $b \div a$.

But in other cases where the question is not of a geometrical nature, the chances involved in it may be conveniently represented by the ratios of geometrical quantities. If an event may happen, or an experiment turn out in several ways not all equally likely, we may represent the probabilities of the several ways by contiguous segments of a straight line, the segments being proportional in length to the respective probabilities. Then if one of the ways must happen the sum of the segments will correspond to certainty, and the ratio of the several segments to the whole will represent the chances of the several ways.

PROPOSITION LXXIII.

To express geometrically the probability of an event Z, which depends upon the way in which a previous event X may have happened, X necessarily happening in one of a finite number of ways.

Suppose that X can happen in a variety of ways denoted by $A, B, C \ldots M$; and let $a, b, c \ldots m$ be the respective chances of these ways; where

$$a + b + c + \ldots + m = 1.$$

Also when A has happened let α be the chance of Z happening; and when B has happened let β be the chance of Z; and when C has happened let γ be the chance of Z, and so on.

Let the straight line PQ of length unity be divided into segments of the respective lengths a, b, $c...m$. And on each of these segments describe a rectangle of height unity. And from the rectangles whose bases are a, b, c, &c., cut off segments of height α, β, γ, &c., and let these segments be shaded.

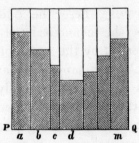

Then the area of the first shaded segment is $a\alpha$, and it therefore represents the chance that X should happen in the first way (A), and that Z should then happen.

So the area of the second shaded segment represents the chance that X should happen in the second way (B), and that Z should then happen. And so on.

Hence the whole shaded area (or its ratio to the area of the great square which is unity) will represent the total chance of the event Z, which was required.

PROPOSITION LXXIV.

To express geometrically the probability of an event Z, which depends upon the way in which a previous event X shall have happened, X necessarily happening in one (and only one) of an infinitely great number of ways.

Make the same construction as in the last case, but with the provision that the number of the segments of PQ is ultimately to be increased indefinitely, and therewith the number of the rectangles upon the segments.

If the problem be determinate at all, the height of the shaded rectangles must follow some definite law, and this law will determine a curve $FGHK$ such that each rectangle is inscribed with one of its angular points upon the curve.

Then (as in Newton, Book I., Lemmas 2 and 3), when the number of the rectangles is increased indefinitely and

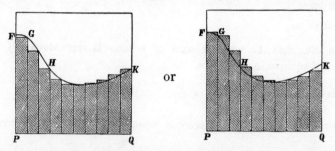

or

their breadth diminished indefinitely, the sum of their areas will be the area bounded by the curved line $FGHK$, and the straight lines FP, PQ, QK. This curvilinear area (or its ratio to the square which is unity) will therefore express the chance required.

EXAMPLE I. A and B each throw once with a common die. What is the chance that A throws higher than B?

Let the straight line AG representing unity be divided into six equal segments AB, BC, CD, DE, EF, FG, representing respectively the (equal) chances of B throwing 1, 2, 3, 4, 5, 6. On each segment erect a rectangle of height unity. Then

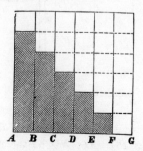

AB represents the chance of *B* throwing 1. In this case *A*'s chance of throwing higher is $\frac{5}{6}$. Therefore we may take $\frac{5}{6}$ ths (shaded) of the rectangle on *AB* to represent *A*'s chance of success in this case.

BC represents the chance of *B* throwing 2. We must take $\frac{4}{6}$ ths (shaded) of the rectangle on *BC* to represent *A*'s chance of success in this case.

And so on.

We thus find *A*'s whole chance of success is represented by the 15 shaded squares in the figure.

His chance is therefore $\frac{15}{36}$ or $\frac{5}{12}$.

NOTE. Of course *B*'s chance is equally $\frac{5}{12}$, and the chance of a tie is $\frac{1}{6}$.

EXAMPLE II. The sides of a rectangle are taken at random, each less than 1 inch, and all lengths equally likely. What is the chance that the diagonal is less than 1 inch?

Let *HK* be a line of length one inch, from which we are to cut off the base of the rectangle. Then the ratio of the small segment *PQ* to the whole line *HK* will represent the chance that the end of the base measured from *H* falls on that segment *PQ*.

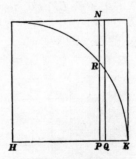

On *HK* describe a square, and suppose it divided into rectangles on small bases such as *PQ*. Let *NQ* be the rectangle on *PQ*. Let a circle from centre H, radius HK, cut PN in R.   Then the other side of the rectangle, of which one side is HP, may be any segment of PN, and the diagonal will be greater or less than the radius HR, according as the segment is greater or less than PR.   That is, the diagonal will be less than 1 inch, provided the extremity of the segment of PN lie in PR, and the chance of this is proportional to PR.   Hence the question comes under Prop. LXXIV., and the required chance will be the ratio of the quadrant of the circle to the square on HK.   That is, the chance is $\dfrac{\pi}{4}$.

EXAMPLE III. A and B are going to a garden party for an hour each. A will arrive between 3 and 5 p.m., all times within these limits being equally likely ; and B will arrive between 4 and 7 p.m., all times equally likely.   What is the chance that they are there together ?

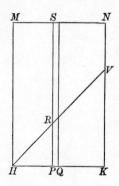

Take the straight line HK to represent the two hours during which A may arrive, so that the ratio of any segment PQ to the whole HK expresses the chance of A arriving in the interval of time represented by the segment PQ.

And on the same scale let HM (at right angles to HK) represent the three hours during which B may arrive.   Complete the rectangle $MHKN$.

Let HK be divided into very small segments, to be ultimately increased indefinitely in number and diminished indefinitely in magnitude.   And let PQ be one of these segments, and on PQ erect a rectangle QS of height equal to HM.   Bisect the right angle MHK by the straight line HRV, cutting PS and KN in R and V.

Suppose A arrives in the interval of time denoted by PQ. Say at P. He will leave at the expiration of time HP after 4 p.m. If he is to meet B, B must arrive before the expiration of this time, but B may arrive at any instant in the period HM after 4 p.m. Therefore the chance of their meeting (if A arrives at the time PQ) is $HP \div HM$, or $PR \div PS$; or it is the ratio of the rectangle QR to the rectangle QS. Hence the series of rectangles on the segments of NK, bounded by the diagonal NV, will represent by their ratio to the rectangles of height NM, the respective chances of A and B meeting when A arrives at the various instants represented by the segments of HK. Therefore the method of Prop. LXXIV. is applicable, and the whole chance of A and B meeting is the ratio of the triangle HKV to the rectangle MK; that is, the chance is $\dfrac{1}{3}$.

EXERCISES.

Solutions of the questions numbered from 1 *to* 700 *are given in the
Companion Volume* DCC EXERCISES IN CHOICE AND
CHANCE. *Additional exercises are numbered from* 701 *upwards.*

CHOICE.

1. If there are five routes from London to Cambridge, and three routes
from Cambridge to Lincoln, how many ways are there of going from London
to Lincoln viâ Cambridge?

2. Two hostile companies of 100 men each agreed to settle their dispute
by single combat. In how many ways could the two champions be chosen?

3. Having four seals and five sorts of sealing-wax, in how many ways
can we seal a letter?

4. In how many ways can a consonant and a vowel be chosen out of the
letters of the word *almost*?

5. In how many ways can a consonant and a vowel be chosen out of the
letters of the word *orange*?

6. A die of six faces and a teetotum of eight faces are thrown. In how
many ways can they fall?

7. There are five routes to the top of a mountain, in how many ways
can a person go up and down?

8. Out of 20 knives and 24 forks, in how many ways can a man choose
a knife and fork? And then, in how many ways can another man take
another knife and fork?

9. Out of a list of 12 regular and 5 irregular verbs in how many ways
can we choose an example of each?

---

701. In how many ways can two squares be selected on a draught-
board, one black and the other white?

702. In how many ways if the two squares must not be in the same
vertical or horizontal line?

10.   Out of 12 masculine words, 9 feminine and 10 neuter, in how many ways can we choose an example of each?

11.   Having six pairs of gloves, in how many ways can you take a right-hand and a left-hand glove without taking a pair?

12.   Out of 5 bibles and 12 prayer books, in how many ways can I select a bible and a prayer book?

13.   Out of three bibles, seven prayer books and seven hymn books, in how many ways can I select a bible, prayer book and hymn book?

14.   A bookseller shews me six bibles, three prayer books and four hymn books, also five volumes each containing a bible and a prayer book bound together, and seven volumes each containing a prayer book and hymn book bound together. In how many ways can I select a bible, prayer book and hymn book?

15.   If in addition the bookseller produced three volumes, each containing a bible and a hymn book, what would my choice now be?

16.   A basket contains 12 apples and 10 oranges, John is to choose an apple *or* an orange, and then Tom is to choose an apple *and* an orange. Shew that if John chooses an apple, Tom will have more choice than if John chooses an orange.

17.   How many changes can be rung upon eight bells? And in how many of these will an assigned bell be rung last?

18.   There are three teetotums, having respectively 6, 8, 10 sides. In how many ways can they fall? And in how many of these will at least two aces be turned up?

19.   Having bunting of five different colours, in how many ways can I select three colours for a tricolour flag?

20.   In how many ways can I make the tricolour, the three selected colours being arranged in horizontal order?

21.   A publisher proposes to issue a set of dictionaries to translate from any one language to any other. If he confines his system to five languages, how many dictionaries must he publish?

22.   If he extend his system to ten languages, how many *more* dictionaries must he issue?

---

703.   In how many ways can a card of each suit be selected from a pack of cards? And in how many ways without any two of the selected cards forming a *pair*? (N.B. A pair means two aces, or two kings, or &c.)

704.   In how many ways can it be done so that the selected cards may make a black pair and a red pair?

23. A man lives within reach of three boys' schools and four girls' schools. In how many ways can he send his three sons and two daughters to school?

24. If there be 300 Christian names, in how many ways can a child be named without giving it more than three Christian names?

25. In how many ways can four persons sit at a round table, so that all shall not have the same neighbours in any two arrangements?

26. In how many ways can seven persons sit as in the last question? And in how many of these will two assigned persons be neighbours? And in how many will an assigned person have the same two neighbours?

27. Five ladies and three gentlemen are going to play at croquet; in how many ways can they divide themselves into sides of four each, so that the gentlemen may not be all on one side?

28. I have six letters to be delivered, and three boys offer their services to deliver them. In how many ways have I the choice of sending the letters?

29. *A* has seven different books, *B* has nine different books; in how many ways can one of *A*'s books be exchanged for one of *B*'s?

30. In the case of the last question, in how many ways can two books be exchanged for two?

31. Five men, *A*, *B*, *C*, *D*, *E*, are going to speak at a meeting; in how many ways can they take their turns without *B* speaking before *A*?

32. In how many ways, so that *A* speaks *immediately* before *B*?

33. A company of soldiers consists of three officers, four sergeants and sixty privates. In how many ways can a detachment be made consisting of an officer, two sergeants and twenty privates? In how many of these ways will the captain and the senior sergeant appear?

34. Out of a party of twelve ladies and fifteen gentlemen, in how many ways can four gentlemen and four ladies be selected for a dance?

35. A man belongs to a club of thirty members, and every day he invites five members to dine with him, making a different party every day. For how many days can he do this?

36. Shew that the letters of *anticipation* can be arranged in three times as many ways as the letters of *commencement*.

---

705. If in the case of Qn. 23 there were also two *mixed* schools within reach, in how many ways could the children be sent to school?

37. How many five-lettered words can be made out of 26 letters, repetitions being allowed, but no consecutive repetitions (*i.e.* no letter must follow itself in the same word)?

38. A boat's crew consists of eight men, of whom two can only row on the stroke side of the boat, and three only on the bow side. In how many ways can the crew be arranged?

39. Having three copies of one book, two copies of a second book, and one copy of a third book, in how many ways can I give them to a class of twelve boys, (1) so that no boy receives more than one book; and (2) so that no boy receives more than one copy of any book?

40. In how many ways can a set of twelve black and twelve white draught-men be placed on the black squares of a draught-board?

41. In how many ways can the letters of the word *possessions* be arranged?

42. In how many ways can the letters of *c o c k a t o o* be arranged?

43. Shew that the letters of *c o c o o n* can be arranged in twice as many ways as the letters of *c o c o a*.

44. In how many ways can the letters of *p a l l m a l l* be arranged without letting all the *l*'s come together?

45. In how many ways can the letters of *o i s e a u* be arranged so as to have the vowels in their natural order?

46. In how many ways can the letters of *c o c o a* be arranged so that *a* may have the middle place?

47. In how many ways can the letters of *q u a r t u s* be arranged so that *q* may be followed by *u*?

48. In how many ways can the letters of *u b i q u i t o u s* be arranged so that *q* may be followed by *u*?

49. In how many ways may the letters of *q u i s q u i s* be arranged so that each *q* may be followed by *u*?

50. In how many ways can the letters of *i n d i v i s i b i l i t y* be arranged without letting two *i*'s come together?

---

706. Compare the number of orders in which the letters of the following words severally can be arranged: *d e a n, d e a d, d e e d*.

707. Make the like comparison in the case of the following words: *t r u s t e e, l e g a t e e, f e o f f e e*.

51.   In how many ways can the letters of *facetious* be arranged without two vowels coming together?

52.   In how many ways can the letters of *facetious* be rearranged without changing the order of the vowels?

53.   In how many ways can the letters of *abstemiously* be rearranged without changing the order of the vowels?

54.   In how many ways can the letters of *parallelism* be rearranged without changing the order of the vowels?

55.   In how many ways can the letters of *almost* be rearranged, keeping the vowels at their present distance apart?

56.   In how many ways can the letters of *logarithms* be rearranged, so that the second, fourth and sixth places may be occupied by consonants?

57.   In how many ways can two consonants and a vowel be chosen out of the word *logarithms*, and in how many of these will the letter *s* occur?

58.   In how many ways can the letters of *syzygy* be arranged without letting the three *y*'s come together?

59.   In how many ways without letting two *y*'s come together?

60.   In how many ways can we arrange the letters of the words *choice and chance* without letting two *c*'s come together?

61.   In how many ways can ten books be made into five parcels of two books each?

62.   In how many ways can nine books be made up in four parcels of two books each and one book over?

63.   In how many ways can they be made into three parcels of three books each?

64.   Ten men and their wives are to be formed into five parties, each consisting of two men and two women. In how many ways can this be done?

---

708.   If out of an alphabet of six letters all possible 3-lettered words be written down, the number of words containing 3 different letters will be to the number containing two different letters as 4 to 3.

709.   How many numbers less than a million are expressed in the common notation by 9's and 8's only?

710.   How many by 9's 8's and 7's only?

711.   How many by 9's 8's and 0's only?

65. In how many of these ways will an assigned man find himself in the same party with his wife?

66. In how many will two assigned men and their wives be together in one party?

67. In how many ways can a purchaser select half a dozen handkerchiefs at a shop where seven sorts are kept?

68. A choir contains 10 members. In how many ways can a different six be selected every day for three days?

69. A man has six friends and he invites three of them to dinner every day for twenty days. In how many ways can he do this without having the same party twice?

70. Find the total number of selections that can be made out of the letters *ned needs nineteen nets*.

71. Find the total number of selections that can be made out of the letters *daddy did a deadly deed*.

72. How many selections of three letters can be made out of the letters in the last question?

73. How many arrangements of three letters can be made out of the same?

74. Shew that there are 8 combinations 3-together of the letters *veneer*, and 16 combinations 4-together of the letters *veneered*.

75. How many are the combinations 3-together of the letters *wedded?*

76. How many are the combinations 4-together of the letters *redeemed?*

77. The number of combinations 5-together of the letters *ever esteemed* is 63.

78. In how many ways can three persons divide among themselves the letters *ever esteemed?*

---

712. In how many numbers less than 1000 does the digit 9 occur? In how many does it occur twice? In how many does the digit 0 occur? In how many does it occur twice?

713. In how many do 9 and 0 both occur? In how many do 9 and 8 both occur?

714. How many numbers are there less than a million in which no two digits which are alike come together? (that is 1 must not follow 1; 2 must not follow 2; and so on).

79. In how many ways can they divide them so that each may take four?

80. *A* has the letters *esteem*, *B* has *feeble*, and *C* has *veneer*. In how many ways can they exchange so that each shall have six?

81. In how many ways can the letters of *falsity* be arranged, keeping the consonants in their natural order, and the vowels also in their natural order?

82. In how many ways can the letters of *affection* be arranged, keeping the vowels in their natural order and not letting the two *f*'s come together?

83. In how many ways can the letters of *kaffeekanne* be arranged so that the consonants and vowels come alternately?

84. In how many ways can the letters of *delete* be arranged, keeping the consonants in their natural order?

85. In how many ways can the letters of *delete* be arranged, keeping the consonants in their natural order and not letting two *e*'s come together?

86. In how many ways can the letters of *delirious* be arranged, keeping the consonants in their natural order and the vowels in their natural order?

87. What would be the answer of the last question if the two *i*'s must not come together?

88. In how many ways can the letters of *fulfil* be arranged without letting two letters which are alike come together?

89. In how many ways can the letters of *murmur* be arranged without letting two letters which are alike come together?

90. How many selections of four letters can be made out of the letters of *murmur;* and how many arrangements of four letters?

---

715. How many numbers less than a million contain all the digits 1, 2, 3, 4? And how many contain no other digits than these?

716. If the figures 1, 2, 3, 4 be written in all possible orders, and the numbers so expressed be added together, shew that the sum will be 66660.

717. What will be the sum if the figures be 1, 2, 2, 5?

718. What will be the sum if the figures be 1, 3, 3, 3?

719. What will be the sum if the figures be 1, 1, 4, 4?

720. The figures 0, 1, 2, 3, 4 are written in all possible orders without the 0 coming first. What will be the sum of the numbers so written?

91. How many arrangements of four letters can be made out of the letters of *fulfil?*

92. How many arrangements of five letters can be made out of the letters of *pallmall?*

93. How many arrangements of four letters can be made out of the letters of *kaffeekanne* without letting the three *e*'s come together?

94. How many arrangements of six letters can be made out of the letters of *nineteen tennis nets?*

95. How many arrangements of six letters can be made out of the letters of *little pipe* without letting two letters which are alike come together?

96. How many arrangements of five letters can be made out of the letters of *murmurer* without letting the three *r*'s come together?

97. In how many ways can the letters of *quisquis* be arranged without letting two letters which are alike come together?

98. In how many ways can the letters of *feminine* be arranged without letting two letters which are alike come together?

99. In how many ways can the letters of *muhammadan* be arranged without letting three letters which are alike come together?

100. In how many ways can the same letters be arranged without letting two letters which are alike come together?

101. Out of 20 consecutive numbers, in how many ways can two be selected whose sum shall be odd?

102. Out of 30 consecutive integers, in how many ways can three be selected whose sum shall be even?

---

721. There are two high roads from London to Brighton and ten cross roads connecting the two high roads. In how many different ways can the journey be made without traversing the same ground twice in the same journey?

722. If two travellers start from London one on each highway, in how many ways can they finish the journey without both of them traversing in the same direction any part of the road?

723. There are three high roads from London to Cambridge and four cross roads connecting all the high roads. By how many routes can the journey be made without traversing any part of a high road in the direction towards London?

103. Out of an unlimited number of pence, half-pence and farthings, in how many ways can twenty coins be selected?

104. A person holds five coins and asks you to guess what they are. Knowing that he can only have sovereigns, half-sovereigns, crowns, half-crowns, florins, shillings, sixpences, fourpences, or threepences, how many wrong guesses is it possible to make?

105. In the ordinary scale of notation how many numbers are there consisting of five digits? In how many of these is every digit an odd number? In how many is every digit an even number? In how many is there no digit lower than 6? In how many is there no digit higher than 3? How many contain all the digits 1, 2, 3, 4, 5? and how many contain all the digits 0, 2, 4, 6, 8?

106. How many different sums can be thrown with two dice, the faces of each die being numbered 0, 1, 3, 7, 15, 31?

107. How many different sums can be thrown with three dice, the faces of each die being numbered 1, 4, 13, 40, 121, 364?

108. At a post-office they keep ten sorts of postage-stamps. In how many ways can a person buy twelve stamps? In how many·ways can he buy eight stamps? In how many ways can he buy eight different stamps?

---

724. In how many orders can the letters of the words *sells eels* be arranged without letting two letters which are alike come together?

725. In how many orders can the letters of the words *sell less eels* be arranged without letting two letters which are alike come together?

726. If all the numbers from 1 to 999999 be written down, there will be 488889 cyphers, and each of the other digits will occur 600000 times.

727. Among the 46656 ways in which six dice can fall shew that there are

6 ways	in which the faces will be		all alike
930 ways	,,	,,	of two sorts
10800 ways	,,	,,	of three sorts
23400 ways	,,	,,	of four sorts
10800 ways	,,	,,	of five sorts
720 ways	,,	,,	of six sorts.

728. In how many ways can four cards be selected out of an ordinary pack? Shew that the ways in which the four cards are of three suits will be more numerous than the ways in which they are of two suits in the ratio of 39 to 20.

109. In how many ways can a pack of 52 cards be dealt to 13 players, four to each, (1) so that every one may have a card of each suit, (2) so that one may have a card of each suit, and no one else have cards of more than one suit?

110. In how many ways can a pack of cards be dealt to four players, subject to the condition that each player shall have three cards of each of three suits and four cards of the remaining suit?

111. In how many ways can 18 different things be divided among five persons, (1) so that four of them have four each, and the fifth has two things, (2) so that three of them have four each and the other two have three each?

112. If there be 14 sorts of things, and two things of each sort, find the total number of selections that can be made.

113. If there be twenty sorts of things and nine things of each sort, shew that 99999999999999999999 different selections can be made.

114. The game of bagatelle is played with 8 balls all alike and 1 different. The object is to get as many as possible of these balls into 9 different holes, no hole being capable of more than one ball. How many different dispositions of balls in the holes are possible?

---

729. In how many ways can 20 men be placed upon a draught-board so that the configuration may be the same from whichever of the four sides of the board the men be placed?

730. In how many ways can they be placed so that the configuration may be the same from two opposite sides of the board?

731. In how many ways can they be placed on black squares only so as to fulfil the condition of Qn. 730?

732. In how many ways can 12 black men and 12 white men be placed on the black squares so that the configuration from opposite sides of the board may be the same?

733. In how many ways, so that the two configurations may be the same but with colours interchanged?

734. In how many ways can two castles be placed on a chess-board so that either may be able to take the other?

735. In how many ways can a queen and a bishop be placed on a chess-board so that either may be able to take the other? and in how many ways so that neither may be able to take the other?

736. In how many ways can two knights be placed on a chess-board so that either may be able to take the other?

115. If there were 7 balls alike and 2 others alike, how many dispositions would be possible?

116. If there were 7 balls alike and 2 others different, how many dispositions would be possible?

117. In how many ways can 27 different books be distributed to A, B, C, so that A and C together may have twice as many as B?

118. Shew that out of 99 things the number of ways of selecting 70 is to the number of ways of selecting 30 as 3 to 7.

119. Four boys are in attendance at a telegraph office when 8 messages arrive. In how many ways can the messages be given to the boys without leaving any boy unemployed?

120. Out of the first 100 integers, in how many ways can three be selected whose sum shall be divisible by 3?

121. The number of ways of selecting x things out of $2x + 2$ is to the number of ways of selecting x things out of $2x - 2$ as 99 to 7. Find x.

122. If $C_3^n + R_3^n = P_3^n$, find n. If $C_3^n + R_3^n = \frac{3}{4}P_3^n$, find n.

123. If $R_x^y = mR_y^x$ and $C_{x+1}^{x+y} = nC_{y+1}^{x+y}$, find x and y.

124. Shew that $C_5^{n+1} : R_5^{n-1} = C_2^{n-2} : R_2^{n+2}$.

125. Shew that $(n-r)\, R_r^n\, C_r^n = nR_{2r}^{n-r}\, C_r^{2r}$.

126. Shew that $\{C_{r+1}^{n+1} - C_r^n\}\, C_{r-1}^{n-1} \div \{(C_r^n)^2 - C_{r+1}^{n+1} C_{r-1}^{n-1}\} = r$.

127. Shew that out of $m + n - 1$ things the choice in selecting m things is to the choice in selecting n things as n to m.

128. There are m parcels, of which the first contains n things; the second $2n$ things; the third $3n$ things; and so on. Shew that the number of ways of taking n things out of each parcel is $\lfloor mn \div \{\lfloor n\}^m$.

---

737. Shew that $C_1^n + 6C_2^n + 6C_3^n = n^3$ and $1 + 7C_1^n + 12C_2^n + 6C_3^n = (n+1)^3$.

738. Shew that $1 + 14C_1^n + 36C_2^n + 24C_3^n = (n+1)^4 - n^4$

and $C_1^n + 14C_2^n + 36C_3^n + 24C_4^n = n^4$.

739. Shew that

$$1 - 3C_2^n + 9C_4^n - 27C_6^n + \ldots = 3 . 2^{n-1}\{1 + C_3^n + C_6^n + C_9^n + \ldots\} - 2^{2n-1};$$

each series being continued as far as it will go.

740. Shew that

$$C_1^n - 3C_3^n + 9C_5^n - 27C_7^n + \ldots = 2^{n-1}\{C_1^n + C_4^n + C_7^n + \ldots\} - 2^{n-1}\{C_2^n + C_5^n + C_8^n + \ldots\}.$$

129. Shew that the number of ways of dividing $2n+2$ things into two equal parcels is the sum of the number of combinations of $2n$ things, n and $n-1$ together.

130. Shew that when repetitions are allowed the number of selections of n things out of $m+1$ is the same as the number of selections of m things out of $n+1$.

131. Shew that $R_n^{2n} = 2R_{2n}^n$ and $R_n^{3n} = 3R_{3n}^n$.

132. When repetitions are allowed, the choice of m things out of n is to the choice of n things out of m as n to m.

133. A basket contains $2n+r$ apples and $2n-r$ pears. Shew that the choice of n apples and n pears is greatest when $r=0$, n being constant.

134. Out of $3n$ consecutive integers; in how many ways can three be selected whose sum shall be divisible by 3 ?

135. If $pq+r$ different things are to be divided *as equally as possible* among p persons, in how many ways can it be done? $(r<p.)$

136. Prove that the number of ways in which p positive signs and n negative signs may be placed in a row, so that no two negative signs shall be together, is equal to the number of combinations of $p+1$ things taken n together. $(p>n.)$

137. The number of boys in the several classes of a school are in arithmetical progression, and a number of prizes equal to the common difference of the progression is to be given to each class, no boy receiving more than one prize. Shew that if the prizes are all different the number of ways of giving them is the same as if all were to be given to the largest class.

138. The number of *different* throws that can be made with n dice is

$$(1+n)\left(1+\frac{n}{2}\right)\left(1+\frac{n}{3}\right)\left(1+\frac{n}{4}\right)\left(1+\frac{n}{5}\right).$$

----

741. A square window contains 16 panes each one foot square, separated and surrounded by gilt lines. Shew that there are 70 different routes each 8 feet long by which an insect can travel along the gilt lines from the lower left-hand corner to the upper right-hand corner. If he makes all these possible journeys, shew that 4 feet of the gilt lines will be traversed 35 times; 8 feet, 20 times; 4 feet, 18 times; 4 feet, 15 times; 4 feet, 12 times; 4 feet, 10 times; 4 feet, 5 times; 4 feet, 4 times; and 4 feet, once.

742. Shew also that one intersection of the gilt lines will be visited 36 times; four will be visited 35 times; four, 30 times; four, 15 times; and four, 5 times; two will be visited 40 times; two, 16 times; and two, once; exclusive of the points of departure and arrival.

139.   The number of ways of selecting four things out of n different things is one-sixth of the number of ways of selecting four things out of $2n$ things which are two and two alike of n sorts : find n.

140.   If bagatelle is played with n balls alike and one different, and there are $n+1$ holes each capable of receiving one ball, the whole number of ways in which the balls can be disposed is $(n+3)\,2^n-1$.

141.   In how many ways can a triangle be formed, having its angular points at three of the angular points of a given hexagon ?

142.   How many triangles can be formed having every side either 4 or 5 or 6 or 7 inches long ?

143.   How many different rectangular parallelepipeds can be constructed, the length of each edge being an integral number of inches not exceeding 10 ?

144.   If four straight lines be drawn in a plane and produced indefinitely, how many points of intersection will there *generally* be ?

145.   If four straight lines be drawn in a plane, no two being parallel and no three concurrent, how many triangles will they form ?

146.   There are n points in a plane, no three being in a straight line, except p of them which are all in a straight line ; how many triangles can be formed having some of these points for vertices ?

147.   There are p points in a straight line, and q points on a parallel straight line ; how many triangles can be formed having some of these points for vertices ?

148.   If there be r more points lying on another parallel straight line, how many additional triangles can be formed, assuming that no three points lie on any transverse straight line ?

---

743.   In how many ways can three Englishmen, three Frenchmen, and three Germans stand in a line without three compatriots standing together ?

744.   In how many ways without two compatriots standing together ?

745.   In how many ways can they form a ring without two compatriots standing together ?

746.   Shew that four Englishmen, four Frenchmen, and four Germans can stand in a line in 1092×24^3 orders without two compatriots standing together.

747.   If all the numbers from 1 to 10^n be written down, the number of cyphers used will be $\{9n+1+(9n-10)\,10^{n-1}\} \div 9$.

EXERCISES

149. Each side of a square is divided into n parts. How many triangles can be formed having their vertices at points of section?

150. If n straight lines be drawn in a plane, no two being parallel and no three concurrent, how many points of intersection will there be?

151. If n straight lines be drawn in a plane, no two being parallel and no three concurrent, except p, which meet in one point, and q which meet in another point, how many other points of intersection will there be?

152. Into how many parts is an infinite plane divided by n straight lines, of which no three are concurrent and no two parallel?

153.. Into how many parts is infinite space divided by n planes, of which no four meet in a point and no two are parallel?

154. A large floor is paved with square and triangular tiles, all the sides of the squares and triangles being equal. Every square is adjacent to four triangles, and every triangle is adjacent to two squares and a triangle. Shew that the number of angular points must be the same as the number of triangles, and that this must be double of the number of squares.

---

748. A pack of cards is shuffled by the following process. The pack is held in the left hand and the cards are passed one by one in order into the right hand, the second card being placed above the first, the third underneath and so on, the cards as they pass from the left hand being placed alternately at the top and bottom of those in the right hand. Shew that if the pack contain $6n - 2$ cards the $2n$th card will retain its original position in the pack.

749. If 22 cards be repeatedly shuffled by the process of Qn. 748, shew that the 8th card will never change its place; the 5th and 16th will oscillate, exchanging places at every shuffle, while the 3rd, 13th and 18th circulate in an independent cycle regaining their original places at every third shuffle.

750. Shew that a pack of 16 cards will be restored to its original order if it be shuffled 5 times by the process of Qn. 748.

751. A pack of 32 cards will be restored to its original order after 6 shuffles; a pack of 42 cards after 8 shuffles; a pack of 28 cards or 36 cards after 9 shuffles; a pack of 12 cards or 20 cards or 46 cards after 10 shuffles; a pack of 22 cards or 52 cards after 12 shuffles.

752. A pack of $2n$ cards will be restored to its original order in $2n$ shuffles if not earlier: e.g. 14 cards require 14 shuffles; 18 cards require 18; 26 cards require 26; 30 cards require 30; 50 cards require 50 shuffles.

155.   If, in a different pattern, the triangles be placed in blocks of three forming a trapezium, and every trapezium be adjacent to five squares, the same results will hold good as in the last question.

156.   In how many ways can we form a triangle having each of its sides an integral number of inches, greater than n and not greater than $2n$?

157.   How many of these will be isosceles, and how many equilateral?

158.   The number of triangles that can be formed having each of their sides an integral number of inches not exceeding $2n$ is $\frac{1}{6}n(n+1)(4n+5)$. And excluding all equilateral and isosceles triangles it is $\frac{1}{6}n(n-1)(4n-5)$.

159.   If the number of inches is not to exceed $2n-1$, the number of triangles will be $\frac{1}{6}n(n+1)(4n-1)$. And excluding all equilateral and isosceles triangles it will be $\frac{1}{6}(n-1)(n-2)(4n-3)$.

160.   If there be n straight lines in one plane, no three of which meet in a point, the number of groups of n of their points of intersection, in each of which no three points lie in one of the straight lines, is $\frac{1}{2}\lfloor n-1$.

161.   The number of ways of dividing $2n$ different things into two equal parts, is to the number of ways of similarly dividing $4n$ different things, as the continued product of the first n odd numbers to the continued product of the n odd numbers succeeding.

162.   Shew that there are 2^{n-1} ways of selecting an odd number of things out of n things.

---

753.   A pack of $2n$ cards is shuffled by the following process. Divide the pack into two equal parts. Push one half-pack into the other in such a way that the cards of the first half go singly into the interstices between the cards of the second half. Thus the $(n+1)$th card will become top; the 1st card, second; the $(n+2)$th, third; the 2nd, fourth; and so on. Prove that after shuffling r times, the card which was originally in the pth place will now be in the xth place, where x is the remainder when $p \cdot 2^r$ is divided by $2n+1$.

754.   If a pack of $6m+2$ cards be repeatedly shuffled by the process of Qn. 753, shew that the $(2m+1)$th card and the $(4m+2)$th card will oscillate or exchange places at every shuffle.

755.   If a pack of $14m+6$ cards be shuffled three times by the process of Qn. 753, the $(2m+1)$th, $2(2m+1)$th, $3(2m+1)$th, $4(2m+1)$th, $5(2m+1)$th and $6(2m+1)$th cards will regain their original positions.

756.   If 2^x-1 be a multiple of $2n+1$, a pack of $2n$ cards will be restored to its original order after x shuffles by the process of Qn. 753.

163. If there be one card marked 1, two marked 2, three marked 3, and so on, the number of ways of selecting two cards on which the sum of the numbers shall be n is $\frac{1}{12}n(n^2-1)$ or $\frac{1}{12}n(n^2-4)$ according as n is odd or even.

164. There are $3n+1$ things of which n are alike and the rest all different: shew that there are 2^{2n} ways of selecting n things out of them.

165. In how many ways can three numbers in arithmetical progression be selected from the series $1, 2, 3 \ldots 2n$, and in how many ways from the series $1, 2, 3 \ldots (2n+1)$?

166. By considering the selections of n things out of n things with repetitions, writing down separately the number of selections when $1, 2, 3 \ldots$ or n *different* things are selected, shew that

$$\left(\frac{1}{\lfloor n-1}\right)^2 + \frac{1}{\lfloor 1 \lfloor 2}\left(\frac{1}{\lfloor n-2}\right)^2 + \frac{1}{\lfloor 2 \lfloor 3}\left(\frac{1}{\lfloor n-3}\right)^2 + \ldots \text{ to } n \text{ terms} = \frac{\lfloor 2n-1}{(\lfloor n \lfloor n-1)^2}.$$

167. Find the number of ways in which $3n$ different books may be distributed to three different persons so that their shares may be in arithmetical progression. (The cases in which the shares would be $0, n, 2n$ or n, n, n are to be included.)

168. If M_r be the number of permutations of m things taken r together, and N_r the number of permutations of n things taken r together, prove that the number of permutations of $m+n$ things r together will be obtained by expanding $(M+N)^r$, and in the result replacing the indices by suffixes.

169. In the expansion of $(a_1+a_2+\ldots+a_p)^n$ where n is an integer not greater than p, there are C_n^p terms, in none of which any one of the quantities $a_1, a_2 \ldots a_p$ occurs more than once as a factor; and the coefficient of each of these terms is $\lfloor n$.

---

757. On an enlarged chess-board of $n \times n$ squares the number of ways of choosing two squares at a knight's move from one another is $4(n-1)(n-2)$.

758. The number of ways of placing two bishops so that neither may take the other is $\frac{1}{6}n(n-1)(3n^2-n+2)$.

759. If the board be enlarged to $m \times n$ squares, shew that

$$\lfloor m \lfloor n \div \lfloor r \lfloor m-r \lfloor n-r$$

is the number of ways in which r counters can be placed so that no two shall be in the same vertical or horizontal line.

760. On the same board the number of ways of selecting two squares at a knight's move from one another is $(2m-3)(2n-3)-1$ and the number of ways of selecting four squares making a knight's circuit is

$$2[(m-3)(n-3)-1].$$

170. There are $2n$ letters, two and two alike of n different sorts. Shew that the number of orders in which they may be arranged, so that no two letters which are alike may come together, is

$$\frac{1}{2^n} \left\{ \lfloor 2n - \frac{n}{1} 2 \lfloor 2n-1 + \frac{n(n-1)}{1 \cdot 2} 2^2 \lfloor 2n-2 - \&c. \text{ to } n+1 \text{ terms} \right\}.$$

171. The number of ways in which r different things may be distributed among $n+p$ persons so that certain n of those persons may have one at least is

$$(n+p)^r - n(n+p-1)^r + \frac{n(n-1)}{1 \cdot 2}(n+p-2)^r - \&c.$$

172. Shew that, for n different things, $1 -$ (number of partitions into two parts) $+ \lfloor 2$ (number of partitions into three parts) $- \ldots \pm \lfloor n-1$ (number of partitions into n parts) $= 0$.

173. Shew that, if $m > n$,

$$\Sigma_{x=0}^{x=n} \{P_x^n \div P_x^m\} = (m+1) \div (m-n+1).$$

174. Shew that

$$\Sigma_{x=0}^{x=n} \{C_x^n C_r^n \div C_{x+r}^{2n}\} = (2n+1) \div (n+1).$$

175. Prove that, to n terms,

$$R_1^m + 2R_2^m + 3R_3^m + \ldots = (n+1) R_n^{m+1} - R_n^{m+2} = m R_{n-1}^{m+2}$$

and

$$R_1^m + 2^2 R_2^m + 3^2 R_3^m + \ldots = (n+1)^2 R_n^{m+1} - (2n+3) R_n^{m+2} + 2R_n^{m+3}$$
$$= m(m+1) R_{n-2}^{m+3} + m R_{n-1}^{m+2}.$$

Verify the results when $n = 2$.

176. Prove that

$$\frac{m}{1} + \frac{m(m+1)}{1 \cdot 2} + \frac{m(m+1)(m+2)}{1 \cdot 2 \cdot 3} + \ldots \text{ to } n \text{ terms}$$

$$= \frac{n}{1} + \frac{n(n+1)}{1 \cdot 2} + \frac{n(n+1)(n+2)}{1 \cdot 2 \cdot 3} + \ldots \text{ to } m \text{ terms}.$$

---

761. Shew that $2 \div (n+1)$ is the sum to n terms of the series whose xth term is $C_{x-1}^{n-1} \div C_x^{2n-1}$.

762. If the xth term be $C_{x-1}^{n-1} \div C_x^{n+q}$ the sum will be

$$(n+q+1) \div (q+1)(q+2).$$

763. If the xth term be $C_{x-2}^{n-2} \div C_x^{n+q}$ the sum will be

$$2(n+q+1) \div (q+1)(q+2)(q+3).$$

764. If the xth term be $C_{x-p}^{n-p} \div C_x^{n+q}$ the sum will be

$$\lfloor p (n+q+1) \div (q+1)(q+2)(q+3) \ldots (q+p+1).$$

177. Shew that $\lfloor 2n-1 \div (\lfloor n-1)^2$ is the sum to n terms of the series
$$(C_1^n)^2 + 2\,(C_2^n)^2 + 3\,(C_3^n)^2 + \ldots .$$

178. Apply Prop. XIV. to shew that

$$\frac{\lfloor n+r-1}{\lfloor r} - \frac{n}{1}\frac{\lfloor n+r-3}{\lfloor r-2} + \frac{n(n-1)}{1.2}\frac{\lfloor n+r-5}{\lfloor r-4} - \&c. \text{ (till it stops)} = \frac{\lfloor n}{\lfloor r}\frac{\lfloor n-1}{\lfloor n-r}.$$

Or, putting $n=r$,

$$\frac{\lfloor 2n-1}{\lfloor n} - \frac{n}{1}\frac{\lfloor 2n-3}{\lfloor n-2} + \frac{n(n-1)}{1.2}\frac{\lfloor 2n-5}{\lfloor n-4} - \&c. \ldots \ldots = \lfloor n-1.$$

179. Shew that, to n terms,

$$\frac{\lfloor a}{\lfloor b} + \frac{\lfloor a+1}{\lfloor b+1} + \frac{\lfloor a+2}{\lfloor b+2} + \ldots = \frac{\dfrac{\lfloor n+a}{\lfloor n+b-1} - \dfrac{\lfloor a}{\lfloor b-1}}{a-b+1}.$$

180. Shew that, to n terms,

$$\frac{\lfloor a}{\lfloor b} + \frac{\lfloor a-1}{\lfloor b-1} + \frac{\lfloor a-2}{\lfloor b-2} + \ldots = \frac{\dfrac{\lfloor a+1}{\lfloor b} - \dfrac{\lfloor a-n+1}{\lfloor b-n}}{a-b+1}.$$

181. In how many ways can four black balls, four white balls, and four red balls be put into six pockets when one or more may be left empty?

182. In how many ways can 3 sovereigns and 10 shillings be put into 4 pockets? (One or more may be left empty.)

---

765. If $Q_x^n \equiv x^n - C_1^x\,(x-1)^n + C_2^x\,(x-2)^n - \&c.$, the series being continued as far as it will go, shew that the successive values of Q_x^3 are 1, 6, 6; and those of Q_x^4 are 1, 14, 36, 24.

766. Shew that the successive values of Q_x^5 are 1, 30, 150, 240, 120; and those of Q_x^6 are 1, 62, 540, 1560, 1800, 720.

767. Shew that
$$Q_n^n = \lfloor n,$$
$$Q_{n-1}^n = (n-1)\,\lfloor n/2,$$
$$Q_{n-2}^n = (n-2)(3n-5)\,\lfloor n/24,$$
$$Q_{n-3}^n = (n-3)^2\,(n-2)\,\lfloor n/48.$$

768. Prove that
$$C_1^m Q_1^n + C_2^m Q_2^n + C_3^m Q_3^n + \ldots = m^n.$$

769. Prove that
$$Q_1^n + C_1^m Q_2^n + C_2^m Q_3^n + \ldots = (m+1)^n - m^n.$$

183. In how many ways can 12 sovereigns be distributed into five pockets, none being left empty?

184. In how many ways can 20 books be arranged in a bookcase containing five shelves, each shelf long enough to contain all the books?

185. In how many ways can a person wear five rings on the fingers (not the thumb) of one hand?

186. A debating society has to select one out of five subjects proposed. If thirty members vote, each for one subject, in how many ways can the votes fall?

187. A bookbinder has 12 different books to bind in red, green or black cloth. In how many different ways can he bind them, binding at least one in each colour?

188. In how many ways can 26 different letters be made into six words, each letter being used once and only once?

189. The *total* number of partitions of n is equal to the number of n-partitions of $2n$.

190. Shew that the number of $(r+x)$-partitions of $2r+x$ is the same whatever be x.

191. In how many ways can an examiner assign a total of 30 marks to eight questions without giving less than two marks to any question?

192. A body of n members has to elect one member as a representative of the body. If every member gives a vote, in how many ways can the votes be given? And how many different forms may the result of the poll assume, regarding only the number of votes given to each member and not the names of his supporters?

---

770. The number of ways of dividing $2n$ indifferent things into three indifferent parcels, so that every two may be together greater than the third, is the same as the number of ways of dividing n things into three parcels without restriction.

771. The number of ways of dividing $2n-3$ indifferent things into three indifferent parcels, so that every two may be together greater than the third, is the same as when there are $2n$ things.

772. How many triangles can be formed of perimeter 40, each side being an integer? And how many of perimeter 43?

773. Shew that the number of different triangles with integral sides, and with perimeter $4n+3$, exceeds the number with perimeter $4n$ by $n+1$.

193. Find the number of ways in which m indifferent black balls and n indifferent white balls can be arranged in a row, so that there may be $2r-1$ contacts of black with white.

194. In how many ways can the same balls be arranged, so that there may be $2r$ contacts of black with white?

195. The number of ways in which two persons can divide $2n$ things of one sort, and $2n$ of another, and $2n$ of a third sort, so that each person may have $3n$ things, is $3n^2+3n+1$.

196. If there be $2n$ more things of a fourth sort, the number of ways in which the persons can take $4n$ things each is $\frac{1}{3}(2n+1)(8n^2+8n+3)$.

197. In the last two questions if the things were to be equally divided into two *indifferent* parcels, the number of ways would be $\frac{1}{2}(3n^2+3n+2)$ and $\frac{1}{3}(n+1)(8n^2+4n+3)$ respectively. Explain why these results are not the halves of the previous results.

198. If there be m sorts of things and $2n$ things of each sort, the number of ways in which two persons can divide them so that each may have mn things is

$$C_{m-1}^{mn+m-1} - C_1^m\, C_{m-1}^{mn+m-2n-2} + C_2^m\, C_{m-1}^{mn+m-4n-3} - \&\text{c.},$$

the $(x+1)$th term being $\pm C_x^m\, C_{m-1}^{mn+m-1-x(2n+1)}$, and the number of terms being the integer next less than $(mn+2n+1)\div(2n+1)$.

199. In how many ways can five black balls, five red balls, and five white balls be distributed into three different bags, five into each?

200. If there be 3 sorts of things and n things of each sort, the number of ways in which three persons can divide them so as to have n things each is

$$C_2^{n+2}\, C_2^{n+2} - 3C_4^{n+3} = \frac{1}{8}(n+1)(n+2)(n^2+3n+4).$$

---

774. The number of three-partitions of n, subject to the condition that no two parts may be equal, is the greatest integer in

$$(n^2-6n+12)\div 12.$$

775. The number of four-partitions of $12n+5$, subject to the condition that no part is to exceed $6n+2$, is

$$\frac{1}{2}(n+1)(12n^2+9n+2).$$

776. The number of four-partitions of $12n+5$, no part exceeding $6n+2$ and no two parts being equal, is

$$\frac{1}{2}n(12n^2+3n-1).$$

777. Shew that the following problem has 104 solutions : *Find three integers in geometrical progression each less than* 101.

201. In how many ways can six Englishmen, seven Russians, and ten Turks be arranged in a row, so that each Englishman may stand between a Russian and a Turk, and no Russian and Turk may stand together?

202. In how many ways can five Englishmen, seven Russians, and ten Turks be arranged in a row, so that each Englishman may stand between a Russian and a Turk, and no Russian and Turk may stand together?

203. Find the number of combinations that can be formed out of the letters of the following line (Soph. *Philoct.* 746):

$$απαππαπαι \qquad παπαππαπαππαπαππαπαι,$$

taking them (1) 5 together, and (2) 25 together.

204. What is the total number of combinations that can be made out of the same letters?

205. How many solutions can be given to the following problem? "Find two numbers whose greatest common measure shall be G and their least common multiple $M = Ga^α b^β c^γ d^δ$; a, b, c, d being prime numbers."

206. How many solutions can be given to the following problem? "Find two numbers of which G shall be a common measure, and M (as in the last question) a common multiple."

207. Out of 20 letters how many combinations of six letters can be made, no letter occurring more than twice in the same combination?

---

778. A row of n letters is constantly permuted by moving any letter backwards or forwards over the next two letters. Shew that by this process exactly half of the possible permutations can be arrived at.

779. There are $p + q + r$ letters of which p are $α$'s, q are $β$'s, r are $γ$'s. If they are to be arranged so that the $α$'s must begin before the $β$'s, and the $β$'s before the $γ$'s, how many permutations are possible?

780. A pole 30 feet long is to be painted in bands, red, white, blue, red, white, blue, &c. in order, beginning at the bottom with red and ending with blue. Each band must occupy an integral number of feet not less than two, and there must be altogether 10 feet of each colour. Shew that 4720 arrangements are possible.

781. If it is not necessary to end with blue, there are 10946 arrangements.

782. If none of the bands must be less than three feet, there will be 153 arrangements ending with blue, 70 with white and 80 with red.

208. A certain symmetrical function of x, y, z is such that x is found in five of its terms, xy in three terms, xyz in two terms, and there is one term without x, or y, or z. How many terms are there altogether?

209. I have six friends, each of whom I have met at dinner 12 times. I have met every two of them 6 times, every three of them 4 times, and every four of them 3 times, every five twice, all six once, and I have dined out eight times without meeting any of them. How many times have I dined out altogether?

210. Two examiners, working simultaneously, examine a class of 12 boys, the one in classics the other in mathematics. The boys are examined individually for five minutes each in each subject. In how many ways can a suitable arrangement be made so that no boy may be wanted by both examiners at once?

211. Out of six pairs of gloves, in how many ways can six persons take each a right-handed and a left-handed glove without any person taking a pair?

212. Out of nine pairs of gloves, in how many ways can six persons take each a right-handed and a left-handed glove without any person taking a pair?

---

783. If every α must have another α next it, and every β be next another β, and every γ be next another γ, shew that the letters represented by $\alpha^2\beta^2\gamma^2$ can be arranged in 6 orders, $\alpha^3\beta^3\gamma^3$ in 6 orders, $\alpha^4\beta^4\gamma^4$ in 90 orders, and $\alpha^5\beta^5\gamma^5$ in 426 orders.

784. If there be 4 Englishmen, 4 Frenchmen, 4 Germans, 4 Russians and so on, to any number (n) of nationalities, the number of orders in which the men can be arranged in a row so that every man has a compatriot next him is $12^n \lfloor 2n$.

785. If there be 5 of each nationality, the number of orders is

$$120^n \left\{ \lfloor 2n - C_1^n \lfloor 2n-1 + C_2^n \lfloor 2n-2 - \&\text{c.} \right\}.$$

786. Six Englishmen and six Frenchmen stand in a row so that every man has a compatriot next him. Shew that the number of possible arrangements is $34 \left(\lfloor 6 \right)^2$.

787. If there be 7 Englishmen and 7 Frenchmen the number is $84 \left(\lfloor 7 \right)^2$.

788. If there be 8 Englishmen and 8 Frenchmen the number is $208 \left(\lfloor 8 \right)^2$.

789. If there be 8 Englishmen and 7 Frenchmen the number is $129 \lfloor 8 \lfloor 7$.

213. A square is divided into 16 equal squares by vertical and horizontal lines. In how many ways can 4 of these be painted white, 4 black, 4 red, and 4 blue, without repeating the same colour in the same vertical or horizontal row?

214. The number of ways of deranging a row of $m + n$ terms so that m are displaced and n not displaced is $\lfloor m+n \rfloor \div \lfloor m \lfloor n$.

215. Shew that, if n be an integer, $\lfloor n^2$ is divisible by $(\lfloor n)^{n+1}$; and if m and n are odd numbers, $\lfloor mn$ is divisible by

$$\left(\lfloor m\right)^{\frac{n+1}{2}} \left(\lfloor n\right)^{\frac{m+1}{2}}.$$

216. If there be an odd number of dominoes in a set that begins with *double-blank* and if the total number of pips on the whole set be even, the number of pips on the highest domino will be a multiple of 8.

217. If f_n denote the number of derangements of n terms in circular procession so that no term may follow the term which it followed originally,

$$f_n + f_{n+1} = \lfloor n.$$

218. Find the number of positive integral solutions of the equation $x + y + z + \dots$ (p variables) $= m$, the variables being restricted to lie between l and n, both inclusive.

219. If there be seven copies of one book, eight of another, and nine of another, in how many ways can two persons divide them, each taking 12 books?

220. The squares on a chess-board are painted with 8 colours, 8 squares with each colour. The colours are to be arranged so that every horizontal line contains every colour, but the vertical lines are only subject to the condition that no two adjacent squares must be alike. How many arrangements are possible?

221. There are n things alike and n others all different; shew that there are 2^n ways of selecting n things out of them, and that the number of orders in which all the $2n$ things can be arranged is $2^n \cdot 1 \cdot 3 \cdot 5 \dots (2n-1)$.

---

790. If m Frenchmen and n Englishmen are to stand in a row subject to the condition that every man must have at least one compatriot next him, the number of possible orders is $\lfloor m \lfloor n$ multiplied by

$$1 + (C_0^{m-2} + C_1^{m-3})(C_0^{n-2} + C_1^{n-3}) + (C_1^{m-3} + C_2^{m-4})(C_1^{n-3} + C_2^{n-4})$$
$$+ (C_2^{m-4} + C_3^{m-5})(C_2^{n-4} + C_3^{n-5}) + \&c.,$$

the series being continued until the terms vanish.

222. If a set of dominoes be made from double-blank up to double n, prove that the number whose pips are $n-r$ is the same as the number whose pips are $n+r$, and this number is $\frac{1}{4}(2n-2r+3\pm1)$; and the total number of dominoes is $\frac{1}{2}(n+1)(n+2)$.

223. If all the combinations of n letters $(1, 2, 3\ldots$ or n together) be written down, the number of times each letter will occur is 2^{n-1}.

224. The total number of permutations $[1, 2, 3\ldots$ or $(m+n)$ together] which can be made out of m things all alike and n other things all alike is $C_{m+1,\ n+1}-2$.

225. If we write down all possible permutations $[1, 2, 3\ldots$ or $(m+n)$ together] of m a's and n β's, we shall write a and β respectively

$$1+\frac{mn+m-1}{n+2}C_{n+1,\ n+1} \text{ times ; and } 1+\frac{mn+n-1}{m+2}C_{m+1,\ n+1} \text{ times.}$$

226. Write down all the permutations 1, 2, 3, 4 or 5 together of the letters $m\,a\,m\,m\,a$, and verify the result of the last question.

227. The total number of permutations $[1, 2, 3\ldots$ or $(m+n+1)$ together] which can be made out of m things alike, n other things alike, and one different thing, always using the one different thing, is

$$1+\frac{mn+m+n}{m+n+4}C_{m+2,\ n+2}.$$

228. The total number of permutations $[1, 2, 3$ or$\ldots(m+n+1)$ together] which can be made out of m things alike, n other things alike, and one different thing, is

$$\frac{(m+1)(n+1)}{m+n+3}C_{m+2,\ n+2}-1.$$

---

791. I have seven friends. Shew how I may invite three of them to dinner every day for seven days without any two of them meeting more than once.

792. Shew that the parties may be formed in 90 ways, giving $90\,\underline{\vert 7}$ arrangements.

793. If I am to have seven different parties of three, and no friend is to be left out altogether, the number of arrangements is $P_7^{35}-7\cdot P_7^{20}+21\cdot P_7^{10}$.

794. If I am to have seven different parties of three, and no guest is to come every day, the number of arrangements is $P_7^{35}-7\cdot P_7^{15}$.

795. If m men and n women are to enter a room in single file so that there may never be as many women as men in the room, the number of possible orders is $(m-n)\underline{\vert m+n-1}$.

229. Write down all the permutations, one or more together, of the letters *p e p p e r*, and verify the result of the last question.

230. The total number of permutations of n things [1, 2, 3 ... or n together] is the integer nearest to $e \lfloor n-1$.

231. The total number of permutations of n things [1, 2, 3, ... or n together] is greater than $e \lfloor n-1-1 \div n$ and less than $e \lfloor n-1-1 \div (n+1)$.

232. If all the permutations of n letters (1, 2, 3 ... or n together) be written down, the number of times each letter will occur is the integer nearest to $e (n-1) \lfloor n-1$.

233. The integer in the last question is always greater than $e (n-1) \lfloor n-1$ and less than $e (n-1) \lfloor n-1+2 \div (n^2-1)$.

234. In how many different orders can seven men and five women get into a carriage, one by one, so that there may never be more women than men in it?

235. In how many orders can m positive units and n negative units be arranged so that the sum to any number of terms may never be negative?

236. In how many orders can m even powers of x and n odd powers of x be arranged so that when $x = -1$ the sum to any number of terms may never be negative?

---

796. A coin is tossed $2n$ times; shew that Y_n is the number of ways in which the heads will never be in excess of the tails.

797. If it be tossed $2n+1$ times, the number of ways is $\frac{1}{2} Y_{n+1}$.

798. One moves from O to P by 5 horizontal and 3 vertical paces. Through O and P parallel lines are drawn, equally inclined to the vertical and horizontal. Shew that of the 56 routes from O to P, 8 cross both the parallels, 8 cross neither, and 40 cross one only.

799. One moves from O to P by $2n-1$ horizontal and n vertical paces. Parallels are drawn as in Qn. 798. Shew that the number of routes from O to P which cross neither parallel is the same as the number which cross both.

800. One moves from O to P by m horizontal and n vertical paces. Shew that among the $C_{m, n}$ possible routes there are $C_{m+2, n-2}$ which cross both parallels and $C_{m, n} - 2C_{m+1, n-1} + C_{m+2, n-2}$ which cross neither. ($m > 2n - 2$.)

237. In how many orders can a man win m games and lose n games so as at no period to have lost more than he has won?

238. In how many different orders can a man possessed of h pounds win m wagers and lose n wagers of 1 pound each without being ruined during the process?

239. If p, q, r be integers, such that the two lowest are together greater than the highest, and $p+q+r=2s$, the number of ways in which two men can divide p black balls, q white and r red, so that each may take s balls, is $s^2+s+1-\frac{1}{2}(p^2+q^2+r^2)$.

240. If the two lowest are together less than the highest $(q+r<p)$, the result in the last question must be increased by $\frac{1}{2}(p-s)(p-s-1)$.

CHANCE.

241. If a letter be taken at random from the word *organize*, what is the chance that it is a vowel?

242. What is the chance that a letter taken at random from *resplendence* should be e, and what is the chance that it should be n?

243. What is the chance that a letter taken at random from *paraphrase* should be a vowel, and if it be known to be a vowel what is the chance that it is a?

244. If two letters are taken at random out of *esteemed*, shew that the odds against both being e are the same as the odds in favour of one at least being e.

245. If two letters be taken at random out of *murmurer*, what is the chance that they should be both alike?

246. What is the chance that two letters taken at random from *obsequious* should both be vowels?

247. Three letters are taken at random from *association*, what is the chance that one of them is c?

248. What is the chance that at least one of them is s?

249. What is the chance that two of them are alike?

250. What is the chance that one and only one is s?

251. If the letters of *obsequious* be arranged at random, what is the chance that all the vowels come together?

252. If the letters of *o i s e a u* be arranged at random, what is the chance that the vowels occur in their natural order?

253. A letter is taken at random out of *a s s i s t a n t* and a letter out of *s t a t i s t i c s.* What is the chance that they are the same letter?

254. A letter is taken at random out of *e f f e t e* and a letter out of *f e e t;* show that the odds are 5 to 3 against their being the same letter.

255. Two letters are taken at random out of *c o c o a* and two out of *c o c o o n.* Find the chance that the four letters should be all different.

256. If the letters of *r e p l e t e* be arranged at random, find the chance that no two *e*'s come together.

257. Find the chance that all the *e*'s come together.

258. How are the last two results affected if the letters be arranged in a ring instead of a line?

259. What is the chance that three letters taken at random from *m u h a m m a d a n* should be all different?

260. What is the chance that five taken at random should be all different?

261. If ten persons form a ring, what is the chance that two assigned persons will be together?

262. If ten persons stand in a line, what is the chance that two assigned persons will stand together?

263. A letter is chosen at random out of each of the words *t i n s e l* and *s i l e n t.* What is the chance that they are the same letter? And what does the chance become if it is known that they are either both consonants or both vowels?

264. A letter is chosen at random out of each of the words *m u s i c a l* and *a m u s i n g:* what is the chance that the same letter is chosen in each case?

265. A letter is taken at random out of each of the words *c h o i c e* and *c h a n c e :* what is the chance that they should be the same letter?

266. What is the chance that two letters taken at random out of the word *m y r r h* should be the same as two taken at random out of *m e r r y*?

---

801. A letter is taken at random from each of the words *i s l e t, e n l i s t* and *s t e n c i l.* What is the chance that they are all three alike?

802. What is the chance that all three are different?

267. 120 men are to be formed at random into a solid rectangle of 12 men by 10; all sides are equally likely to be in front. What is the chance that an assigned man is in the front?

268. If the 26 letters of the alphabet are written down in a *ring* so that no two vowels come together, what is the chance that *a* is next to *b*?

269. If the 26 letters of the alphabet are written down in a *row* so that no two vowels come together, what is the chance that *a* is next to *b*?

270. *A*, *B*, *C* have equal claims for a prize. *A* says to *B*, let us two draw lots, let the loser withdraw and the winner draw lots with *C* for the prize. Is this fair?

271. *A* and *B* stand in a line with 10 other persons. If the arrangement is made at random what is the chance that there are exactly 3 persons between *A* and *B*?

272. What would the chance be if they stood in a ring instead of a line?

273. Five men, *A*, *B*, *C*, *D*, *E*, speak at a meeting, and it is known that *A* speaks before *B*, what is the chance that *A* speaks *immediately* before *B*?

274. Two numbers are chosen at random, find the chance that their sum is even.

275. A bag contains six black balls and one red. A person is to draw them out in succession, and is to receive a shilling for every ball he draws until he draws the red one. What is his expectation?

276. There are ten tickets, five of which are numbered 1, 2, 3, 4, 5, and the other five are blank. What is the probability of drawing a total of ten in three trials, one ticket being drawn out and replaced at each trial?

277 What is the probability in the preceding question if the tickets are not replaced?

---

803. A common die is thrown repeatedly in presence of six persons. The first is to score every number that turns up until an ace has appeared; the second is to score every number until a 2 has appeared; the third until a 3 has appeared and so on. Shew that their expectations are equal.

804. From 50 cards numbered consecutively two are drawn at random, find the chance that the difference of the numbers drawn is less than 17.

805. Find the chance that the difference is greater than 17.

806. Shew that the average value of the difference is exactly 17.

278. A person has ten coins, which he throws down in succession. He is to receive one shilling if the first falls head, two shillings *more* if the second *also* falls head, four shillings *more* if the third *also* falls head, and so on, the amount doubling each time; but as soon as a coin falls tail, he ceases to receive anything. What is the value of his expectation?

279. *A* and *B* play at chess, and *A* wins on an average two games out of three. Find the chance of *A* winning exactly four games out of the first six, drawn games being disregarded.

280. Four flies come into a room in which there are four lumps of sugar, of different degrees of attractiveness, proportional to the numbers 8, 9, 10, 12; what is the chance that the flies will all select different lumps?

281. A teetotum of eight faces numbered from one to eight, and a common die are thrown: what is the chance that the same number is turned up on each?

282. Out of a set of dominoes, numbered from double one to double six, one is drawn at random. At the same time a pair of common dice are thrown. What is the chance that the numbers turned up on the dice will be the same as those on the domino? and what is the chance that they will have one number at least in common?

283. What are the odds against throwing seven twice at least in three throws with two dice?

284. Two persons play for a stake, each throwing two dice. They throw in turn, *A* commencing. *A* wins if he throws 6, *B* if he throws 7: the game ceasing as soon as either event happens. Shew that *A*'s chance is to *B*'s as 30 to 31.

---

807. I continue to throw a common die until I have thrown an ace. If I succeed the first time I receive £5; if at the second trial £4; if at the third £3 and so on. If I do not succeed till the sixth I receive nothing; or till the seventh I pay £1; or till the eighth I pay £2; and so on ad infinitum until an ace turns up. Shew that the bargain is a fair one.

808. Two dice are thrown and I am to score the difference of the numbers turned up. Shew that my expectation is $\frac{35}{18}$.

809. If three dice are thrown and I am to score the difference between the highest and the lowest of the numbers turned up my expectation is $\frac{35}{12}$.

810. If two dice be thrown shew that the odds are 2 to 1 against one of the numbers turned up being *more than* double of the other, and 2 to 1 in favour of the square of one being more than double of the square of the other.

285. *A, B, C* amongst them stake £9. 2*s*., and throw in turn with a single die, until an ace is thrown, the thrower of the ace to take all the stakes. In what proportion ought they to contribute the stakes?

286. Two faces of a die are marked with even numbers and the other four faces with odd numbers. Shew that the odds are 41 to 40 in favour of the sum of four throws being an even number.

287. An archer hits his target on an average 3 times out of 4, find the chance that in the next four trials he will hit it three times exactly.

288. A man wins on an average 3 games out of 5, find the chance that out of the next five games he wins exactly 3.

289. On an average out of 10 games a player wins 3, loses 5, and the others are drawn. Find the chance that out of the next ten games he wins exactly 3, and loses exactly 5.

290. An experiment succeeds twice as often as it fails. Find the chance that in the next six trials there will be at least four successes.

291. A bag contains four red balls and two others, each of which is equally likely to be red or white. Three times in succession a ball is drawn and replaced. Find the chance that all the drawings are red.

---

811. If a common die be thrown *two* or *three* times the chance that the highest throw is exactly twice the lowest is $\frac{1}{8}$.

812. If the die be thrown twice the chance that the highest throw is at least twice the lowest is $\frac{1}{2}$.

813. If it be thrown three times the chance that the highest throw is at least twice the lowest is $\frac{3}{4}$.

814. If the die be thrown twice the chance that the highest throw is exactly three times the lowest is $\frac{1}{9}$, and the chance that it is at least three times the lowest is $\frac{5}{18}$.

815. If the die be thrown three times the chance that the highest throw is exactly three times the lowest is $\frac{1}{6}$, and the chance that it is at least three times the lowest is $\frac{1}{2}$.

816. A common die is to be thrown 5 times and I am to score the sum of the greatest and least throws. Shew that my expectation is 7. But when the first throw has been seen my expectation will be approximately $6\frac{1}{4}$, $6\frac{11}{16}$, $6\frac{15}{16}$, $7\frac{1}{16}$, $7\frac{5}{16}$, $7\frac{3}{4}$ according as the throw is 1, 2, 3, 4, 5, 6. [For absolute accuracy the numerators of the fractions are 325, 951, 1215, 81, 345, 971, to the common denominator 1296.]

292. A bag contains a £5 note (V), a £10 note (X), and six pieces of blank paper (O^6). If a man is to draw them one by one and to go on drawing till he draws a blank, what is his expectation?

293. A box contains 10 pairs of gloves. A draws out a single glove: then B draws one: then A draws a second: then B draws a second. Shew that A's chance of drawing a *pair* is the same as B's and that the chance of neither drawing a pair is $290 \div 323$.

294. A boy tries to jump a ditch: in jumping from the upper bank to the lower he succeeds five times out of six, in jumping from the lower to the upper he succeeds three times out of five. What is the chance that after four trials he leaves off on the same side on which he began?

295. Shew that the odds are eleven to three against a month selected at random containing portions of *six* different weeks.

296. A walks at an uniform speed known to be greater than 3 and less than 4 miles an hour between 2 places 20 miles apart. An hour having elapsed since A's departure, B starts after him for the same place walking at the uniform speed of 4 miles an hour. Find the odds against B's overtaking A, (1) on the hypothesis that within the given limits all distances per hour are equally likely, (2) on the hypothesis that within the limits all times per mile are equally likely.

297. Three different persons have each to name an integer not greater than n. Find the chance that the integers named will be such that every two are together greater than the third.

---

817. I draw a card from an ordinary pack. If it be king, queen or knave I pay 14 pence: if it be any other card I receive as many pence as there are pips upon the card. What is the value of my expectation?

818. I throw a common die. If an even number turns up I receive that number of pence. If an odd number turns up I pay that number of pence. What is the value of my expectation?

819. If a common die be thrown 6 times the expectation of the lowest throw is $\frac{67171}{46656}$.

820. The expectation of the highest throw is $\frac{259421}{46656}$.

821. From 15 tickets numbered consecutively 1, 2, 3...15, A and B each draw one. If A's is known to be a multiple of 5 and B's to be a multiple of 3, shew that the odds are 47 to 43 that A has drawn a higher number than B.

822. Shew that the odds were *à priori* 13 to 2 against the highest ticket being drawn, but after the observation made the odds become 4 to 3.

298. *A* and *B* play at chess, and *A* wins on an average five games out of nine. Find *A*'s chance of winning a majority (1) out of three games, (2) out of four games, drawn games not being counted.

299. If the odds on every game between two players are two to one in favour of the winner of the preceding game, what is the chance that he who wins the first game shall win at least two out of the next three?

300. *A*, *B*, *C* play at a game in which each has a separate score, and the game is won by the player who first scores 3. If the chances are respectively $\frac{1}{2}$, $\frac{1}{4}$, $\frac{1}{4}$, that any point is scored by *A*, *B*, *C*, find the respective chances of the three players winning the game.

301. The chance of one event happening is the square of the chance of a second event, but the odds against the first are the cube of the odds against the second. Find the chance of each.

302. With two dice having their faces numbered *alike* in any way whatever, the chance of throwing an even number can never be less than $\frac{1}{2}$.

303. If *mn* men are formed into a solid column with *m* men in front and *n* in depth, find the chance that a given man will be on the outside of the column.

---

823. If three squares be chosen at random on a chess-board the chance that no two are in the same vertical or horizontal line is $\frac{4}{7}\frac{8}{1}$.

824. Find the chance that no two are in the same diagonal line.

825. A purse contains 80 coins of which 8 have been specially marked. I draw coins one by one until all the marked coins are drawn. Shew that on an average 8 coins will be left in the purse.

826. Eleven cricketers make a total score of 100. In how many ways can the score be made up? If all these ways be deemed equally probable what is the chance that some player makes at least 50.

827. Twelve sovereigns are made into three parcels, all three-partitions being equally probable. If I am to take the largest parcel my expectation is £6. 15*s*.

828. Twelve sovereigns are placed in three drawers, all distributions being equally probable, no drawer being left empty. If I am to take the sovereigns from the drawer which contains the most my expectation is £6. 17*s*. 10*d*. nearly.

829. If one or two drawers may be left empty my expectation will be £7. 10*s*. 1½*d*. nearly.

830. *A* is twice as good a player as *B*. If they engage in a match to win six consecutive games the odds are 3328 to 95 in favour of *A*.

304. If n men, among whom are A and B, stand in a row, what is the chance that there will be exactly r men between them?

305. If they stand in a ring instead of a row, the chance will be independent of r.

306. If A agrees to pay B a shilling for every man who stands between them, what is B's expectation when the n men are arranged at random in a row?

307. What is B's expectation if they stand in a ring and count the shortest distance between them?

308. What is it, in the last case, if they count from A's right to B?

309. A bag contains m white and n black balls. (1) If they are drawn out one by one, find the chance of first drawing a white and then a black, and so on alternately, until the balls remaining are all of one colour. (2) If m balls are drawn at once, what is the chance that all the white balls will be drawn at the first trial?

---

831. If S_k denote the number of times we may expect to have to toss a coin in order to obtain k consecutive heads, shew from elementary considerations that $\frac{1}{2} S_k = 1 + S_{k-1}$. Hence deduce an elementary proof of Prop. LIV. for the case when $\mu = \frac{1}{2}$.

832. In the general case of Prop. LIV. shew from elementary considerations that $S_k = 1 + S_{k-1} + \nu S_k$. Hence prove the Proposition.

833. If a coin be tossed n times, prove that the chance that there are not two consecutive heads is

$$\frac{(1 + \sqrt{5})^{n+2} - (1 - \sqrt{5})^{n+2}}{4^{n+1} \sqrt{5}}.$$

834. Each of two urns contains n cards numbered successively 1, 2, 3, ... n. I draw a card from each urn and receive a number of shillings equal to the difference between the numbers on the two cards drawn. I repeat this operation, again receiving the difference in shillings between the two numbers which I draw; and so on, until at the nth operation the cards are exhausted. Shew that my expectation is worth $\frac{1}{3}(n^2 - 1)$ shillings.

835. A bag contains mr balls of r different colours, m balls of each colour. I draw n balls and receive a shilling for every colour drawn. Shew that my expectation of shillings is

$$r \{1 - C_n^{mr-m} \div C_n^{mr}\}.$$

310. A boy who on an average does four sums out of five correctly is given five sums to do. Shew that the odds are more than two to one against their being all right.

311. A spins a teetotum with a faces, numbered 1, 2, 3...a respectively, B spins one with b faces, similarly numbered from 1 to b. Each spins once and the highest number wins. Shew that if $a > b$, A's chance is $1 - \dfrac{b+1}{2a}$, B's chance is $\dfrac{b-1}{2a}$, and the chance of a tie is $\dfrac{1}{a}$.

312. If in the last exercise they are to spin again in case of a tie, A's chance of winning will be $\dfrac{2a-b-1}{2a-2}$, and B's chance will be $\dfrac{b-1}{2a-2}$.

313. Out of $2n$ tickets, numbered consecutively, three are drawn at random. Find the chance that the numbers on them are in A.P.

314. Out of $2n+1$ tickets, consecutively numbered, three are drawn at random. Find the chance that the numbers on them are in A.P.

315. A and B shoot at a mark, and A hits it once in n times, and B once in $n-1$ times. If they shoot alternately, A commencing, compare their chances of first hitting the mark.

316. If there be m sorts of things and n things of each sort, shew that the chance that $m-r$ things selected at random may be all different is

$$n^{m-r}\, C_r^{mn+r} \div C_m^{mn+r}.$$

---

836. One boy has six coins, another has five. They play pitch and toss with them until one boy has won them all. Shew that they may expect 30 tosses.

837. A throws a die whose faces are numbered 2, 4, 6, 8, 10, 12. B throws one whose faces are numbered 1, 3, 5, 7, 9, 11. What is the chance that at a single throw A throws higher than B?

838. They throw for penny stakes, the higher throw winning; and they go on throwing until one has lost all his money. If each had three pence to begin with they may expect to make $8\frac{5}{13}$ throws.

839. If they have four pence each to begin with they may expect over 14 throws.

840. If they begin with five pence each they may expect over 51 throws.

841. If they make three throws each the odds are 9907 to 5645 in favour of A's aggregate being greater than B's.

317. If n things (a, β, γ, &c.) be arranged in a row subject to the condition that a comes before β, what is the chance that a comes *next* before β?

318. There are n counters marked with odd numbers, and n more marked with even numbers; if two are drawn at random shew that the odds are n to $n-1$ against the sum of the numbers drawn being even.

319. If a head counts for *one* and a tail for *two*, shew that $3n$ is the most likely number to throw when $2n$ coins are tossed. Also shew that the chance of throwing $3(n+1)$ with $2(n+1)$ coins is less than the chance of throwing $3n$ with $2n$ coins in the ratio $2n+1 : 2n+2$.

320. A red card has been removed from a pack. Thirteen cards are then drawn and found to be all of one colour. Shew that the odds are 2 to 1 that this colour is black.

321. Two squares are marked at random on a chess-board. Shew that the odds are 17 to 1 against their being adjacent.

322. If two squares of opposite colour are marked at random on a chess-board the chance that they are adjacent is $\frac{7}{64}$.

323. If two squares are marked at random on a chess-board the chance that they have contact at a corner is $\frac{7}{144}$.

324. If two squares of the same colour are marked at random on a chess-board the chance that they have contact at a corner is $\frac{49}{496}$.

325. Two squares are chosen at random on a chess-board: what is the chance that one is a castle's move from the other?

326. What is the chance that both are the same colour, and one a castle's move from the other?

327. Two squares are chosen at random on a chess-board: what is the chance that one is a knight's move from the other?

328. What is the chance that one is a bishop's move from the other?

329. What is the chance that one is a queen's move from the other?

330. What is the chance that one is a king's move from the other?

---

842. If two dice be thrown, shew that the mean value of the quotient of the numbers turned up is 343/240.

843. If the numbers turned up be unequal and the larger be divided by the smaller, the mean value of the quotient is 759/300; but if the smaller be divided by the larger, the mean value is $\frac{1}{2}$.

331.   Four squares are chosen at random on a chess-board : what is the chance that they should form a knight's circuit?

332.   Two black squares and two white squares are chosen at random on a chess-board : what is the chance that they should form a knight's circuit?

333.   Two boards are divided into squares coloured alternately like a chess-board.   One has 9 rows of 16 squares each.   The other has 12 rows of 12 squares.   If two squares are chosen at random, shew that they are more likely to be adjacent on the square board than on the oblong one, in the ratio of 264 to 263.

334.   In the last question, if the squares were chosen at random of opposite colours, the square board would still have the same advantage over the oblong.

335.   The two squares in Qn. 333 are more likely to have corner-contact on the square board than on the oblong one, in the ratio of 121 to 120.

336.   If three squares be chosen at random on a chess-board, the chance that they are in the same line, excluding diagonal lines, is $\frac{2}{93}$.

337.   The chance that they should be in a diagonal line is $\frac{7}{744}$.

338.   If four squares be chosen at random on a chess-board, find the chance that they be at the corners of a square having its sides parallel to the sides of the board.

339.   Find the chance that they be at the corners of a square having its sides parallel to the diagonals of the board.

340.   What would be the chance in the last question if the four squares were taken at random of one colour?

341.   In a single throw with four dice, what is the chance of throwing two doublets?

342.   What is the chance of the throw containing a single doublet?

---

844.   A die is thrown 6 times in succession.   If the same face turns up 6 times A is to score all the throws.   If a face turns up 5 times in succession B is to score the sequence.   So C is to score a sequence of 4, and D any sequences of 3, and E any sequences of 2.   Also F is to score any throws which do not come in sequences.   Prove that their expectations are as 3 : 25 : 170 : 990 : 4860 : 17280.

845.   A die is thrown 10 times.   I am to score all throws that occur in sequences of two or more.   My opponent is to score all that occur singly.   Shew that his expectation is greater than mine in the ratio 13 to 5.

343. If six dice are thrown together, what is the chance that the throw will be (1) three doublets, (2) two triplets, (3) a quartett and a doublet ?

344. Compare the chances of throwing four with one die, eight with two dice, and twelve with three dice, having two trials in each case.

345. What is the probability of throwing not more than eight in a single throw with three dice ?

346. There is a greater chance of throwing nine in a single throw with three dice than with two dice. Shew that the chances are as 25 to 24.

347. In a single throw with three dice, the chance that the sum turned up will be a multiple of three is one-third ; and the chance that it will be a multiple of six is one-sixth.

348. A prize is to be won by A as soon as he throws five with two dice, or by B as soon as he throws ten with three dice. If they throw alternately, A commencing, shew that their chances of winning are equal.

349. A and B have each a pair of dice : shew that the odds are nearly 19 to 1 against their making the same throw in one trial. And if they throw with three dice each, the odds are nearly 46 to 1.

350. The chance of throwing 14 is the same whether we throw with three dice or with five.

351. The chance of throwing 15 is less with three dice than with five as 360 to 651.

352. If we throw with two dice and count the difference of the two numbers which turn up, this is as likely as not to be *one-or-two*. Also the chance of *zero* is the same as the chance of *three*, and is the same as the chance of *four-or-five*.

353. A, B, C, D throw with two dice in succession, the highest throw winning a prize of one guinea. If two or more throw equal sums (higher than their competitors) they divide the prize. A having thrown 9, what is the value of his expectation ?

354. A die is loaded so that *six* turns up twice as often as *ace* and three times as often as any other face. Another die is loaded so that *six* turns up three times as often as *ace* and twice as often as any other face. If these dice be thrown together what is the chance of throwing *sixes* ?

---

846. If two dice be thrown, the expectation of the square of the sum of the numbers turned up is $54\frac{5}{6}$, and if three dice be thrown the expectation is 119.

847. The expectation of the cube of the sum of the numbers turned up by two dice is $465\frac{1}{2}$, and with three dice the expectation is $1433\frac{1}{4}$.

355. What is the chance of throwing at least one *six*?

356. What is the chance of throwing at least eleven?

357. What is the chance of throwing doublets?

358. What is the chance of throwing seven?

359. Shew that if each die is loaded so that *six* turns up oftener than any other face in the ratio 7 : 4, the odds are 41 to 40 in favour of a throw with two dice exceeding *seven*.

360. If each be so loaded that *six* turns up less often than any other face in the ratio 2 : 5, the odds will be 55 to 26 against the throw exceeding *seven*.

361. Eleven cards are marked with the letters of the word *Hammersmith*, and one is lost. Out of the remaining ten a card is drawn and is found to be *m*. What is the chance that the lost letter was *m*?

362. If in the last question the drawn card is replaced and again a card drawn at random is found to be *m*, what is the chance that the lost letter was *m*? And if the same operation be repeated again with the same result, what does the chance then become?

363. If in the last question the drawn card had not been replaced, what would the chances have been after each operation?

364. It is not known whether a set of dominoes goes to double eight or double nine, each being equally likely. Two dominoes are drawn and found to contain no number higher than eight. Shew that the odds are now three to two in favour of the set going only to double eight.

365. Two letters have fallen out of the word *Mississippi*; they are picked up and placed at random in the two blank spaces. Find the chance that the letters are in right order.

---

848. A die is thrown twice. I score the higher number that turns up. Shew that my expectation is $4\cdot47\dot2$.

849. If I score the highest of three throws, my expectation is $4\cdot958\dot3$.

850. If I score the highest of four throws, my expectation is $5\cdot2446$ nearly.

851. A bag contains 13 counters representing £1, £4, £9, £16, and so on (successive square numbers). If I am allowed to draw one, my expectation is £63. But if I draw three and reject the highest and lowest of the three, my expectation will be only £56.

366. A box contains four dice two of which are true, and the others are so loaded that with either of them the chance of throwing six is $\frac{1}{4}$ and the chance of throwing ace is $\frac{1}{12}$. I take two dice at random out of the box and throw them. If they turn up *sixes* find the chance (1) that both are loaded, (2) that one only is loaded, and (3) that neither is loaded.

367. What would be the chances in the last question, if *six and five* had turned up?

368. What would be the chances in the same question, if *six and one* had turned up?

369. One card out of a pack has been lost. From the remainder of the pack thirteen cards are drawn at random, and are found to consist of two spades, three clubs, four hearts, and four diamonds. What are the respective chances that the missing card is a spade, a club, a heart, or a diamond?

370. A man has left his umbrella in one of three shops which he visited in succession. He is in the habit of leaving it, on an average, once in every four times that he goes to a shop. Find the chance of his having left it in the first, second, and third shops respectively.

371. Eleven cricketers had to elect a captain. Each was as likely as not to vote for himself. Otherwise he voted at random. What are the odds that a man who polled five votes voted for himself?

372. The odds are estimated as 2 to 1 that a man will write *r i g o r o u s* rather than *r i g o u r o u s*. Out of the word which he writes a letter is taken at random and is found to be *u*. What are now the odds that he wrote the word in the former way?

373. If two letters had been taken at random out of the word and found to be *both alike*, what would be the odds that the word was written in the former way?

———

852. Three terms are selected at random from the series $1, 2, 3, \ldots n$. Shew that if n is even, the sum of the three terms is equally likely to be odd or even. But if n be odd, the sum is more likely to be even than odd in the ratio $n^2 - 2n + 3$ to $n^2 - 2n - 3$.

853. Out of $2n$ consecutive numbers $2r$ numbers are selected at random. Shew that if r be even, the odds are $C_{2r}^{2n} + C_r^n$ to $C_{2r}^{2n} - C_r^n$ in favour of the sum of the selected numbers being even; but if r be odd, there are the same odds in favour of the sum being odd.

854. If $2r + 1$ numbers be selected, their sum is equally likely to be odd or even.

374. The face of a die, which should have been marked ace, has been accidentally marked with one of the other five numbers. A six is thrown twice in two throws. What is the chance that the third throw will give a six?

375. Reference is made to a month which contains portions of six different weeks: what is the chance that it contains thirty-one days?

376. One card has been lost out of a pack. From the remainder 13 cards are drawn and are found to be all black. Find the chance that the lost card is red.

377. A bag contains seven cards inscribed with the letters of the word *singing*. Another bag contains the letters of *morning*, and a third bag the letters of *evening*. From one of the bags two letters are drawn and are found to be n and g. What is the chance that it was the first bag?

378. From one of the bags in the last question two letters are drawn and are *both alike*; what are the respective chances of the bag having been the first, the second or the third?

379. One letter each is drawn from two of the bags, and the two letters drawn are found to be both alike. What are the respective chances that the bag not drawn from was the first, the second or the third?

380. In six trials, on an average, A hits the centre 3 times, the outer twice, and misses once. B misses 3 times, hits the outer twice, and the centre once. A man who is equally likely to be A or B is observed to fire three shots, two of which hit the centre and one misses. Shew that the odds are now 3 to 1 that the man is A.

381. If two letters are taken at random out of *little lilies*, shew that the odds are 5 to 1 against their being both alike.

382. If three of the letters are taken at random the odds are 6 to 5 against two (at least) being alike.

---

855. Out of $2n+1$ consecutive numbers $2r$ numbers are selected at random. Shew that if r be even, the odds are $C_{2r}^{2n+1}+C_r^n$ to $C_{2r}^{2n+1}-C_r^n$ in favour of the sum of the selected numbers being even; but if r be odd, there are the same odds in favour of the sum being odd.

856. If $2r+1$ numbers be selected the odds are $C_{2r+1}^{2n+1}+C_r^n$ to $C_{2r+1}^{2n+1}-C_r^n$ in favour of the sum being even if r is even, and odd if r is odd, provided the first of the consecutive numbers be odd; but if the first of the consecutive numbers be even the odds are reversed.

383. Four persons draw each a card from an ordinary pack. Find the chance (i) that one card is of each suit: (ii) that no two cards are of equal value: (iii) that one card is of each suit and no two of equal value.

384. Each of four persons draws a card from an ordinary pack. Find the chance that one card is of each suit, and that in addition, on a second drawing, each person shall draw a card of the same suit as before.

385. All the cards marked 1, 2, 3, 4, 5 are dealt into one heap, and all marked 6, 7, 8, 9, 10 into another. If a card be taken at random out of each heap, what is the chance that the sum of the numbers on them is eleven?

386. If two cards be taken out of each heap what is the chance that the sum is twenty-two?

387. A bag contains m black balls and n white balls $(m>n)$. These are drawn out in succession. Shew that the chance that there shall never be an equal number of black and white balls drawn is $(m-n)\div(m+n)$.

388. A man undertakes to win two games consecutively out of three games, playing alternately with two opponents of unequal skill. Shew that it is to his advantage to begin by playing with the more skilful opponent.

389. When A and B play at chess A wins on an average two games out of three. What are the respective chances of A winning each of the following matches, A undertaking (1) to win two games out of the first three, (2) to win two consecutive games out of the first four, (3) to win four games out of the first six?

390. Two men engage in a match to win two games out of three, the odds in every game being three to two in favour of the player who begins. If the winner of any game always begins the next game, shew that the odds on the match are 69 : 56 in favour of the player who begins the first game.

857. If three numbers be chosen at random out of 1, 2, 4, 5, 6, 7, 8, 10, 11, their continued product is equally likely to be of any of the forms $3N-1$, $3N$, $3N+1$.

858. Shew that the odds are 11 to 10 in favour of the continued product being divisible by 8.

859. Three numbers are selected at random out of $3n$ consecutive integers, the chances of their sum being of the forms $3N-1$, $3N$, $3N+1$ are as $3n^2-3n$, $3n^2-3n+2$, $3n^2-3n$.

860. The chances of their continued product being of the forms $3N-1$, $3N$, $3N+1$ are as $4n^2-6n+2$, $19n^2-15n+2$, $4n^2-6n+2$.

391. *A* and *B* play at chess. If *A* has the first move the odds are eleven to six in favour of his winning the game, but if *B* has the first move the odds are only nine to five in *A*'s favour. It is known that *A* has won a game, what are the odds that he had first move?

392. In the last question, if *A* has the first move in the first game, and the loser of each game plays first in the next game, what is *A*'s chance of winning at least two out of the first three games?

393. A marksman's score is made up of *centres* counting 2 each and *outers* counting 1 each. He finds that he hits the centre once in five trials and he hits the outer ring as often as he misses altogether. What score may he expect to make in 5 shots, and what is the chance that he makes exactly this?

394. What is the chance that he makes more than the expected score, and what is the chance that he makes less?

395. There are ten counters in a bag marked with numbers. A person is allowed to draw two of them. If the sum of the numbers drawn is an odd number, he receives that number of shillings; if it is an even number, he pays that number of shillings. Is the value of his expectation greater when the counters are numbered from 0 to 9 or from 1 to 10?

396. A bag contains six shillings and two sovereigns. What is the value of one's expectation if one is allowed to draw till one draws a sovereign?

397. One of two bags contains ten sovereigns, and the other ten shillings. One coin is taken out of each and placed in the other. This is repeated ten times. What is now the expectation of each bag?

398. Four whist players cut for partners (i.e. each draws a card, the two highest to play together and the two lowest together), what is the chance that they will have to cut again?

---

861. From a pack of $3n$ cards numbered 1, 2, 3, ... $3n$ my opponent and I each draw a card. If mine is known to be a multiple of 3, my chance of having drawn the higher card is $\frac{1}{2} (3n+1)/(3n-1)$.

862. If three cards are drawn and mine is known to be a multiple of 3, what is the chance that it is the highest of the three cards?

863. From mn tickets numbered 1, 2, 3, ... mn, *A* and *B* each draw one. If *A*'s ticket is known to be a multiple of m the odds are $mn+m-2$ to $mn-m$ in favour of *A* having drawn the larger number.

864. If it is *also* known that *B* has not drawn a multiple of m the odds in *A*'s favour are $n+1$ to $n-1$.

399. The whole number of possible ways in which four whist players can have 13 cards each is 53644,737765,488792,839237,440000. Hence shew that if a party play a hundred millions of games the odds are more than ten billions to one against their ever having the same distribution of cards twice.

400. A and B play at cards. A's skill : B's :: 3 : 2. Nothing is known as to whether either has a confederate; if one has and the other has not, the odds on the dishonest player are doubled; B wins 3 games successively, what is the chance he will win the next game?

401. What is the chance that two persons aged 33 and 57 should both be alive two years hence?

402. What is the chance that they should both be dead?

403. Find the chance that one and only one is dead.

404. If it be known that one and only one is alive, find the chance that the younger is alive.

405. If at the age of 89 the expectation of life is 2·95 years, what is the expectation at the age of 88?

406. What is the expectation at the age of 87?

407. Given that at the age of four the expectation of life is 52·1 shew that this is greater than the expectation either at three or five.

408. I promise to pay a boy's school fees for the next five years provided we both live. The fees are £50 per annum payable yearly in advance. If my age is 52 and the boy's age 13 what is the present value of the boy's expectation? (Interest at 5 per cent.)

409. Twelve months later we are both alive; for what immediate sum might I fairly compound the future payments?

410. What is the expectation of life at the age of 90, if among 100 persons reaching this age the deaths in successive years are 19, 17, 15, &c.?

411. Compare the chance of a person aged 20 living to be 60, with the chance of a person aged 60 living to be 80.

---

865. If a die of any number of faces be so numbered that the chances of the number turned up being of the forms $3N-1$, $3N$, $3N+1$ are respectively $\frac{1}{3}(1-\mu)$, $\frac{1}{3}(1+2\mu)$, $\frac{1}{3}(1-\mu)$, shew that when n such dice are thrown the chances of the sum of the numbers turned up being of the stated forms are $\frac{1}{3}(1-\mu^n)$, $\frac{1}{3}(1+2\mu^n)$, $\frac{1}{3}(1-\mu^n)$.

412. A person is now aged 20, shew that the chance of his dying before he is 60 is nearly equal to the chance of his dying between 60 and 80.

413. Shew that the odds are 2 to 1 against a child 5 years old living to be 70.

414. Shew that the odds are 2 to 1 (nearly) in favour of a child 5 years old living to be 50.

415. A man emigrated leaving two brothers aged 51 and 61. Five years afterwards he hears that one is alive and one is dead. Find the odds in favour of the younger one being alive.

416. Three men are known to have been alive four years ago when their ages were 34, 59 and 70. Find the chance that they are all alive now.

417. Find the chance that two and only two are alive now.

418. Find the chance that one and only one is alive now.

419. If it be known that one and only one is alive find the chance that it is the youngest.

420. Find the chance that it is the eldest.

421. What is the chance that a hand of 5 cards contains at least two aces?

422. What is the chance that it contains exactly three aces?

423. What is the chance that it contains a pair?

424. What is the chance that it contains two pairs and no more?

425. What is the chance that it contains exactly three pairs?

426. What is the chance of having six pairs exactly in a hand of six cards?

427. What is the chance of having seven pairs in a hand of six cards?

---

866. Five points are taken, viz. four at the corners of a square and the fifth at the intersection of the diagonals. If the side of the square be unity what is the mean distance between any two of the points, and what is the mean value of the square of the distance?

867. What are the mean values if seven points be taken, viz. six at the angles of a regular hexagon and the seventh at the centre of the figure?

868. A church stands in the centre of a circular parish (radius one mile) and the density of the population varies inversely as the distance from the centre. What is the mean distance of the people from church?

428. What is the chance of having a sequence of three cards and no more in a hand of five cards?

429. What is the chance that a hand of four cards should be a sequence?

430. *A* has a hand of four cards containing three aces. *B* has a hand of four cards out of the same pack. What is the chance that he has at least three cards alike?

431. Two aces, three kings and a queen having been removed from a pack, what is the chance that a hand of four cards should contain at least two alike?

432. All the sevens having been removed from a pack what is the chance that a hand of six cards should be a sequence?

433. What would the chance be, if all the tens were removed instead of all the sevens?

434. Three cards out of a hand of six are seen to be *seven, eight, nine*. What is the chance that the whole hand forms a sequence?

435. What is the chance that it consists of three pairs?

436. What is the chance that it contains no pair?

437. If the three cards seen were *seven, eight, ten*, what would be the chance of the whole hand forming a sequence?

438. *A* and *B* have each a hand of five cards out of the same pack. If *A*'s cards form a sequence of five beginning from ace, what is the chance that *B*'s cards also form a sequence?

439. *A* draws a black and a red card from a pack and *B* draws two black. Shew that *A*'s chance of drawing a pair is greater than *B*'s in the ratio of 25 : 13.

---

869. On $2r$ occasions the congregation at a certain church numbered $n+a$, $n-a$, $n+b$, $n-b$, $n+c$, $n-c$, &c. If every person accurately estimates the numbers that he witnesses present, shew that the average of the observations will exceed the true average congregation by

$$(a^2+b^2+c^2+ \ldots) \div rn.$$

[Hence the average of unequal congregations is apt to be over-estimated : more people see the large congregations than the small.]

870. If on n occasions the congregations were in geometrical progression (common ratio $= r$), shew that the average of observed attendance will be to the average of actual attendance as

$$n\,(r^n+1)\,(r-1) \text{ to } (r^n-1)\,(r+1).$$

440. Shew that in the last question B's chance is the same whether A's cards be replaced or not.

441. Shew that the chance of throwing doublets with two dice one of which is true and the other loaded is the same as if both were true.

442. Shew that the chance of throwing seven is the same as if both were true.

443. There are three dice A, B, C, two of which are true and one is loaded so that in twelve throws it turns up *six* 3 times, *ace* once, and each of the other faces twice. Each of the dice is thrown three times and A turns up 6, 6, 1; B turns up 6, 5, 4; and C turns up 3, 2, 1. What are now the respective chances that A, B or C is loaded?

444. If the dice in the last question are thrown once more and A turns up 6, B 1, and C 4, what are now the respective chances that A, B or C is loaded?

445. If two dice are loaded *alike* in any way whatever, shew that the chance of throwing doublets is increased by the loading.

446. Shew that the chance of throwing *doublets-or-seven* is increased by the loading, except in one particular case in which it is unaltered.

447. In the case where two dice are loaded alike, so that the chance of throwing *doublets-or-seven* is unaltered, if $\frac{1}{6}+f$ be the chance of throwing doublets, the chance of throwing triplets with three such dice will be $\frac{1}{36}+\frac{1}{2}f$.

448. The chance of throwing three such dice so that two may turn up alike and the other different is $\frac{5}{12}+\frac{3}{2}f$.

---

871. If three cards of each suit be taken from a pack, what is the chance that among the twelve cards there will be no pair?

872. If 27 things be made at random into three parcels containing respectively 11, 10, and 6 things, what is the chance that the two best will be in the same parcel?

873. If $3n$ persons (among whom are A, B, C) take their places at random in three railway carriages holding respectively $n-r$, n and $n+r$ persons, what is the chance that A, B, C will be in the same carriage? And what is the chance that they will be all in different carriages?

874. A circular plate 12 inches in diameter is exposed to a hail-storm until 10 hailstones have struck it. Find the chance that at least 3 of the hailstones will strike within three inches of the centre.

449. The chance of throwing the same three dice so that all may turn up different is $\frac{5}{9} - 2f$.

450. There are $1 + 2^n$ dice of which one is loaded so that the chance of throwing *six* with it is $\frac{1}{3}$; the rest are all true. If one of the dice selected at random be thrown n times and always turns up *six*, shew that it is as likely as not to be the loaded one.

451. If in the n throws there be only r *sixes* the odds will be 5^{n-r} to 2^{n-r} against the die being the loaded one.

452. If there be two dice, loaded so that with either the chances of throwing 1, 2, 3, 4, 5, 6 are as $1-x : 1+2x : 1-x : 1+x : 1-2x : 1+x$, shew that the chances of throwing *more-than-seven*, *seven*, and *less-than-seven* are as $5+2x^2 : 2-4x^2 : 5+2x^2$.

453. Shew that with three dice loaded as in the last question the odds against throwing *more-than-ten* are as $18+x+5x^3$ to $18-x-5x^3$.

454. Shew that the most likely sum to be thrown with $2n$ dice is $7n$; and with $2n+1$ dice the most likely sums are $7n+3$ and $7n+4$.

455. If n dice be thrown the chance of an even number of aces turning up is one-half of $1 + \left(\frac{2}{3}\right)^n$, and the chance that the number of aces is a multiple of 4 is one-fourth of the sum of the nth powers of the roots of the equation $(6x-5)^4 = 1$.

456. A and B play for a stake which is to be won by him who makes the highest score in four throws of a die. After two throws, A has scored 12, and B 9. What is A's chance of winning?

---

875. The faces of a die are numbered 1, 2, 4, 8, 16, 32. It is thrown four times and the continued product of the numbers turned up is 64. Shew that the mean value of their sum is 20·1.

876. A coin is to be tossed seven times. A is to score the longest sequence of heads, B the longest sequence of tails and C the longest sequence whether of heads or tails. Shew that A and B have each an expectation of 2·34375 and C an expectation of 3·15625.

877. If the coin be tossed eight times the expectations will be 2·51171875 and 3·34375.

878. Shew that whatever be the number of throws, C will have an expectation exceeding by unity that which A would have with one throw less.

457. A and B throw for a stake, A having a die whose faces are numbered 10, 13, 16, 20, 21, 25; and B a die whose faces are numbered 5, 10, 15, 20, 25, 30. The highest throw to win, and equal throws to go for nothing. Prove that the odds are 17 to 16 in favour of A.

458. A die of any number of faces has μ of its faces marked 1, and ν marked -1, the rest being zero. It is repeatedly thrown until the sum of the numbers turned up no longer lies between the limits m and $-n$. Shew that either extreme of these limits is *equally* likely to be reached if

$$\mu^{m+n} + \nu^{m+n} = 2\mu^m\nu^n.$$

459. A and B throw each with a pair of dice until one of them throws sixes. A's dice are true, but one of B's is loaded so that the chance of its turning up *six* is $\frac{6}{35}$. Shew that if A has the first throw their expectations are equal.

460. A and B throw each with a pair of dice until one of them has thrown *six-and-one*. A's dice are true, but one of B's is loaded so that *six* turns up three times as often as any other face. Shew that the odds are 17 to 12 against A if he begins, and 18 to 11 against A if B begins.

461. A bag contains $2n$ counters, of which half are marked with odd numbers and half with even numbers, the sum of all the numbers being S. A man is to draw two counters. If the sum of the numbers drawn be an odd number, he is to receive that number of shillings; if an even number, he is to pay that number of shillings. Shew that his expectation is worth (in shillings) $S \div n\,(2n-1)$.

---

879. If a common die be thrown n times, the chance that the highest throw is exactly twice the lowest is $(4^n - 3^n - 1) \div 6^n$.

880. The chance that the highest throw is at least twice the lowest is $1 - \left(\frac{1}{2}\right)^{n-1}$.

881. Shew that the last result holds good if the die have any even number of faces.

882. The chance that the highest throw is exactly three times the lowest is

$$(5^n - 2 \cdot 4^n + 2 \cdot 3^n - 2 \cdot 2^n + 1) \div 6^n.$$

883. The chance that the highest throw is at least three times the lowest is

$$1 - \left(\frac{2}{3}\right)^n + (1 - 2^n + 3^n - 4^n) \div 6^n.$$

884. If the die have $3p$ faces the last result will become

$$1 - \left(\frac{2}{3}\right)^n + \{1 - 2^n + 3^n - \ldots - (2p)^n\} \div (3p)^n.$$

462. If in the case of the last question there be $m+n$ counters, of which m are marked with odd numbers amounting to M, and n with even numbers amounting to N, the man's expectation is worth

$$\frac{M+N-(m-n)\,(M-N)}{\tfrac{1}{2}\,(m+n)\,(m+n-1)}\,.$$

463. A says that B says that C says that D says that a certain coin turned up head. If the odds are $a : b$ in favour of any person making a true report, shew that the odds are $a^4+6a^2b^2+b^4$ to $4a^3b+4ab^3$ in favour of the coin having turned up head.

464. In the last question if the evidence came through a chain of n witnesses, shew that the odds in favour of the event would be

$$(a+b)^n+(a-b)^n \text{ to } (a+b)^n-(a-b)^n.$$

465. All the combinations of n letters, r together, repetitions permissible, are written down. Find the chance that a combination selected at random will contain no repetition. $(n>r.)$

466. All the combinations of n letters, r together, repetitions permissible, are written down. Find the chance that a combination selected at random will contain all the n letters. $(n<r.)$

467. All the combinations n together of mn letters being written down, a person selects m of these combinations at random. Find the chance that the resulting combination will contain all the mn letters.

468. A reading society of 13 members passes books in circular rotation from member to member in defined order. If for a new year the order be rearranged at random, what is the chance that no one will pass his books to the same member as in the previous year?

———

885. At a seaside resort the numbers of bathers on five days were 50, 55, 60, 65, 70. B bathed on three of the days; what is the chance that he bathed on the first day?

886. If C bathed on two days what is the chance that B and C did not bathe on the same day?

887. In a table of 5-figure logarithms the average number of *different* figures in an entry is 4·0951; and in two entries taken at random the average number of different figures is 6·513....

888. If a die of m faces be thrown n times the average number of *different* faces turned up is $m-(m-1)^n/m^{n-1}$.

469. In a company of sixty members, each member votes for one of the members to fill an office. If the votes be regarded as given at random, what is the chance that some member shall get a majority of the whole number of votes? Also determine the chance of the same event on the hypothesis that every different result of the poll is equally likely to occur.

470. A boy has done n sums; the odds are $h : 1$ against any given sum being wrong; and the odds are $k : 1$ against the examiner seeing that any given wrong sum is wrong. If the examiner discovers that r sums are wrong, shew that the most likely number to be wrong is the greatest integer in $(k + nk + rh + rhk) \div (h + k + hk)$.

471. If the odds against your getting full marks for any answer you send up be $10 : 1$, how many must you send up to make it as probable as not that you will get full marks for one at least?

472. A series is summed to the number of terms given by the throw (1) of a single die, (2) of a pair of dice. Find the expectation, in each case, when the series is $1 + 3 + 5 + \dots$.

473. Find the expectation when the series is $1 + 4 + 9 + 16 + \dots$.

474. If the throw be made with two dice, the expectation will be equal to the sum of seven terms, if the series be such that the 8th term is equal to the 7th, the 9th to the 6th, and so on.

For example: let the series be $1 . 14 + 2 . 13 + 3 . 12 + \dots$.

475. Three customers order amongst them $3n$ copies of a pamphlet. In how many proportions may their orders have been given? and if all proportions are equally likely, what is the chance that the numbers ordered are unequal and in arithmetical progression?

---

889. A purse contains sovereigns, all numbers from 90 to 110 being equally likely. Another purse contains sovereigns, all numbers from 95 to 105 being equally likely. Shew that the odds are 11 to 10 in favour of the difference between the two being less than 6 and also 11 to 10 in favour of the total number of sovereigns lying between 195 and 205 inclusive.

890. Two dice are thrown, one of m faces, the other of n. Find the chance that the sum of the numbers turned up lies between $m + 1$ and $n + 1$ inclusive.

891. A can have any integral value from 0 to $a - 1$, the chance of any value x varying as $a - x$; and B can have any integral value from 0 to $b - 1$, the chance of any value y varying as $b - y$ (where $a > b$); shew that the chance of A and B being equal is $2 (3a - b + 1) \div 3a (a + 1)$.

476. Of three independent events the chance that the first *only* should happen is a; the chance of the second *only* is b; the chance of the third *only* is c. Shew that the independent chances of the three events are respectively

$$\frac{a}{a+x}, \qquad \frac{b}{b+x}, \qquad \frac{c}{c+x},$$

where x is a root of the equation

$$(a+x)(b+x)(c+x) = x^2.$$

477. The theorem of the last question can be extended to the case of n events, x being then a root of the equation

$$(a+x)(b+x)(c+x)\ldots \text{to } n \text{ factors} = x^{n-1}.$$

478. If three numbers be named at random it is just as likely as not that every two of them will be greater than the third.

479. If the chance of any given person being ill at any given time is θ, what is the most likely population of a parish in which there are r persons ill? And what is the most likely number of persons to be ill at once in a parish of population n?

480. It is not known whether a set of dominoes goes to double six, double eight, or double nine. All three are equally likely. n dominoes are drawn from the set and contain no number higher than six. What are now the respective chances that the set goes to double six, double eight, or double nine?

481. A floor is paved with tiles, each tile being a rhomboid whose breadth measured perpendicularly between two opposite sides is a, and perpendicularly between the other two opposite sides is b; and one of the diagonals is d. A stick of length c is thrown upon the floor so as to fall parallel to this diagonal. Shew that the chance that it lies entirely on one tile is $\left(1 - \dfrac{c}{d}\right)^2$.

---

892. P is a random point on a line AB. O is a fixed point on the same line, so that $OA=a$, $OB=b$. Shew that

$$\mathfrak{E}(OP^m) = \frac{a^{m+1} + b^{m+1}}{(m+1)(a+b)}.$$

893. P is a random point on a line AB. O is a fixed point on the same line *produced*, so that $OA=a$, $OB=b$. Shew that

$$\mathfrak{E}(OP^m) = \frac{a^{m+1} - b^{m+1}}{(m+1)(a-b)}.$$

482. A circle, of diameter c, is thrown down on the same floor, shew that the chance that it lies on one tile is $\left(1 - \dfrac{c}{a}\right)\left(1 - \dfrac{c}{b}\right)$.

483. A ball of diameter c inches is thrown at random against a trellis composed of bars of width b inches crossing one another at right angles so as to leave openings of a inches square: shew that the chance of the ball passing clear through the trellis is $(a - c)^2 \div (a + b)^2$.

484. An indefinitely large piece of bread contains a spherical plum of diameter b. If the bread is cut up into cubical dice (each side $= a > b$), find the chance that the plum is cut.

485. A shot fired at a target of radius a makes a hole of radius b. If the centre of the shot is equally likely to hit all points of the target, find the chance that the hole made is completely within the circumference of the target.

486. If a point be taken at random on a finite line it is as likely as not that one of the parts into which it divides the line will be at least three times as great as the other.

487. If two points be taken at random on the circumference of a circle, it is as likely as not that one of the arcs into which they divide the circumference will be at least three times as great as the other.

488. In either of the last two questions the chance that one part should be at least m times the other is $\dfrac{2}{m + 1}$.

489. If two points be taken at random on the circumference of a circle, the odds are 2 to 1 that their (rectilinear) distance apart will be greater than the radius of the circle.

490. The odds are also 2 to 1 that their distance apart will be less than $\sqrt{3}$ times the radius of the circle.

491. Their distance is as likely as not to exceed $\sqrt{2}$ times the radius of the circle.

------

894. A rod of length a is broken at random subject only to the condition that the fracture must not be within a distance b of either end. Shew that the expectation of the greater part is $\frac{1}{4}(3a - 2b)$ and of the lesser $\frac{1}{4}(a + 2b)$.

895. Two equal rods are broken at random and the four pieces arranged in order of magnitude. Shew that their expectations are as $1 : 2 : 4 : 5$.

896. If n such rods be broken the expectations will be proportional to the numbers $1, 2, 3, \dots (2n + 1)$, omitting the middle number of the series.

492. If a chord equal to the radius be drawn in a circle, and taken as the base of a triangle whose vertex is a point taken at random on the circumference, the area of the triangle is as likely as not to exceed the area of an equilateral triangle whose sides are equal to the radius.

493. The odds are 5 to 1 against the area of the triangle being more than double that of the equilateral triangle.

494. Two chords each equal to the radius are placed at random in a circle so as not to intersect. If they become the opposite sides of a quadrilateral, the area of the quadrilateral is as likely as not to be more than 3 times as great as its least possible area.

495. A point is taken at random in each of two adjacent sides of a square. Shew that the average area of the triangle formed by joining them is one-eighth of the area of the square.

496. If the points be taken on two adjacent sides of a triangle the average area will be one-fourth of the area of the triangle.

497. If n points be taken at random on a finite line the average distance between any two consecutive points will be one $(n+1)$th of the line.

498. On opposite sides of a rectangle two points are taken at random and are joined by a straight line, dividing the rectangle into two quadrilaterals. Find the chance that the area of one is more than n times the area of the other.

499. A coin whose diameter is one third of a side of a tile is thrown on the pavement of Question 154. Find the chance that it falls entirely on one tile.

500. On a chess-board, in which the side of every square is a, there is thrown a coin of diameter b, so as to be entirely on the board, which includes a border of width c outside the squares. Find the chance that the coin is entirely on one square. $(a > b > c.)$

501. A purse contains 2 sovereigns and 10 shillings. The coins are to be drawn out one by one and I am to receive all the shillings that are drawn between the two sovereigns. What is my expectation?

---

897. A magnitude is divided at random into three parts. Shew that the expectation of the difference between the greatest two is double of the expectation of the difference between the least two.

898. A magnitude is divided at random into four parts. A is to take the greatest and least parts and B the other two. Shew that their expectations are as 7 to 5.

308 EXERCISES

502. A die is thrown until every face has turned up at least once. Shew that on an average $14\frac{7}{10}$ throws will be required.

503. A pack of cards is repeatedly cut until at least one card of every suit has been exposed. Shew that on an average it must be cut $8\frac{1}{3}$ times.

504. Cards are drawn one by one from a pack until at least one card of every suit has been drawn. Shew that on an average $7\frac{419}{630}$ cards must be drawn.

505. A deals from a pack of cards till he has dealt a spade: B takes the remainder of the pack and deals till he has dealt a spade: C takes the remainder and deals till he has dealt a spade. Shew that their expectations (of the number of cards they will deal) are equal.

506. A person draws cards one by one from a pack until he has drawn n hearts. Shew that his expectation is $\frac{53}{14}n$ cards.

507. A person draws cards one by one from a pack until he has drawn all the aces. How many cards may he expect to draw?

508. A person draws cards one by one from a pack and replaces them till he has drawn two consecutive aces. How many cards may he expect to draw?

509. If he draw till he have drawn four consecutive spades, how many cards may he expect to draw?

510. One throws a die until one has thrown two consecutive *sixes*, and then receives a shilling for every *six* he has thrown. What is the value of his expectation?

511. A pair of dice is to be thrown until doublets have turned up in every possible way. How many throws are to be expected?

---

899. If a straight line be divided at random into two parts the expectation of their difference is equal to half the line.

900. The expectation of the square on the difference of the two parts is equal to one-third of the square on the line.

901. The expectation of the difference of the squares on the two parts is equal to half the square on the line.

902. The expectation of the cube on the difference of the two parts is equal to a quarter of the cube on the line.

903. The expectation of the difference of the cubes on the two parts is equal to seven-sixteenths of the cube on the line.

512. A bag contains m sovereigns and n shillings. A man is allowed to draw coins one by one until he has drawn p shillings. Shew that the value of his expectation is $\dfrac{mp}{n+1} + \dfrac{p}{20}$ pounds.

513. What would be the expectation in the last question if each coin drawn were scored to the drawer's credit and replaced before the next drawing?

514. If he were to draw until he had drawn p pounds his expectation would be worth $\dfrac{np}{m+1} + 20p$ shillings.

515. If an experiment is equally likely to succeed or fail, the chance that it will succeed exactly n times in $2n$ trials is the ratio of the product of the first n odd numbers to the product of the first n even numbers.

516. If an experiment succeeds $n+1$ times for n times that it fails, the chance that it will succeed exactly $n+1$ times in $2n+1$ trials is to the chance in the last question as $\{1 - (2n+1)^{-2}\}^n$ to 1, or nearly as $4n+3$ to $4n+4$.

517. If on an average 18 male children are born for 17 female, find the chance that among the next 35 births there are exactly 18 males.

518. If the odds are m to n (where $m > n$) in favour of an experiment succeeding, the most likely number of successes in $m+n$ trials is m; and $m+1$ is a more likely number than $m-1$ in the ratio of $mn+m$ to $mn+n$; but less likely than m in the ratio of m to $m+1$.

519. If the chance of a trial succeeding is to its chance of failing as $m : n$, the most likely event in $(m+n)r$ trials is mr successes and nr failures.

---

904. If a straight line be divided at random into three parts the expectation of the rectangle contained by the greatest and least parts is less than the expectation of the square on the mean part, the difference being the square on one-sixth part of the line.

905. If a straight line be divided at random into four parts the expectation of the rectangle contained by the greatest and the least will be to the expectation of the rectangle contained by the other two parts as 21 to 29.

906. The expectation of the sum of the squares on the greatest and least will be to the expectation of the sum of the squares on the other two parts as 106 to 65.

310 EXERCISES

520. A candidate who correctly solves on an average $n-1$ questions out of n goes in for an examination in two parts. In each part n questions are proposed and he is required to solve $n-1$ of them. Shew that if the two parts were merged in one and he were required to solve $2(n-1)$ questions out of the $2n$, his chance of passing would be improved in the ratio of 4 to 5 very nearly. [Accurately as $4n^2-4n+1$ to $5n^2-5n+1$.]

521. A raffling match is composed of five persons each throwing three times with seven coins, the one turning up the greatest number of heads to be the winner. A player having turned up 20 heads, it is required to find his chance of winning.

522. A and B play at a game which is such that no two consecutive games can be drawn. Their skill is such that when a game may be drawn the probability of it is q. Prove that the chance of r games being drawn out of p is $C_r^{p-r} q^r (1-q)^{p-2r} \{p-(q+1)r+1\} \div (p-2r+1)$.

523. In a game of mingled chance and skill, which cannot be drawn, the odds are 3 to 1 that any game will be decided by superiority of play and not by luck. A plays three games with B, and wins two. Prove that the odds are 3 to 1 in favour of A being the better player. If also B beat C two games out of three, prove that the chance of A winning the first three games he plays with C is $\frac{103}{352}$.

524. My chance of winning a game against A is a; against B it is β; against C it is γ; and so on. One of these players in disguise enters into play with me and I win the first n games, shew that the chance of my winning the next game is $(a^{n+1}+\beta^{n+1}+\gamma^{n+1}+...) \div (a^n+\beta^n+\gamma^n+...)$.

525. At a chess tournament the players are supposed to be divisible into 2 classes, the odds on a member of the first in a game with a member of the second being 2 to 1. The second class is twice as numerous as the first. A player is observed to win a game, and a bet of 7 to 10 is made that he belongs to the first class. Shew that this is fair if there are 18 players.

---

907. If in making a reputed linear foot all lengths between 11·91 inches and 12·09 inches are equally likely, the mean value of the reputed square foot will be 1·001875 and of the reputed cubic foot 1·005625.

908. If in measuring the linear unit all errors between μ and $-\mu$ are equally likely, the mean value of the square unit will be $1+\frac{1}{3}\mu^2$, and the mean value of the cubic unit will be $1+\mu^2$.

909. If x is equally likely to have any value between a and b shew that the mean value of x^2 is $\frac{1}{3}(a^2+ab+b^2)$, and the mean value of x^3 is $\frac{1}{4}(a^3+a^2b+ab^2+b^3)$; and generally the mean value of x^{n-1} is

$$(a^n-b^n) \div n(a-b).$$

526.   A player has reckoned his chance of success in a game to be a, but he considers that there is an even chance that he has made an error in his calculation affecting the result by β (either in excess or defect).   Shew that this consideration does not affect his chance of success in a single game, but increases his chance of winning a series of games.

527. A and B play at draughts and bet £1 even on every game; the odds are $\mu : 1$ in favour of the player who has the first move.   If it be agreed that the winner of each game have the first move in the next, shew that the advantage of having the first move in the first game is £$\mu - 1$.

528.   Seven clubs compete annually for a challenge cup, which is to become the property of any club which wins it three consecutive years. Assuming all the clubs to be equally good, what is the chance that last year's winner (not having won the previous year) will ultimately own the cup?

529.   What is the chance of a club that has won the last two years?

530.   If there be n clubs and the cup have to be won k years in succession, what is the chance of a club that has won the last r years ultimately owning the cup?

531.   Two players of equal skill engage in a match to play at draughts until one of them has won k games *in succession*.   Shew that after A has won r games in succession, the odds are $2^k + 2^r - 2$ to $2^k - 2^r$ in favour of his winning the match.

532. A and B agree to play at chess until one has won k games more than the other.   If they play equally well, when one has won r games more than the other, the odds are $k + r : k - r$ in favour of his winning the match. But if A plays μ times as well as B, then when A has won r games the odds are $\mu^{2k} - \mu^{k-r} : \mu^{k-r} - 1$ in favour of his winning the match.

---

910.   Three magnitudes are taken, each less than a and greater than b, all values between these limits being equally likely.   If G be the greatest, M the next, and L the least, shew that

$$\epsilon\,(L^2) = (a^2 + 3ab + 6b^2) \div 10,$$

$$\epsilon\,(M^2) = (a + b)^2 \div 4,$$

$$\epsilon\,(G^2) = (6a^2 + 3ab + b^2) \div 10.$$

911.   Shew that

$$\epsilon\,(L^n) = \frac{1 \cdot 2\,a^n + 2 \cdot 3\,a^{n-1}b + 3 \cdot 4\,a^{n-2}b^2 + \ldots + (n+1)\,(n+2)\,b^n}{\tfrac{1}{3}\,n\,(n+1)\,(n+2)}.$$

533. A's chance of scoring any point being better than B's chance in the ratio of five to four, A engages to score 14 in excess of B before B shall have scored three in excess of A. Shew that the odds are very slightly (about 331 to 330) in favour of A winning the match.

534. A and B play at a game which cannot be drawn, and the odds are seven to five in favour of A winning any assigned game. They agree to play until either A shall win by scoring 10 points ahead of B, or B shall win by scoring two points ahead of A. Shew that the odds are about 176 to 175 in favour of B winning the match.

535. A and B play at a game which cannot be drawn. A undertakes to win rn games in excess of B, before B has won n in excess of A. Shew that, if the match is fair, A's chance of winning a single game must exceed B's chance in the ratio

$$\sqrt[n]{2 - \frac{1}{2^r - \frac{1}{2}r}} : 1 \text{ very nearly.}$$

536. A and B play a set of games, in which A's chance of winning a single game is p, and B's chance q. Find

(i) the chance that A wins m out of the first $m+n$,

(ii) the chance that when A has won m games, $m+n$ have been played,

(iii) the chance that A wins m games before B wins n games.

537. A number of persons A, B, C, D ... play at a game, their chances of winning any particular game being α, β, γ, δ ... respectively. The match is won by A if he gains a games in succession; by B if he gains b games in succession; and so on. The play continues till one of these events happens. Shew (i) that their chances of winning the match are proportional to

$$\frac{(1-\alpha)\,\alpha^a}{1-\alpha^a}, \quad \frac{(1-\beta)\,\beta^b}{1-\beta^b}, \quad \frac{(1-\gamma)\,\gamma^c}{1-\gamma^c}, \&\text{c.}$$

and (ii) that the average no. of games in the match will be

$$1 \div \left\{ \frac{(1-\alpha)\,\alpha^a}{1-\alpha^a} + \frac{(1-\beta)\,\beta^b}{1-\beta^b} + \frac{(1-\gamma)\,\gamma^c}{1-\gamma^c} + \dots \right\}.$$

912. A line is equally likely to be of any length between a and b. If n such lines be taken, and the greatest and least of them selected, the expectation of the difference of the squares on the two selected lines will be $(a^2 - b^2)\,(n-1) \div (n+1)$.

913. The expectation of the sum of the cubes on the two selected lines is

$$a^3 + b^3 - 3\,(a+b)\,(a-b)^2\,n \div (n+1)\,(n+2).$$

538. A man possessed of $a+1$ pounds plays even wagers for a stake of 1 pound. Find the chance that he is ruined at the $(a+2x+1)$th wager and not before.

539. If a man playing for a constant stake win $2n$ games and lose n games, the chance that he is never worse off than at the beginning and never better off than at the end is $(n^2+n+2) \div (4n^2+6n+2)$.

540. If he win $2n+1$ games and lose $n+1$ games, the chance is

$$n \div (4n+6).$$

541. Prove that at birth the expectation of life is

$$\tfrac{1}{2} + R_1 + R_2 + R_3 + \dots .$$

542. Prove that the expectation at the age of x years will be

$$\tfrac{1}{2} + (R_{x+1} + R_{x+2} + R_{x+3} + \dots) \div R_x.$$

543. Thirteen persons meet at dinner, their ages being n, $n+1$, $n+2$, and so on, to $n+12$. Shew that the chance that they will all be alive a year hence is $R_{n+13} \div R_n$, and express the chance that they will all be alive five years hence.

544. Three persons born on the same day keep their 21st birthday together. They agree to keep in like manner their 31st, 41st, 51st, &c., as long as they are all alive. How many such celebrations are there likely to be?

545. An aunt aged 70 has a nephew born to-day and she promises to make him three annual payments of £100 commencing on his 15th birthday, subject to their both being alive. What is the chance that the nephew will be entitled to all the three payments? And what is the chance that he will receive none of them?

---

914. If a coin is tossed $2n-1$ times or $2n$ times, the expectation of the difference between the number of heads and tails is

$$1 + \frac{Y_1}{4} + \frac{Y_2}{4^2} + \frac{Y_3}{4^3} + \dots \text{ to } n \text{ terms.}$$

915. A coin is tossed n times. Shew that we may expect $\tfrac{1}{4}n$ sequences of two or more heads or tails and $\tfrac{1}{4}(n+2)$ single heads or tails. More generally, we may expect $(\tfrac{1}{2})^r(n-r+2)$ sequences of r or more heads or tails.

916. I am to throw a coin n times and to score 1 for a head, 4 for a sequence of 2 heads, 9 for a sequence of 3 heads, and so on throughout the play. Shew that the expectation of my score is $(\tfrac{1}{2})^{n-1} + \tfrac{1}{2}(3n-4)$.

546. What is the present value of the aunt's gift? *Questions of Present Value are to be solved approximately, interest being calculated at 5 per cent.*

547. If aunt and nephew are both alive 5 years hence, what will then be the value of the nephew's expectation?

548. If out of 100 persons who reach the age of 87 years, 19 die in the first year, 17 the next year, 15 the next and so on in A.P., shew that the expectation of life at 87 is $3\cdot35$ years, at 88 it is $3\cdot01\dot85$, and at 89 it is $2\cdot6875$.

549. On the hypothesis of the last question what is the present value of an annuity of £100 per annum on the life of a person aged 87: the first payment being due a year hence?

550. On the same hypothesis what annual premium should a person pay for an insurance of £1000, the first payment being made on his 87th birthday?

551. A who is aged 87 is entitled to the reversion of an annuity of £100 a year on his own life after the death of B who is just three years older than himself. What is the present value of A's expectation on the hypothesis of the last three questions?

552. What is the value of his expectation on the hypothesis that out of 9 persons who reach the age of 87, two die in the first year and one every year afterwards till all are dead?

553. If (on another planet) the conditions of life are such that out of every 95 persons who reach the age of 5 years one dies every year till all are dead, what is the chance that a person aged m years will outlive another person whose age is n years? $(n>m>5.)$

554. If out of n persons who reach the age of N years one dies every year till all are dead, shew that the expectation of life at the age of $N+r$ is $\frac{1}{2}(n-r)$.

---

917. If μ be the chance of an experiment succeeding, shew that in a series of n trials we may expect a series of *at least* r consecutive successes to occur $(n-r+1)\,\mu^r-(n-r)\,\mu^{r+1}$ times and a series of exactly r consecutive successes $\mu^r\,\{(n-r)\,(1-\mu)^2-(1-\mu^2)\}$ times.

918. A die of n faces is to be thrown repeatedly and I am to score the difference between the highest and lowest numbers turned up. Shew that two throws give me an expectation of $(n^2-1)\div3n$; three throws $(n^2-1)\div2n$; four throws $(n^2-1)(9n^2-1)\div15n^3$.

555. On the hypothesis of the last question the chance that three persons aged N, $N+a$, $N+2a$ respectively should all be alive a years hence is $(n-3a) \div n$.

556. On the same hypothesis find the present value of an annuity of £1 on the life of a person aged N years, £t being the interest on £1 for 1 year.

557. On the same hypothesis find the present value of an annuity of £1 to continue during the joint lives of two persons now aged N and $N+a$.

558. What would be the present value of the annuity in the last question if it were to continue until both persons were dead?

559. If out of n^2 persons who reach the age of N years, $2n-1$ die in the first year, $2n-3$ in the second, $2n-5$ in the third, and so on, shew that the expectation of life at the age of $N+r$ is $\dfrac{n-r}{3} + \dfrac{1}{6\,(n-r)}$.

560. On the hypothesis of the last question, shew that the chance that p persons, whose ages are N, $N+1$, $N+2$, ... $N+p-1$, will live another year is $\left(1 - \dfrac{p}{n}\right)^2$, and the chance that they will all live for r years is $\{C_r^{n-p} \div C_r^{n}\}^2$.

561. A bag contains $2m$ balls of which $2n$ are white. A second contains $3m$ balls of which $3n$ are white. If two balls are to be drawn from each bag, which bag is the more likely to give both white? and which is the more likely to give at least one white?

562. Each of two bags contains m sovereigns and n shillings. If a man draw a coin out of each bag he is more likely to draw two sovereigns than if all the coins were in one bag and he drew two.

---

919. If three numbers be selected at random from the series 1, 2, 3 ... n, and if the greatest and least of the three be rejected, the mean value of the number retained is $\frac{1}{2}(n+1)$; the mean value of its square is $\frac{1}{10}(n+1)(3n+1)$; and the mean value of its cube is $\frac{1}{10}(n+1)^2(2n-1)$.

920. From a series of successive square numbers 1, 4, 9, 16, &c. I was about to draw one at random, when it was suggested that I should draw three and reject the highest and lowest of the three. My expectation was thus reduced in the ratio of 19 to 17. Find how many numbers were in the series.

921. From a series of n tickets numbered 1, 4, 9, 16, ... we draw r tickets. If A scores the highest number drawn, and B the lowest, their expectations are as $r(rn+n+r)$ to $2n-r+2$.

316 EXERCISES

563. There are 3 balls in a bag, and each of them may with equal probability be white, black, and red. A person puts in his hand and draws a ball. It is white. It is then replaced. Find the chance (i) of all the balls being white, (ii) that the next drawing will give a red ball.

564. A bag contains a black balls and b white balls. A second bag contains $a+c$ black balls and $b-c$ white balls. m balls are drawn from one and n from the other, and are found to be all black. Shew that the odds are $C_{c,\,a-m} : C_{c,\,a-n}$ in favour of the m balls having been drawn from the first bag.

565. A bag contains counters, one marked 1, two marked 4, three marked 9, &c. A person draws out a counter marked at random, and is to receive as many shillings as the number marked on it. Prove that the value of his expectation varies as the number of counters in the bag.

566. Counters (n) marked with consecutive numbers are placed in a bag, from which a number of counters (m) are to be drawn at random. Shew that the expectation of the sum of the numbers drawn is the arithmetic mean between the greatest and least sums which can be indicated by the number of counters (m) to be drawn.

567. There are n tickets in a bag numbered 1, 2, 3, ... n. A man draws two tickets at once, and is to receive a number of sovereigns equal to the product of the numbers drawn. What is his expectation?

568. What would be the expectation in the last exercise if three tickets were drawn and their continued product taken?

---

922. (Notation of Qn. 765.) Shew by considerations of chance that $Q_x^n = x\,(Q_x^{n-1} + Q_{x-1}^{n-1})$. Hence shew that, if $n > 6$ and $x > n-6$, Q_x^n will be divisible by 42. Shew also that

$$Q_n^{n+4} = \lfloor n+4\,(15n^3 + 30n^2 + 5n - 2)\,n \div 5760.$$

923. The *Century Dictionary* consists of 8 equal volumes. If I have to look out 6 words the respective chances that I have to take down 1, 2, 3, 4, 5 or 6 volumes are as

$$1 : 217 : 3780 : 13650 : 12600 : 2520.$$

924. If I look out 11 words the chance that I have to take down all the volumes is $\lfloor 12 \div 8^{11}$.

925. If I look out words at random until I have used every volume I must expect to look out 22 words.

569. A bag contains m counters marked with odd numbers, and n counters marked with even numbers. If r counters be drawn at random the chance that the sum of the numbers drawn be even is $\frac{1}{2}(1+\mu)$, and that it be odd $\frac{1}{2}(1-\mu)$, where μ is the coefficient of x^r in the expansion of $(1-x)^m(1+x)^n \div C_r^{m+n}$.

570. A bag contains a number of counters known not to exceed m, numbered in order from 1 upwards. A person draws r times, replacing the counters drawn, and the highest number drawn is found to be n. What is the chance that the number of counters does not exceed p?

571. A bag contains balls, some of which are white, and I am entitled to receive a shilling for every ball I draw as long as I continue to draw white balls only; the balls drawn not being replaced. But an additional ball, not white, having been introduced into the bag, I claim as a compensation to replace every white ball I draw. Shew that this is a fair equivalent.

---

926. A and B play until one of them has won two consecutive games. If A's chance of winning a game is μ, and B's chance is ν (where $\mu+\nu=1$), they must expect to play $(2+\mu\nu) \div (1-\mu\nu)$ games. (*This can be easily proved from first principles without reference to Prop. LIV.*)

927. If the match is decided in favour of the player who first wins two consecutive games, A's chance is to B's as $\mu(1-\nu^2) : \nu(1-\mu^2)$.

928. If they continue to play till *each* has won two consecutive games, the expectation of the number of games is

$$\frac{1-\mu\nu}{\mu^2\nu^2} - \frac{2+\mu\nu}{1-\mu\nu}.$$

929. If the issue be the winning of n consecutive games, A's chance is to B's as $\mu^{n-1}(1-\nu^n)$ to $\nu^{n-1}(1-\mu^n)$. In this case they may expect to play N games, where

$$\frac{1}{N} = \frac{\mu^n\nu}{1-\mu^n} + \frac{\nu^n\mu}{1-\nu^n}.$$

930. If at the beginning A has m times the stake and B has n times the stake and they play till one of them has nothing left, the number of games played may be expected to be

$$\frac{n\mu^n(\mu^m-\nu^m) - m\nu^m(\mu^n-\nu^n)}{(\mu-\nu)(\mu^{m+n}-\nu^{m+n})}.$$

If $\mu=\nu$ this reduces to mn, and if $m=n$ it becomes

$$n(\mu^n-\nu^n) \div (\mu-\nu)(\mu^n+\nu^n).$$

572. There are m white balls and m black ones: m balls are placed in one bag, and the remaining m in a second bag, the number of white and black in each being unknown. If one ball be drawn from each bag, find the chance that they are of the same colour.

573. In the last exercise, if $m=4$, and a ball of the same colour has been drawn from each, find the chance that a second drawing will give balls of the same colour: (i) if the balls drawn at first have been replaced, and (ii) if they have not been replaced.

574. A bag contains m white and n black balls, and from it balls are drawn one by one till a white ball is drawn. A bets B at each drawing, x to y, that a black ball is drawn. Prove that the value of A's expectation at the beginning of the drawing is $\dfrac{ny}{m+1} - x$.

575. From a bag containing m gold and n silver coins, a coin is drawn at random, and then replaced; and this operation is performed p times. Find the chance that all the gold coins will be included in the coins thus drawn.

576. A bag contains a £10 note (X), two £5 notes (V^2) and three pieces of blank paper (O^3). I find that I succeed twice out of three times, by the aid of the sense of touch, in drawing a bank note. What ought I to give for the privilege of drawing one piece of paper from the bag?

---

931. A and B divide a bag of counters between them and begin to play for them in a game in which A's chance of winning any point is the double of B's. They agree to go on playing until one of them has won all the counters. Shew that their chances will be approximately equal if A takes one of the counters and gives B the rest. (If there be $n+1$ counters in the bag their expectations will be as 2^n to $2^n - 1$.)

932. From a bag containing p black balls, q white balls and r red balls, balls are drawn one by one till all the colours have appeared. Shew that the chance that red is the last to appear is

$$pq\,(p+q+2r) \div (p+r)\,(q+r)\,(p+q+r),$$

and that this result will not be affected if each ball is replaced before the next is drawn.

933. If n more balls be introduced of another colour, the chance becomes $npqf \div (n+p+q+r)$, where f is the sum of the three expressions obtained by permuting n, p, q in

$$\left(\frac{1}{p}+\frac{1}{q}\right)\left(\frac{1}{n+r} - \frac{1}{p+q+r}\right).$$

577. On the principle of Prop. LXX. what should I give for the expectation in the last question when my available funds are (1) twenty pounds or (2) five hundred pounds?

578. Nine black balls and 5 white balls are drawn, one by one, from a bag. Find the chance that throughout the process there shall never have been more white than black drawn.

579. If mn balls have been distributed into m bags, n into each, what is the chance that two specified balls will be found in the same bag? And what does the chance become when r bags have been examined and found not to contain either ball?

580. A bag contains m white balls and n black balls, and balls are to be drawn from it so long as they are all drawn of the same colour. If this be white, A pays B x shillings for the first, rx for the second, $\dfrac{r\,(r+1)}{2}\,x$ for the third, $\dfrac{r\,(r+1)\,(r+2)}{\lfloor 3}\,x$ for the fourth, and so on; but if black, B pays A y shillings for the first, ry for the second, and so on. Find the value of A's expectation at the beginning of the drawing.

581. If two milestones be selected at random on a road n miles long, shew that their average distance apart will be $\frac{1}{3}\,(n+2)$.

582. A town is surrounded by a road n miles long. If two milestones be selected at random, find their average distance apart measured the shortest way along the road.

583. If the road form a regular hexagon six miles long with a milestone at every angle, find the average distance measured in a straight line from one milestone to the other.

584. If two squares be taken at random on a chess-board as the opposite corners of a rectangle formed of complete squares, find the average number of squares in the rectangle.

------

934. If in Qn. 504 the pack had been composed of four suits of n cards each, the expectation would have been

$$(5n+1)\,(10n^2+5n+1)\div(n+1)\,(2n+1)\,(3n+1).$$

935. If it had consisted of m suits of n cards each, the expectation would have been $(mn+1)f$, where

$$f=\frac{C_1^m}{n+1}-\frac{C_2^m}{2n+1}+\frac{C_3^m}{3n+1}-\frac{C_4^m}{4n+1}+\ldots\pm\frac{1}{mn+1}.$$

585. Two squares are marked at random on a chess-board. If we are to move from one to the other by stepping from every square to an adjacent one (not diagonally), what is the average number of steps required?

586. What will the average be reduced to if diagonal steps are admissible?

587. Two squares are marked at random on a chess-board and a knight moves (by as short a route as possible) from one to the other. Shew that if one of the squares be at a corner of the board the average number of moves is $3\frac{31}{63}$; but if one of the squares be one of the four central ones the average will be only $2\frac{26}{63}$.

588. If a knight be placed at random on a chess-board the odds are 3 to 1 against his having 8 possible moves; and his expectation is $5\frac{1}{4}$ moves.

589. A rectangular parallelepiped a feet long, b wide, and c high, is formed of wire, and is divided by wires into abc cubes, of one foot each; by how many routes can a fly travel along the wires from one corner to the opposite corner without travelling more than $a+b+c$ feet?

590. How many joints will there be in the parallelepiped? And if two of the joints be marked at random what will be their average distance apart, measured as shortly as possible along the wires?

591. What is the chance that two joints marked at random are connected by one straight line of wire?

---

936. A window m feet long and n feet wide is glazed with mn square panes. If two panes at random be broken, the chance that these are in the same diagonal line is
$$2(n-1)(3m-n-1)\div 3m(mn-1).$$

937. A draught board is extended to $m \times n$ squares ($m > n$), and two men are placed on squares of the same colour. The chance that they are in the same diagonal is
$$4(n-1)(3m-n-1)\div 3m(mn-2),$$
except when m and n are both odd, in which case the chance is
$$4n(n-1)(3m-n-1)\div 3(mn-1)^2.$$

938. If three squares be taken at random on a chess board of $n \times n$ squares, the chance that no two will be on the same diagonal is
$$\frac{2n^6 - 8n^5 + 15n^4 - 20n^3 + 16n^2 - 8n + 3}{2n^6 - 6n^4 + 4n^2},$$
the last term ($+3$) in the numerator being omitted if n is even.

592. A pyramidal pile of cannon balls is formed as follows:—the base is an equilateral triangle with n balls along each side: on this balls are placed forming another triangle with $n-1$ along each side: and so on until the pile is crowned by a single ball. Find the chance that an assigned ball will be on one of the sloping faces of the pyramid.

593. Find the chance that two assigned balls will touch one another.

594. Find the chance that two assigned balls will be at the same height from the ground.

595. Find the chance that two assigned balls shall be in a line parallel to one of the edges.

596. Find the average distance apart of two balls which are known to be in a line parallel to one of the edges.

597. If the centres of the balls in any layer be at a height b above the centres in the next lower layer, and if the lowest layer be sunk into the ground up to their centres, find the average height of all the balls above the ground.

598. If two lengths be taken at random each greater than b and less than a, the chance that their sum shall be less than $2b+c$ is $\frac{1}{2} c^2 \div (a-b)^2$: and the chance that their difference shall exceed c is $(a-b-c)^2 \div (a-b)^2$. Express also the chance that the sum of their squares shall exceed a^2.

599. If a point taken at random within a triangle be joined to the two extremities of the base, the chance that the triangle thus formed will bear to the whole triangle a ratio greater than $n-1$ to n is $1 \div n^2$.

600. Within the area of a triangle another triangle is formed with its sides parallel to the sides of the original triangle. Shew that if all possible triangles are equally likely the average area is one-tenth of the area of the original triangle.

---

939. Let x, y, z be the numbers turned up when three common dice are thrown, and let Δ be the area of the triangle whose sides are $y+z$, $z+x$, $x+y$. Shew that the mean value of Δ^2 is $557\frac{3}{8}$.

940. Let x, y, z be integers whose sum is 10, and let Δ be the area of the triangle whose sides are $y+z$, $z+x$, $x+y$. Shew that the mean value of Δ^2 is 220.

941. Let x, y, z be parts into which a length 10 is broken at random, and let Δ be the area of the triangle whose sides are $y+z$, $z+x$, $x+y$. Shew that the mean value of Δ^2 is $166\frac{2}{3}$.

601. An omnibus makes m journeys and carries a total of n passengers. If each passenger is equally likely to take any journey, find the chance that on a given journey there will be no passengers.

602. Find the chance that on r given journeys there will be no passengers.

603. Shew that the expectation of a person who is to receive £1 for every journey until the first passenger is carried, will be (in pounds)

$$(1^n + 2^n + 3^n + \ldots \text{to } m-1 \text{ terms}) \div m^n.$$

604. If the omnibus make 10 journeys and carry 15 passengers, what is the chance that there will be at least one passenger on every journey?

605. If 20 omnibuses an hour pass my house, what is the chance that in the next five minutes none will pass?

606. If 100 persons an hour cross a certain bridge, each taking a minute to traverse it, what is the chance that at a given instant no one will be on the bridge?

607. If there pass over the bridge in an hour a persons who traverse it in α minutes each, b persons who traverse it in β minutes each, c persons who traverse it in γ minutes each, and so on, shew that the chance that at a given instant there is no one on the bridge is

$$1 \div \sqrt[60]{e^{a\alpha + b\beta + c\gamma + \ldots}}.$$

608. A railway company carries n passengers an average of 10 miles each for every one passenger who is fatally injured. What is the chance that a passenger makes a given journey of 100 miles in safety?

609. In reading a French book I have to refer to a dictionary for two words a page on an average; what is the chance that I shall read the next page I come to without referring to a dictionary?

---

942. A point is taken at random within a cube. Shew that the mean value of its distance from the nearest face is one-eighth of the edge of the cube; and the mean value of the sum of its distances from the three nearest faces is three-fourths of the edge of the cube.

Shew also that the mean value of the square on its distance from the nearest vertex is one-fourth of a face of the cube.

943. Ten boys go in for an examination. The highest gets 75 per cent. of the possible marks and the lowest 12 per cent. If all positions between these limits are equally likely, the chance that the fifth boy gets at least 40 per cent. is $32290625 \div 43046721$.

610. A rider on a bicycle has a fall on an average once in 10 miles. What is the chance that he will perform a given journey of 15 miles without a fall?

611. If all the permutations (1, 2, 3 or more together) of the 26 letters of the alphabet be written down, and one of them be selected at random, the chance that this one contains a is very nearly $\frac{25}{26}$.

612. The chance that the selected permutation contains all the letters of the alphabet is very nearly $\frac{227}{617}$.

613. If a man can throw a pair of dice 10 times in a minute, how many hours must he expect to play before he throws double sixes five times in succession?

614. Shew that when a whist player has dealt more than $C_{12}^{51}\log_e 2$ times it is more likely than not that he has held at some time all the trumps.

615. Two players of equal skill play for 36 nights, stopping each night as soon as one of them has won three games in succession. The winner of each game begins the next game and this gives him an advantage over his opponent in the ratio 3 : 2. Shew that their expectation is 196 games. But if the loser of each game were to begin the next game their expectation would be 351 games.

---

944. If $a, \beta, \gamma \ldots$ be n integers (zero not admissible) taken at random, subject only to the condition that their sum is s, then

$$\mathcal{E}(a) = \frac{s}{n}, \quad \mathcal{E}(a^2) = \frac{s(2s-n+1)}{n(n+1)}, \quad \mathcal{E}(a\beta) = \frac{s(s+1)}{n(n+1)},$$

$$\mathcal{E}(a^3) = \frac{6s^2(s-n+1)+(n-1)(n-2)s}{n(n+1)(n+2)},$$

$$\mathcal{E}(a^2\beta) = \frac{s(s+1)(2s-n+2)}{n(n+1)(n+2)}, \quad \mathcal{E}(a\beta\gamma) = \frac{s(s+1)(s+2)}{n(n+1)(n+2)}.$$

945. If $a, \beta, \gamma \ldots$ be n integers (zero admissible) taken at random, subject only to the condition that their sum be s, then

$$\mathcal{E}(a) = \frac{s}{n}, \quad \mathcal{E}(a^2) = \frac{s(2s+n-1)}{n(n+1)}, \quad \mathcal{E}(a\beta) = \frac{s(s-1)}{n(n+1)},$$

$$\mathcal{E}(a^3) = \frac{6s^2(s+n-1)+(n-1)(n-2)s}{n(n+1)(n+2)},$$

$$\mathcal{E}(a^2\beta) = \frac{s(s-1)(2s+n-2)}{n(n+1)(n+2)}, \quad \mathcal{E}(a\beta\gamma) = \frac{s(s-1)(s-2)}{n(n+1)(n+2)}.$$

616.   A die is thrown m times : shew that the chance that every face has turned up at least once is $\left(\frac{1}{6}\right)^m \lfloor m$ times the coefficient of x^m in $(e^x - 1)^6$. For instance if it be thrown 10 times the chance is $38045 \div 139968$.

617.   If $x > y$, both being even or both odd, so that $x + y = 2s$; and if x be expressed as the sum of y integers, all the ways of so expressing it being equally likely, the chance of all the y integers being odd is $\Pi_y^s \div \Pi_y^x$.

618.   A pack of cards consists of p suits of q cards each, numbered from 1 up to q.   A card is drawn and turned up: and r other cards are drawn at random.   Find the chance that the card first drawn is the highest of its suit among all the cards drawn.

619.   A pack of n different cards is laid face downwards on a table. A person names a card.   That and all the cards above it are shewn to him, and removed.   He names another; and the process is repeated until there are no cards left.   Find the chance that, in the course of the operation, a card was named which was (at the time) at the top of the pack.

620.   If the birth rate is double the death rate, shew that the annual multiplier is given by the equation

$$\frac{R_1}{\mu} + \frac{R_3}{\mu^3} + \frac{R_5}{\mu^5} + \dots = \frac{1 - R_2}{\mu^2} + \frac{1 - R_4}{\mu^4} + \frac{1 - R_6}{\mu^6} + \dots .$$

621.   A man writes a number of letters greater than eight, and directs the same number of envelopes.   If he puts one letter into each envelope at random, the chance that all go wrong is (to six decimal places) $\cdot 367879$.

622.   A class of twelve men is arranged in order of merit: find the chance that no name is in the place it would have occupied if the class had been in alphabetical order.

623.   A list is to be published in three classes.   The odds are m to 1 that the examiners will decide to arrange each class in order of merit, but if they are not so arranged, the names in each will be arranged in alphabetical order.   The list appears, and the names in each class are observed to be in alphabetical order, the numbers in the several classes being a, b, and c. What is the chance that the order in each class is also the order of merit?

_____

946.   If s be the sum of n throws with a common die, the mean value of s^2 is $7n\,(21n + 5) \div 12$, and the mean value of s^3 is $49n^2\,(7n + 5) \div 8$.

947. n integers are selected, not necessarily different, all selections equally likely.   Their sum is known to be s.   Shew that the expectation of their continued product is $C_{n,\,s-1} \div C_{n,\,n-1}$.

624.   A goes to hall p times in q consecutive days and sees B there r times.   What is the most probable number of times that B was in hall in the q days?

Ex.   Suppose $p=4$, $q=7$, $r=3$.

625.   If n witnesses concur in reporting an event of which they received information from another person, the chance that the report is true will be $(p^{n+1}+q^{n+1}) \div (p^n+q^n)$, where $p=1-q$ is the chance of the correctness of a report made by any single person.

626.   A judges correctly 5 times out of 6, and B 3 times out of 4.   The same four £5 notes have been submitted to them both independently. A declares that 3 of the notes are good without specifying them.   B declares that only one is good.   How much ought one to give for the notes?

627.   There are two clerks in an office, each of whom goes out for an hour in the afternoon, one may start at any time between two and three o'clock, the other at any time between three and four, and all times within these limits are equally likely.   Find the chance that they are not out together.

628.   The reserved seats in a concert-room are numbered consecutively from 1 to $m+n+r$.   I send for m consecutive tickets for one concert and n consecutive tickets for another concert.   What is the chance that I shall find no number common to the two sets of tickets?

---

948.   n integers are selected, not necessarily different, none less than p nor greater than $p+q$, all selections equally likely.   If s denote their sum, find $\mathfrak{E}(s)$, $\mathfrak{E}(s^2)$, $\mathfrak{E}(s^3)$.

949.   A pack consists of n cards numbered 1, 2, 3, ... n.   If I am to draw two at random and score the difference of the numbers upon them, shew that my expectation is $\frac{1}{3}(n+1)$.   If I score the difference of the squares my expectation is $\frac{1}{3}(n+1)^2$, and if I score the product of the two numbers my expectation is $(n+1)(3n+2) \div 12$.

950.   If three numbers be drawn and I score their continued product my expectation is $n(n+1)^2 \div 8$.   If I score the difference of the cubes of the highest and lowest my expectation is $(n+1)(3n+1)(3n+4) \div 20$.

951.   If p cards be drawn, the expectation of the lowest is $(n+1)/(p+1)$, and the expectation of the highest is $p(n+1)/(p+1)$.   If I score the product of the highest and lowest, my expectation is $(n+1)(np+n+p) \div (p+1)(p+2)$, and if I score the sum of the cubes of the highest and lowest it is

$$\{(p^2+2)(n+1)-3p\}(n+1)^2 \div (p+1)(p+2).$$

629. Two persons are known to have passed over the same route in opposite directions within a period of time $m+n+r$, the one occupying time m, and the other time n: find the chance that they will have met.

630. A writes to B requiring an answer within n days. It is known that B will be at the address on some one of these days, any one equally likely. It is a p-days' post between A and B. If one in every q letters is lost in transit, find the chance that A receives an answer in time. $(n > 2p.)$

631. There are n vessels containing wine, and n vessels containing water. Each vessel is known to hold a, $a+1$, $a+2$, ... or $a+m-1$ gallons. Find the chance that the mixture formed from them all will contain just as much wine as water.

632. A vessel is filled with three liquids whose specific gravities in descending order of magnitude are S_1, S_2, S_3. All volumes of the several liquids being equally likely, prove that the chance of the specific gravity of the mixture being greater than S is

$$\frac{(S_1 - S)^2}{(S_1 - S_2)(S_1 - S_3)}, \text{ or } 1 - \frac{(S - S_3)^2}{(S_2 - S_3)(S_1 - S_3)},$$

according as S lies between S_1 and S_2, or between S_2 and S_3.

633. A man drinks in random order n glasses of wine and n glasses of water (all equal); shew that the odds are n to 1 against his never having drunk throughout the process more wine than water.

634. If n men and their wives go over a bridge in single file, in random order, subject only to the condition that there are to be never more men than women gone over, prove that the chance that no man goes over before his wife is $(n+1)\,2^{-n}$.

635. A dinner party consists of n gentlemen and their wives. When $n-1$ gentlemen have taken $n-1$ ladies down to dinner, no gentleman taking his own wife, and all possible arrangements being equally likely, the odds are $\lfloor\!\lfloor n$ to $\lfloor\!\lfloor n-1$ against the gentleman and lady remaining being husband and wife.

---

952. If a die of m faces be thrown n times the expectation of the lowest throw is M/m^n, and the expectation of the highest throw is $m + 1 - M/m^n$; where $M = 1^n + 2^n + 3^n + ... + m^n$. Shew also that the chance that β shall be the difference between these two throws is

$$\{(\beta+1)^n - 2\beta^n + (\beta-1)^n\}\,(m-\beta) \div m^n.$$

953. I am to receive a number of pounds represented by the sum of x terms of the series 1, 4, 9, 16, &c., x being the highest throw with a die of m faces thrown until n different faces have turned up. What is the value of my expectation?

636. A coin is tossed $m + n$ times, where $m > n$. Shew that the chance of there being at least m consecutive heads is $(n + 2) \div 2^{m+1}$.

637. If a coin be tossed n times, the chance that there will not be κ consecutive heads is the coefficient of x^n in the expansion of

$$(1 + x + x^2 + \ldots + x^{\kappa-1}) \div 2^n (1 - x - x^2 - \ldots - x^{\kappa}).$$

638. A person throws up a coin n times: for every sequence of m throws, heads or tails, for all possible values of m, he is to receive $2^m - 1$ shillings; prove that the value of his expectation is $3n (n + 3)$ pence.

639. A having a single penny, throws for a stake of a penny with B, who has at least 8 pence. Shew that the chance that A loses his penny at the 17th throw and not before is $1430 \div 2^{17}$.

640. If a player repeatedly stake the same sum in a series of either $2n$ or $2n - 1$ even wagers, the chance that throughout the play he is never worse off than he was at the beginning is expressed by the ratio of the product of the first n odd numbers to the product of the first n even numbers.

641. A bag contains $m + n + r$ sovereigns of which n are of the Victorian Jubilee issue, m of the previous issue, and r of the subsequent issue. I am allowed to draw them one by one as long as those drawn are all of one issue. What is my expectation?

642. If in the last question there were n coins of each of p different issues, what would my expectation be?

643. A person throws a die until some face has turned up k times in succession. How many throws must he expect to make?

---

954. A bag contains m black balls and n white balls $(m > n)$. I draw them out one by one. Shew that the chance of my ever holding an equal number of black and white is $2n/(m + n)$.

955. A bag contains n black balls and n white balls. I draw the balls one by one until I have got an equal number of black and white. Shew that I may expect to draw $4^n \div Y_n$ balls.

956. Two men agree to play until their scores are equal. Shew that if their skill is equal they must expect to play an infinite number of games. If however their skill be unequal the consummation will not be secured by an infinite duration of play, and the chance that it is reached at all is the double of the chance of the weaker player winning any point. Also, if equality of points is reached at all, the average duration of play will be $2a \div (2a - 1)$ points, where a is the chance of the better player winning any point.

644. From a point P within the rectangle $OADB$, perpendiculars OM, ON are let fall on OA, OB. Shew that if P be taken at random within the rectangle, $\mathfrak{C}(OM.ON) = \frac{1}{4}OA.OB$. But if P be restricted to lie on the diagonal OD, then $\mathfrak{C}(OM.ON) = \frac{1}{3}OA.OB$; and if on the diagonal AB, then $\mathfrak{C}(OM.ON) = \frac{1}{6}OA.OB$.

645. A man plays continuously, always staking one-tenth of his fund in an even wager. Shew (i) that after 70 gains and 70 losses he will have lost more than half his fund; and (ii) that it will require 304 gains to balance 275 losses.

646. Shew the fallacy of the following argument: "*Three persons A, B, C blind-folded, place themselves at random in a straight line; required the chance that both B and C will place themselves to the right of A. The chance that B is to the right of A is $\frac{1}{2}$; the chance that C is to the right of A is also $\frac{1}{2}$; $\therefore$ the chance that both are to the right of $A = \frac{1}{4}$.*" Obviously the correct result is $\frac{1}{3}$.

647. A table of logarithms is constructed to 10 places of decimals. In what proportion of the entries shall we expect less than one cypher and in what proportion more than one cypher?

---

957. A bag contains m black balls and n white balls. They are drawn one by one till both colours have appeared. Shew that on an average the number of balls drawn will be

$$1 + \frac{m}{n} + \frac{n}{m}, \text{ or } 1 + \frac{m}{n+1} + \frac{n}{m+1},$$

according as the balls drawn are—or are not—replaced.

958. A bag contains s balls of which m are black and n are white. They are drawn one by one until both a black and a white ball have been drawn. Shew that the average number of balls drawn is

$$\frac{s+1}{m+n+1}\left\{1 + \frac{m}{n+1} + \frac{n}{m+1}\right\} = (s+1)\left\{\frac{1}{m+1} + \frac{1}{n+1} - \frac{1}{m+n+1}\right\}.$$

959. A purse contains m sovereigns of the first Victorian issue, n of the second, and r of the third. If I am allowed to draw coins one by one until I have drawn at least one of each issue, the value of my expectation is $£(m+n+r+1)f$, where

$$f = \frac{1}{m+1} + \frac{1}{n+1} + \frac{1}{r+1} - \frac{1}{n+r+1} - \frac{1}{m+r+1} - \frac{1}{m+n+1} + \frac{1}{m+n+r+1}.$$

648. I offer a boy $4n$ oranges, apples, pears and plums, in any proportion he likes. If all proportions be equally probable, the chance that he takes exactly n oranges is less than $27 \div 64n$, and the oranges are more likely to be in defect that in excess of n, in the ratio greater than 37 : 27.

649. If a train consisting of p carriages, each of which will hold q men, contains $pq - m$ men, find the chance that another man B getting in, and being equally likely to take any vacant place, will travel in the same carriage with a given passenger A.

650. Shew that with n dice the no. of ways of throwing a sum s is

$$C_{n-1}^{s-1} - C_1^n \, C_{n-1}^{s-7} + C_2^n \, C_{n-1}^{s-13} - \&c.$$

651. In a game of mixed chance and skill the odds are $k : 1$ that any given game shall be won by the superior player. A, B, C are unequal players. A plays $m+1$ games with B and wins m of them. He plays $n+1$ games with C and wins n of them. Shew that the odds are

$$(1 + k)\,(1 + k^{m+n}) + k^m + k^{n+1} : (1 + k)\,(1 + k^{m+n}) + k^{m+1} + k^n$$

that B will win the first game he plays with C.

652. Shew that the no. of squares visible on an enlarged chess-board with n squares along each side is the sum of the first n square numbers, and the no. of rectangles visible is the sum of the first n cube numbers.

653. If from a random point on the diameter of a semi-circle a perpendicular be erected to meet the arc, its average length will be $\pi \div 4$ of the radius. But if from a random point on the arc a perpendicular be let fall on the diameter, its average length will be $2 \div \pi$ of the radius.

---

960. If a random point be taken within a parallelogram $ABCD$, the expectations of the areas PAB, PBC, PCD, PDA are all equal.

961. If a random point be taken within a circle, the expectation of its shortest distance from the boundary of the figure is $\frac{1}{3}$-radius. If it be taken in a triangle, or in a square or any regular polygon, the expectation is $\frac{1}{3}$-radius of inscribed circle.

962. If the point be taken on a rectangle, length $= a$, breadth $= b$, the expectation is $(3a - b)\,b \div 12a$. If it be taken on a parallelogram of which the longer side is a, the shorter b, and the perpendicular breadth b', the expectation is $(3a - b)\,b' \div 12a$.

963. A random point is taken on a quadrilateral $ABCD$ of which two sides are parallel (viz. $AB = a$ and $CD = b$), and the other two sides are equal. Shew that the expectations of the areas PAB, PBC, PCD, PDA are as

$$a^2 + 2ab : a^2 + ab + b^2 : 2ab + b^2 : a^2 + ab + b^2.$$

654. In a circle the average length of a random chord is a third proportional to the semi-circumference and the diameter.

655. If it be stipulated that the chord must be greater than the chord of a quadrant, its average length will be multiplied by $\sqrt{2}$.

656. P, Q are random points on the circumference of a circle, on opposite sides of a fixed chord AB which subtends an angle $2a$ at the centre. Shew that the average area of the quadrilateral $APBQ$ is

$$\frac{AB^2}{4}\left\{\frac{1}{a}+\frac{1}{\pi-a}\right\}.$$

657. If two points be taken at random on a straight line of length a the chance that the distance between them exceeds a given length b is

$$(a-b)^2 \div a^2.$$

658. If a point be taken at random on the area of a circle (or of a sector of a circle) its average distance from the centre is two-thirds of the radius. And if it be taken on the annulus between two concentric circles of radii a and b (or on any sector of this annulus), the average distance is

$$\tfrac{2}{3}(a^2+ab+b^2)\div(a+b).$$

659. A random point P is taken on the area of a triangle ABC. AP is produced to meet BC in D; shew that D is equally likely to fall on any point in BC.

660. In the last question

$$\mathfrak{E}(PBC)=\mathfrak{E}(PCA)=\mathfrak{E}(PAB)=\tfrac{1}{3}ABC.$$

661. Two points P, Q, equidistant from the base BC, are taken at random on the area of a triangle. Shew that if all possible positions of the pair P, Q are equally likely $\mathfrak{E}(PQ)=\tfrac{1}{4}BC$. But if all positions of P are equally probable, and then all possible positions of Q equally probable, $\mathfrak{E}(PQ)=\tfrac{2}{3}BC$.

———————

964. If P be a point taken at random within a triangle ABC, then

$$\mathfrak{E}(PA^2+PB^2+PC^2)=\tfrac{5}{12}(BC^2+CA^2+AB^2),$$

and

$$\mathfrak{E}(PA^4+PB^4+PC^4)=\tfrac{7}{30}(BC^4+CA^4+AB^4).$$

Also if G be the centre of gravity of the triangle

$$\mathfrak{E}(PG^2)=\tfrac{1}{36}(BC^2+CA^2+AB^2).$$

965. If a, β, γ be the trilinear co-ordinates of a point taken at random within the triangle of reference, then with the usual notation

$$\mathfrak{E}(a\beta\gamma)=2\Delta^3 \div 15abc.$$

662. A random point P is taken in the base BC of a triangle ABC, and another random point Q anywhere on the area of the triangle. Shew that PQ produced is equally likely to cut AB or AC.

663. A random point P is taken on a side of a parallelogram and another random point Q anywhere on the area. Shew that the chance of PQ (produced if necessary) cutting a given diagonal (not produced) is $\frac{3}{4}$.

664. On each of three assigned faces of a tetrahedron a random point is taken : shew that the chance of the plane thus determined cutting any given edge of the fourth face is $\frac{1}{2}$: and the chance of its cutting the fourth face is $\frac{3}{4}$.

665. A fixed point O outside a closed area or on its perimeter is joined to a random point P within the area. Two other random points H, K are taken within the area. Find the chance that H, K are on opposite sides of OP. (N.B. If the boundary of the area be re-entrant or inflected the point O must be assumed to be external to a string tightly wrapped round the figure.)

666. A line of length c is divided into n segments by $n-1$ random points. Find the chance that no segment is less than a given length a, where $c > na$. (Say $c - na = ma$.)

667. In the last question find the chance that r of the segments shall be less than a and $n - r$ greater than a.

668. In a circle whose circumference is c there are placed at random n equal chords, each subtending an arc a. Find the chance that none of the chords will intersect, where $c > na$. (Say $c - na = ma$.)

---

966. If a straight line 36 inches long be divided at random into three parts, the expectations of the pieces in order of magnitude are 4, 10 and 22 inches. But if the operation be subject to the condition that the pieces must be capable of forming a triangle, the expectations are 7, 13 and 16 inches.

967. If α, β, γ be random magnitudes so that $\alpha + \beta + \gamma = 1$, we have

$$\mathfrak{E}(\alpha) = \tfrac{1}{3}, \quad \mathfrak{E}(\alpha^2) = \tfrac{1}{6}, \quad \mathfrak{E}(\alpha^3) = \tfrac{1}{10}, \quad \mathfrak{E}(\alpha^m) = \frac{2}{(m+1)(m+2)}.$$

But if α, β, γ be further subject to the condition that any two must be greater than the third, we have

$$\mathfrak{E}(\alpha) = \tfrac{1}{3}, \quad \mathfrak{E}(\alpha^2) = \tfrac{1}{8}, \quad \mathfrak{E}(\alpha^3) = \tfrac{1}{20}, \quad \mathfrak{E}(\alpha^m) = \frac{1}{(m+2)\,2^{m-1}}.$$

Also, in the latter case,

$$\mathfrak{E}(\alpha\beta) = 5/48, \quad \text{and} \quad \mathfrak{E}(\alpha\beta\gamma) = 7/240.$$

669. In the last question find the chance that there shall be one and only one intersection.

670. A circular slate is handed to two blind men and each draws a chord across it. Find the chance that the chords intersect.

671. If $2n$ points be given on the circumference of a circle (or other closed curve without cusps or inflections), in how many ways can they be joined two and two so as to form n chords?

672. In how many ways can the chords in the last question be drawn so that each may intersect all the rest? And in how many ways so that the no. of intersections may be one less than the maximum?

673. If a random chord is the line joining two random points on a curve, find the respective chances that three random chords will give 0, 1, 2 or 3 points of intersection, and shew that the average expectation is *one* such point.

674. If n random chords be drawn as in the last question, the expectation of intersections is $\frac{1}{6}n(n-1)$.

675. If n random chords be drawn, the chance that there shall be no intersection is $2^n \div \lfloor n+1$.

676. The chance that there shall be one and only one intersection is

$$2^n n (n-1) \div \lfloor n+2.$$

677. If a straight line be broken at random into three parts the odds are 3 to 1 against their making the sides of a triangle; but if the line be first broken into two parts and then the longer portion be broken into two parts, the odds are 2 to 1.

678. If a straight line be broken at random into three parts the odds are about 10 : 9 in favour of the square on the *middle* part being greater than the rectangle contained by the other two parts, and about 7 : 5 in favour of the square on the *mean* part being greater than the rectangle contained by the other two parts.

---

968. If a magnitude s be divided at random into n parts subject to the condition that no part shall exceed $s \div (n-1)$, the expectation of the largest part will be $s(n+1) \div n^2$, and the expectation of the mth power of any part will be $s^m \div (n+m-1)(n-1)^{m-1}$.

969. P is a random point on a straight line AB in which the density varies as the distance from A. Shew that $\mathfrak{E}(AP^m) = (m+1)\mathfrak{E}(BP^m)$, but if the density varied as the square of the distance from A, we should have

$$\mathfrak{E}(AP^m) = \tfrac{1}{2}(m+1)(m+2)\mathfrak{E}(BP^m).$$

679. A is to have the larger and B the smaller of two parcels into which $2n$ things (or $2n+1$ things) are divided at random. Find the ratio of the expectations (i) when the things are indifferent and all possible numbers (zero included) in either parcel are equally likely; and (ii) when the things are all different and every possible selection in either parcel is equally likely.

680.   A stick is broken at random into three parts. I am to take the largest piece, my wife the next larger, and my child the smallest. Shew that our expectations are as $11:5:2$.

681.   A lump of dough is divided at random into three parts, and each of these is made into a circular cake, all the cakes equally thick. Shew that the chance that the diameters will make the sides of a triangle is $\pi \div 3\sqrt{3}$.

682.   The value of a rough diamond varying as the square of its weight, shew that if a diamond of value V be broken at random into three parts, the value of the three parts together lies between $\frac{1}{3}V$ and V; the most likely value is $\frac{1}{2}V$; and the chance that the value is less than μV is

$$\frac{\pi}{3\sqrt{3}}(6\mu-2), \quad \text{or} \quad \frac{\pi-3(\theta-\cos\theta\sin\theta)}{3\sqrt{3}}(6\mu-2),$$

according as $\mu < \frac{1}{2}$ or $\mu > \frac{1}{2} = \frac{1}{2} + \frac{1}{6}\tan^2\theta$, suppose.

683.   If three magnitudes are chosen at random between the limits m and n, the odds are 2 to 1 that their sum will lie between the limits $2m+n$ and $m+2n$.

684.   A bag contains n coins, some of which are sovereigns and the rest worthless imitations, all numbers of each being equally likely; r coins are drawn and found to be sovereigns. What is the expectation of the value of the remainder?

---

970.   On a horizontal base of 462 square feet a hollow pyramid is built. Within it four points are taken at random and through each point a horizontal floor is constructed. Shew that the expectations of the areas of the floors are 396, 324, 243 and 163·8 square feet. If however the floors be built at random heights above the base, the expectations of their areas will be 308, 184·8, 92·4, 30·8 square feet.

971.   If a spherical plum pudding contain n indefinitely small plums, the expectation of the distance of the nearest one from the surface is one $(2n+1)$th of the radius.

972.   If unity be divided at random into n parts, the expectation of the continued product of the parts is $\lfloor n-1 \div \lfloor 2n-1$, and the expectation of the sum of the mth powers of the parts is $\lfloor m \lfloor n \div \lfloor m+n-1$.

685.   A die of p faces is being repeatedly thrown (i) until r specified faces have all turned up or (ii) until r different faces (unspecified) have turned up. Shew that the no. of throws which we must expect to make is (i) pH_r and (ii) $p(H_p - H_{p-r})$, where H_n denotes the sum to n terms of the Harmonic progression $1 + \frac{1}{2} + \frac{1}{3} + \frac{1}{4} + \dots$.

686.   Shew that the no. of orders in which $3n$ letters, n alike and n alike and n alike, can be written down without two letters alike coming together is

$$2 \{ C_{n+1}^{2n+1} + k_0 k_1 C_{n+1}^{2n} + k_1 k_1 C_{n+1}^{2n-1} + k_1 k_2 C_{n+1}^{2n-2} + \dots \text{ to } n+1 \text{ terms} \},$$

where k_r denotes C_r^{n-1}.

687.   If n red beads, n white beads, and n black beads be strung at random to make a necklace, the chance that no two beads of the same colour come together is

$$6 \{ C_{n-1}^{2n-1} + k_1 k_1 C_{n-1}^{2n-3} + k_2 k_2 C_{n-1}^{2n-5} + \&c. \} \, (\underline{|n})^3 \div \underline{|3n}.$$

688.   If a coin be repeatedly thrown the chance that heads and tails are equal at the $2n$th throw is $Y_n \div 4^n$, and the chance that they are equal for the first time at the $2n$th throw is $Y_n \div 4^n (2n - 1)$.

689.   The chance that in $2n$ throws the heads and tails are never equal is $Y_n \div 4^n$.

690.   The chance that in $2n$ throws the heads and tails have been equal once and once only is $Y_n \div 4^n$.

691.   The chance that the heads and tails are equal for the pth time at the $2n$th throw is $pR_{n-p}^n \div n 2^{2n-p}$.

---

973.   From a random point within a triangle perpendiculars are let fall upon the sides.   Shew that the expectation of their sum is

$$\frac{r}{3} (a+b+c) \left(\frac{1}{a} + \frac{1}{b} + \frac{1}{c} \right),$$

r being the radius of the inscribed circle.   Also the expectation of the least perpendicular is $\frac{1}{3} r$, and of the next

$$\frac{r}{3} \left(1 + \frac{a}{b+c} + \frac{b}{c+a} + \frac{c}{a+b} \right),$$

and of the greatest

$$\frac{r}{3} \left(1 + \frac{b+c}{a} + \frac{c+a}{b} + \frac{a+b}{c} - \frac{a}{b+c} - \frac{b}{c+a} - \frac{c}{a+b} \right).$$

692. The chance that in $2n$ throws the heads and tails shall have been equal exactly p times is $R_{n-p}^{n+1} \div 2^{2n-p}$.

693. A die of k faces is thrown nk times, and n aces have turned up. Shew that the chance that the ratio (one ace to $k-1$ not-aces) has never previously occurred in the course of the play is $(k-1) \div (nk-1)$.

694. The chance that the ratio (one ace to $k-1$ not-aces) should occur at the nkth throw and not before is $C_{n-1}^{nk-2} (k-1)^{nk-n} \div nk^{nk-1}$.

In the Questions 695 to 700 a knowledge of the Integral Calculus is assumed.

695. If à priori a man's skill (i.e. the chance of his succeeding in a given experiment) is equally likely to have any value from 0 to 1, shew that after he has succeeded p times in n trials his skill must be estimated at

$$(p+1) \div (n+2).$$

696. If A be a fixed point on the circumference of a circle, and P, Q random points within the circle, find $\mathfrak{E}(AP)$ and $\mathfrak{E}(PQ)$.

697. Find also $\mathfrak{E}(AP^{2n})$ and $\mathfrak{E}(AP^{2n-1})$; also $\mathfrak{E}(PQ^{2n})$ and $\mathfrak{E}(PQ^{2n-1})$.

698. Two arrows are sticking on a circular target; what is the chance that their distance is greater than the radius of the target?

699. An indefinitely large plane area is ruled with parallel equidistant lines. An ellipse whose major axis is less than the distance between the lines is thrown down on the area. Shew that the chance of the ellipse falling on one of the lines is the ratio of its perimeter to the perimeter of the circle which touches two successive lines.

700. A fixed point O within a triangle is joined to a random point P within the triangle. Two other random points H, K are taken within the triangle. Find the chance that H, K are on opposite sides of OP.

---

974. P is a point taken at random within a triangle ABC. PD, PE are drawn parallel to AB, AC to meet BC in D, E. Shew that the expectations of BD, DE, EC are equal, but that the expectations of the areas of the triangles on these bases, with P as vertex, are unequal.

975. If through a random point within a triangle straight lines be drawn parallel to the sides, shew that the areas of the six compartments into which the triangle is divided are of equal expectation.

976. If P, Q be random points within a triangle $ABC = \Delta$, then will $\mathfrak{E}(APQ) = \frac{4}{27}\Delta$. But if D be any fixed point (or a random point) on the base BC, and P, Q be required to be on opposite sides of AD, then

$$\mathfrak{E}(APQ) = \tfrac{2}{9}\Delta.$$

977. If P, Q be random points within the triangle, so that AP is nearer to AB and AQ nearer to AC, then $\mathfrak{E}(BPQC) = \frac{11}{27}\Delta$ and

$$\mathfrak{E}(AP^2) = \tfrac{1}{12}(4c^2 + 2b^2 - a^2), \quad \mathfrak{E}(AQ^2) = \tfrac{1}{12}(4b^2 + 2c^2 - a^2).$$

978. Two random points are taken within a triangle. Shew that the straight line through them is equally likely to cut any two of the sides.

979. Four points are taken at random in a plane. Shew that the quadrilateral is equally likely to be convex or re-entrant.

980. If the four points be taken within a triangle, the odds are 2 to 1 in favour of the quadrilateral being convex.

981. On each side of a quadrilateral two points are marked at random and each corner is cut off by joining the two nearer points so as to form an octagon. Shew that the expectation of the area of the octagon is seven-ninths of the area of the quadrilateral.

982. Two points P, Q are taken at random on a line AOB in which the density varies as the distance from O. Shew that, if $AO = a$ and $OB = b$,

$$\mathfrak{E}(PQ) = \tfrac{4}{3} \cdot \frac{a^3 + b^3}{a^2 + b^2} - \tfrac{16}{15} \cdot \frac{a^5 + b^5}{(a^2 + b^2)^2}.$$

983. If in the last question the density of the line were to vary as the square of the distance from O, we should have

$$\mathfrak{E}(PQ) = \tfrac{9}{2} \cdot \frac{a^4 + b^4}{a^3 + b^3} - \tfrac{30}{7} \cdot \frac{a^7 + b^7}{(a^3 + b^3)^2}.$$

984. If any number of points be taken at random within a circle, the expectations of the distances from the centre, of the two points nearest to the centre, will be as 2 : 3. If the points be taken within the volume of a sphere, the ratio will be 3 : 4.

985. At a game of bowls A plays with one ball and B with two. Assuming equal skill in the two players, required their respective chances in one trial. Wherein consists the error of the following solution? *Suppose A to have delivered his ball: the chance that B will succeed with his first ball is $\frac{1}{2}$: the chance that B will fail with his first but succeed with his second is $\frac{1}{2} \times \frac{1}{2}$; therefore B's chance is $\frac{3}{4}$.* Compare Qn. 646.

986. Shew that if m be any odd number,

$$1 + \frac{m-1}{m-2} + \frac{(m-1)(m-3)}{(m-2)(m-4)} + \frac{(m-1)(m-3)(m-5)}{(m-2)(m-4)(m-6)} + \ldots \text{ to } \frac{m+1}{2} \text{ terms} = m.$$

And if m be an integer of the form $3N+1$,

$$1 + \frac{m-1}{m-3} + \frac{(m-1)(m-4)}{(m-3)(m-6)} + \frac{(m-1)(m-4)(m-7)}{(m-3)(m-6)(m-9)} + \ldots \text{ to } \frac{m+2}{3} \text{ terms} = m.$$

987. If a globule of mercury (O) be divided at random into n globules, of which A is the least and M is any one, shew that (i) the expectations of the *volumes* of A, M, O, are as $1 : n : n^2$; (ii) the expectations of the *surfaces* of A, M, O are as

$$1 : \sqrt[3]{n^2} : \sqrt[3]{n^2} \frac{5 \cdot 8 \cdot 11 \ldots (3n-1)}{3 \cdot 6 \cdot 9 \ldots (3n-3)};$$

(iii) the expectations of the *diameters* of A, M, O are as

$$1 : \sqrt[3]{n} : \sqrt[3]{n} \frac{4 \cdot 7 \cdot 10 \ldots (3n-2)}{3 \cdot 6 \cdot 9 \ldots (3n-3)}.$$

988. If O be a fixed point within the triangle ABC so that the areas OBC, OCA, OAB, ABC are as $\alpha : \beta : \gamma : 1$, and if P be a random point within the same triangle, then

$$\mathfrak{E}(OP^2) = a^2(\tfrac{1}{4} - \tfrac{1}{3}\alpha - \beta\gamma) + b^2(\tfrac{1}{4} - \tfrac{1}{3}\beta - \alpha\gamma) + c^2(\tfrac{1}{4} - \tfrac{1}{3}\gamma - \alpha\beta).$$

989. If P, Q be random points within the triangle ABC, then

$$\mathfrak{E}(PQ^2) = \tfrac{1}{18}(a^2 + b^2 + c^2).$$

990. If θ denote the angle PAQ we may write

$$\mathfrak{E}(AP \cdot AQ \cos\theta) = \tfrac{1}{6}(b^2 + c^2 + 2bc \cos A)$$

and $$\mathfrak{E}(AP \cdot AQ \sin\theta) = \tfrac{4}{27}bc \sin A.$$

Does it follow that

$$\mathfrak{E}(\cot\theta) = \tfrac{9}{4}(b^2 + c^2 + 2bc \cos A) \div bc \sin A?$$

991. If a random point be taken within the volume of a regular tetrahedron, the expectation of the square of its distance from a given vertex is 9/20 of the square on one of the edges.

992. If P, Q, R be random points on BC, CA, AB respectively, shew that

$$\mathfrak{E}(AP^2 + BQ^2 + CR^2) = 2\mathfrak{E}(QR^2 + RP^2 + PQ^2),$$

and $$\mathfrak{E}(AP^4 + BQ^4 + CR^4) = 3\mathfrak{E}(QR^4 + RP^4 + PQ^4).$$

993. If P be a random point within an equilateral triangle ABC, the expectation of AP^{2n} is

$$\frac{BC^{2n}}{4^n (n+1)} \left\{ \frac{3^n}{1} + \frac{C_1^n 3^{n-1}}{3} + \frac{C_2^n 3^{n-2}}{5} + \ldots \text{ to } n+1 \text{ terms} \right\}.$$

994. Within the triangle ABC, n points are taken at random. Shew that the chance that the point nearest to AB is also the nearest to AC is $1/(2n-1)$.

995. The mean value of the triangle formed by three random points within a fixed triangle is one-twelfth of the area of the fixed triangle.

996. If n points be taken at random within a parallelogram $ABCD$, the chance that the point nearest to AB is also the nearest to BC is $1/n$.

997. If n points be taken at random within a parallelepiped of which OA, OB, OC are edges, the chance that the point nearest to OAB is also the nearest to OBC is $1/n$, and that it is also the nearest to OCA is $1/n^2$.

998. A large quantity of pebbles lie scattered uniformly over a circular field: compare the labour of collecting them one by one;—(i) at the centre (O) of the field;—(ii) at a point (A) on the circumference.

999. The average area of a quadrilateral inscribed in a given circle is to the area of the circle as 3 to π^2.

1000. The average area of a triangle inscribed in a given circle is to the area of the circle as 5 to $2\pi^2$.

ANSWERS TO THE EXERCISES.

1. 15.   **2.** 10000.   **3.** 20.   **4.** 8.   **5.** 9.   **6.** 48.
7. 25.   **8.** 480, 437.   **9.** 60.   **10.** 1080.   **11.** 30.   **12.** 60.
13. 147.   **14.** 134.   **15.** 143.   **16.** 110 > 108.   **17.** 40320,
5040.   **18.** 480, 22.   **19.** 10.   **20.** 60.   **21.** 20.   **22.** 70.
23. 432.   **24.** 26820600.   **25.** 3.   **26.** 360, 120, 24.   **27.** 30.
28. 729.   **29.** 63.   **30.** 756.   **31.** 60.   **32.** 24.
33. $18 \lfloor 60 \div \lfloor 20 \lfloor 40,\ 3 \lfloor 60 \div \lfloor 20 \lfloor 40.$ **34.** 675675.   **35.** 118755.
37. 10156250.   **38.** 1728.   **39.** 55440, 174240.   **40.** $\lfloor 32 \div \lfloor 12 \lfloor 12 \lfloor 8.$
41. 166320.   **42.** 3360.   **44.** 780.   **45.** 6.   **46.** 6.

47. 720. **48.** 90720. **49.** 90. **50.** 3386880. **51.** 2880.

52. 3023. **53.** 332639. **54.** 277199. **55.** 144. **56.** 1058399.

57. 63, 18. **58.** 96. **59.** 24. **60.** 1234926000. **61.** 945.

62. 945. **63.** 280. **64.** 107163000. **65.** 21432600.

66. 264600. **67.** 924. **68.** 9129120. **69.** $\lfloor 20$. **70.** 3023.

71. 1919. **72.** 43. **73.** 183. **75.** 6. **76.** 12. **78.** 19071.

79. 690. **80.** 19193. **81.** 35. **82.** 5880. **83.** 900.

84. 20. **85.** 4. **86.** 126. **87.** 56. **88.** 84. **89.** 30.

90. 6, 54. **91.** 102. **92.** 265. **93.** 548. **94.** 12289.

95. 4020. **96.** 416. **97.** 864. **98.** 2220. **99.** 88080.

100. 20040. **101.** 100. **102.** 2030. **103.** 231. **104.** 1286.

105. 90000, 3125, 2500, 1024, 768, 120, 96. **106.** 21. **107.** 56.

108. 293930, 24310, 45. **109.** $\left(\lfloor 13\right)^4$, $\left(\lfloor 13\right)^5 \div 2^{40} . 3^{16}$.

110. $\left(\lfloor 13\right)^4 \div 2^{21} . 3^{15}$. **111.** $5\lfloor 17 \div 2^{12} . 3^2$, $5\lfloor 17 \div 2^9 . 3^3$.

112. 4782968. **114.** 2815. **115.** 7405. **116.** 14308.

117. 1228613679150. **119.** 40824. **120.** 53922. **121.** 5.

122. 4, 5. **123.** $y = mx = (mn - m^2) \div (m^2 - n)$. **134.** $\frac{1}{2}n(3n^2 - 3n + 2)$.

135. $C_r^p . \lfloor pq + r \div (q+1)^r (\lfloor q)^p$. **141.** 20. **142.** 20. **143.** 220.

144. 6. **145.** 4. **146.** $C_3^n - C_3^p$. **147.** $\frac{1}{2}pq(p+q-2)$.

148. $\frac{1}{2}r(p+q)(p+q+r-2)$. **149.** $2(n-1)^2(5n-8)$. **150.** $\frac{1}{2}n(n-1)$.

151. $C_2^n - C_2^p - C_2^q$. **152.** $\frac{1}{2}(n^2+n+2)$. **153.** $\frac{1}{6}(n+1)(n^2-n+6)$.

156. $\frac{1}{6}n(n+1)(n+2)$. **157.** n^2-n, n. **165.** $n(n-1)$, n^2.

167. $3 . 2^{2n}C_n^{3n}$. **181.** 2000376. **182.** 5720. **183.** 330.

184. $\lfloor 23$. **185.** 6720. **186.** 46376. **187.** 519156.

188. $1151150\lfloor 23$. **191.** 116280. **192.** n^n, C_n^{2n-1}. **193.** $2C_{r-1}^{m-1}C_{r-1}^{n-1}$.

194. $C_r^{m-1}C_{r-1}^{n-1} + C_{r-1}^{m-1}C_r^{n-1}$. **199.** 231. **201.** $1980\lfloor 6\lfloor 7\lfloor 10$.

202. $1080\lfloor 5\lfloor 7\lfloor 10$. **203.** 15, 12. **204.** 623. **205.** 8.

206. $\frac{1}{2}n(n-1)$ where $n = (a+1)(\beta+1)(\gamma+1)(\delta+1)$. **207.** 146490.

208. 9. **209.** 36. **210.** $479001600 \times 176214841$. **211.** 190800.

212. 1852925760. **213.** 576. **218.** Coeff. of x^m in $(x^l - x^{n+1})^p \div (1-x)^p$.

219. 60. **220.** $40320 \times (14833)^7$. **234.** 179625600. **235,**

236, 237. $C_{m, n} - C_{m+1, n-1}$. **238.** $C_{m, n} - C_{m+h, n-h}$. **241.** $\frac{1}{2}$.

242. $\frac{1}{3}$, $\frac{1}{6}$. **243.** $\frac{2}{5}$, $\frac{3}{4}$. **245.** 5/28. **246.** $\frac{1}{3}$. **247.** 3/11.

248. 27/55. **249.** 12/55. **250.** 24/55. **251.** 1/42.

252. 1/120.　**253.** 19/90.　**255.** 1/15.　**256.** $\frac{2}{7}$.　**257.** $\frac{1}{4}$.

258. $\frac{1}{5}$, $\frac{1}{5}$.　**259.** 19/30.　**260.** $\frac{1}{6}$.　**261.** $\frac{2}{9}$.　**262.** $\frac{1}{5}$.

263. $\frac{1}{6}$, $\frac{1}{3}$.　**264.** 5/49.　**265.** $\frac{1}{6}$.　**266.** 1/10.　**267.** 11/120.

268. 1/10.　**269.** 2/21.　**270.** Chances as $1:1:2$.　**271.** 4/33.

272. 2/11.　**273.** $\frac{2}{7}$.　**274.** $\frac{1}{2}$.　**275.** 3 shillings.　**276.** 33/1000.

277. 1/60.　**278.** 5 shillings.　**279.** 80/243.　**280.** 2560/28561.

281. $\frac{1}{8}$.　**282.** 1/21; 61/126.　**283.** 25 to 2.　**285.** 72, 60, 50 shillings.　**287.** 27/64.　**288.** 216/625.　**289.** 1701/20000.

290. 496/729.　**291.** 265/432.　**292.** £2$\frac{1}{7}$.　**294.** Starting from the upper bank ·439105 ; from the lower ·596111.　**296.** 2 to 1; 3 to 2.　**297.** $(n^2+1)\div 2n^2$.　**298.** 425/729; 875/2187.　**299.** 16/27.

300. As $1354:347\cdot:347$.　**301.** $\frac{1}{5}$, $\frac{1}{3}$.　**303.** $2(m+n-2)\div mn$.

304. $2(n-r-1)\div n(n-1)$.　**305.** $2\div(n-1)$.　**306.** $\frac{1}{3}(n-2)$.

307. $\frac{1}{4}(n-3)$ if n be odd ; $\frac{1}{4}(n-2)^2\div(n-1)$ if n be even.　**308.** $\frac{1}{2}(n-2)$.

309. In each case $1\div C_{m,\,n}$.　**310.** 2101 to 1024.　**313.** $3\div(4n-2)$.

314. $3n\div(4n^2-1)$.　**315.** Equal.　**317.** $2/n$.　**325.** $\frac{2}{5}$.

326. 2/21.　**327.** 1/12.　**328.** 5/36.　**329.** 13/36.

330. 5/48.　**331.** 37/158844.　**332.** 37/61504.　**338.** 5/22692.

339. 1/11346.　**340.** 7/8990.　**341.** 5/72.　**342.** $\frac{5}{9}$.

343. 25/648 ; 25/3888 ; 25/2592.　**344.** As $14256:12060:10175$.

345. 7/27.　**353.** 1379/2916 of a guinea.　**354.** 9/85.

355. 93/170.　**356.** 33/170.　**357.** 33/170.　**358.** 27/170.

361. $\frac{1}{5}$.　**362.** $\frac{1}{7}$; 1/10.　**363.** $\frac{1}{6}$; 0.　**365.** 34/55.

366. As $9:24:4$.　**367.** As $3:10:2$.　**368.** As $3:16:4$.

369. As $11:10:9:9$.　**370.** As $16:12:9$.　**371.** 95 to 6.

372. 9 to 8.　**373.** 12 to 7.　**374.** $\frac{1}{4}$.　**375.** $\frac{1}{3}$.　**376.** $\frac{2}{5}$.

377. $\frac{1}{2}$.　**378.** $\frac{1}{2}$, $\frac{1}{6}$, $\frac{1}{3}$.　**379.** As $3:4:4$.　**383.** $13^4/C_4^{52}$; $256C_4^{13}/C_4^{52}$; $24C_4^{13}/C_4^{52}$.　**384.** $6.12^4.13^3\div P_7^{51}$.　**385.** $\frac{1}{5}$.

386. 1261/9025.　**389.** 20/27 ; 20/27 ; 496/729.　**391.** 154 to 153.

392. 1441/2023.　**393.** 4 ; 144/625.　**394.** 1173/3125.　**395.** The latter.　**396.** 22 shillings.　**397.** $21\pm 19(\frac{4}{5})^{10}$ crowns.　**398.** 461/4165.

400. 62129617/126854980.　**401.** 13/14.　**402.** 5/4788.

403. 337/4788.　**404.** 247/337.　**405.** 2·96.　**406.** 3·19.

408. £216·83.　**409.** £129·53.　**410.** 3·35.　**411.** As 24649 : 10286.　**415.** 245 to 124.　**416.** 16898/28125.

417. 88231/253125. **418.** 12392/253125. **419.** 4165/6196.

420. 135/1549. **421.** 2257/54145. **422.** 94/54145.

423. 2053/4165. **424.** 198/4165. **425.** 88/4165.

426. 144/195755. **427.** 9/195755. **428.** 7632/54145.

429. 512/54145. **430.** 543/52969. **431.** 3679/10879.

432. 1024/1533939. **433.** 2048/1533939. **434.** 32/2303.

435. 27/18424. **436.** 960/2303. **437.** 24/2303. **438.** 137/32637.

443. As $9 : 12 : 4$. **444.** As $27 : 12 : 8$. **456.** 173/216.

465. $C_r^n \div R_r^n$. **466.** $C_n^r \div R_n^r$. **467.** $\lfloor mn \rfloor N - m \div (\lfloor n \rfloor)^m \lfloor N$ where

$N = C_n^{mn}$. **468.** $\cdot 3397\ldots$. **471.** 7. **472.** $15\frac{1}{6}$; $54\frac{5}{6}$.

473. $32\frac{2}{3}$; $183\frac{3}{4}$. **475.** $12(n-1) \div (3n-1)(3n-2)$. **480.** Inversely

as $C_n^{28} : C_n^{45} : C_n^{55}$. **484.** $1 - (a-b)^3 \div a^3$. **485.** $(a-b)^2 \div a^2$.

498. $4 \div (n+1)^2$. **499.** $(34\sqrt{3} - 56) \div 9$. **500.** $64(a-b)^2 \div (8a - b + 2c)^2$.

501. $3s.\ 4d.$ **507.** $42 \cdot 4$. **508.** 182. **509.** 340.

510. 7 shillings. **511.** $88 \cdot 2$. **513.** $(20m + n) p \div n$ shillings.

528. 3/19. **529.** 5/19. **530.** $(n^r - n^{r-1} + n^{k-1} - 1) \div (n^k - 1)$.

536. $C_{m,n} p^m q^n$; $C_{m,n} p^{m+1} q^n$; First n terms in expansion of $p^m (1-q)^{-m}$.

538. $(\frac{1}{2})^{a + 2x + 1} C_{x-1}^{2x+a} (a+1) \div x$. **545.** 2547/40000; 1429/1600.

546. £11·83. **547.** £30·5. **549.** £248·4. **550.** £344·06.

551. £218·785. **552.** £219·38. **553.** $\frac{1}{2} + \frac{1}{2}(n-m) \div (100 - m)$.

556. $\{nt - t - 1 + (1+t)^{-n+1}\} \div nt^2$. **561.** The second; the first.

562. $\frac{1}{9}$, $\frac{2}{9}$. **567.** $(n+1)(3n+2) \div 12$. **568.** $n(n+1)^2 \div 8$.

572. $(m-1) \div (2m-1)$. **573.** 9/20, 7/15. **576.** £40÷9.

577. £4·11; £4·3 approximately. **578.** $\frac{1}{2}$. **579.** $(n-1) \div (mn-1)$;

$(n-1) \div (mn - rn - 1)$. **580.** $\{y C_{n-1, m+r} - x C_{m-1, n+r}\} \div C_{m, n}$.

582. $\frac{1}{4}(n+1)$ if n is odd; $\frac{1}{4} n^2 \div (n-1)$ if n is even. **583.** $(4 + 2\sqrt{3}) \div 5$.

584. 16. **585.** $5\frac{1}{3}$. **586.** $(7n^2 + 2)/15n$. **589.** $\lfloor a + b + c \div \lfloor a \rfloor b \rfloor c$.

590. $(a+1)(b+1)(c+1) = N$ suppose; $\frac{1}{3} \dfrac{N}{N-1} \left\{ \dfrac{a(a+2)}{a+1} + \dfrac{b(b+2)}{b+1} + \dfrac{c(c+2)}{c+1} \right\}$.

591. $(a + b + c) \div (N+1)$. **592.** $(9n^2 - 9n + 6) \div (n^3 + 3n^2 + 2n)$.

593. $72 \div (n+2)(n^2 + 4n + 6)$. **594.** $9(n+3) \div 5(n^2 + 4n + 6)$.

595. $18 \div (n^2 + 4n + 6)$. **596.** $(n+3) \div 5$. **597.** $(n-1) b \div 4$.

598. $(a - b - c)^2 \div (a-b)^2$. **601.** $(1 - m^{-1})^n$. **602.** $(1 - r/m)^n$.

605. $e^{-5/3}$. **606.** $e^{-5/3}$. **608.** $e^{-10/n}$. **609.** e^{-2}. **610.** $e^{-3/2}$.

613. $103656 \cdot 3$. **618.** $\{1 - C_{r+1}^{pq-q} / C_{r+1}^{pq}\} p / (r+1)$. **619.** $1 - \lfloor n / \lfloor n$.

622. ·367879.   **623.** $(m+1) \div (m + \lfloor a \rfloor \lfloor b \rfloor c)$.   **624.** Greatest integer in $(q+1) r \div p$.   **626.** £11·85 or £11·25 according to hypothesis.   **627.** $\frac{1}{2}$.   **628.** $(r+1)(r+2) \div (m+r+1)(n+r+1)$.

629. $(mn + mr + nr) \div (m+r)(n+r)$.   **630.** $(n - 2p)(q-1)^2 \div nq^3$.

631. Coeff. of middle term of $\{1 - x^m \div m (1-x)\}^{2n}$.

641. $m/(n+r+1) + n/(m+r+1) + r(m+n+1)$.   **642.** $pn \div (pn - n + 1)$.

643. $(6^k - 1) \div 5$.   **647.** About 4 entries with defect for 3 with excess.

649. $(q - 1) \div (pq - 1)$.   **665.** $\frac{1}{3}$.   **666, 668.** $m^{n-1} \div (m+n)^{n-1}$.

667. $\dfrac{m^{n-1} - C_1^r (m+1)^{n-1} + C_2^r (m+2)^{n-1} - \&c. \pm (m+r)^{n-1}}{\pm (m+n)^{n-1}}$.

669. $2\{(m+1)^{n-1} - m^{n-1}\} \div (m+n)^{n-1}$.   **670.** $\frac{1}{3}$.   **671.** $\lfloor 2n \div 2^n \rfloor n$.

672. $1; n$.   **673.** As $5 : 6 : 3 : 1$.   **679.** ($2n$ things) $3 : 1$; $(2^{2n-1} + Y_n) : 2^{2n-1}$; ($2n+1$ things) $3n + 2 : n$; $(2^{2n} + Y_n) : (2^{2n} - Y_n)$.

684. $(n - r)(r+1) \div (r+2)$.   **696.** $32a \div 9\pi$; $128a \div 45\pi$.

697. $a^{2n} Y_{n+1} \div 2(n+1)$; $32(4a)^{2n-1} \div \pi (n+1)(2n+1) Y_{n+1}$: $a^{2n} Y_{n+1} \div (n+1)(n+2)$; $128(4a)^{2n-1} \div \pi (2n+1)(2n+3) Y_{n+1}$.

698. 35/88 nearly.   **701.** 1024.   **702.** 768.   **703.** 28561; 17160.

704. 169.   **705.** 4500.   **706.** As $4 : 2 : 1$.   **707.** As $9 : 6 : 1$.

709. 126.   **710.** 1092.   **711.** 728.   **712.** 271; 28; 180; 9.

713. 36; 54.   **714.** 597870.   **715.** 23160 : 5460.   **717.** 33330.

718. 11110.   **719.** 16665.   **720.** 2599980.   **721.** 2048.

722. 1024.   **723.** 243.   **724.** 174.   **725.** 1092.

729. $C_{5,11} = 4368$.   **730.** $C_{10,12}$.   **731.** $C_{10,6}$.   **732.** $C_{6,6,4}$.

733. $2^{12} C_{4,12}$.   **734.** 448.   **735.** 560; 2576.   **736.** 168.

743. 283824.   **744.** 37584.   **745.** 3168.   **772.** 33; 44.

779. $\lfloor p+q+r-1 \div (q+r) \lfloor p-1 \rfloor q-1 \rfloor r$.   **801.** 1/42.   **802.** $\frac{1}{2}$.

804. 664/1225.   **805.** 528/1225.   **817.** One penny.   **818.** One halfpenny.   **824.** 1637/2604.   **826.** $C_{10,100}$; $11\{C_{10,50} - 5\} \div C_{10,100}$.

837. 7/12.   **862.** $(3n^2 - 1) \div (3n - 1)(3n - 2)$.   **868.** $\frac{1}{2}$ mile.

871. $2100 \div 143^3$.   **872.** 115/351.

873. $(n-1)(n^2 - 2n + 2r^2) \div n (3n - 1)(3n - 2)$; $2(n^2 - r^2) \div (3n - 1)(3n - 2)$.

887. $10 - 9^5/10^4$ and $10 - 9^{10}/10^9$.   **890.** $(m - n + 1)/m$.   **920.** 28.

948. N; $N^2 + (n+q+1) nq/12$: $N^3 + N(n+q+1) nq/4$; where $N = n(p + \frac{1}{2}q)$.

998. 3π to 16.